Anansi and the Moss-Covered Rock

retold by Eric A. Kimmel
illustrated by Janet Stevens

SCHOLASTIC INC.
New York Toronto London Auckland Sydney

To Jonny

ISBN 0-590-43164-1

Text copyright © 1988 by Eric A. Kimmel.
Illustrations copyright © 1988 by Janet Stevens.

All rights reserved. Published by
Scholastic Inc., 730 Broadway, New York, NY 10003,
by arrangement with Holiday House, Inc.

12 11 10 9 8 7 6 5 4 3 2 1   0 1 2 3 4 5/9
Printed in the U.S.A.   23
First Scholastic printing, January 1990

Once upon a time Anansi the Spider was walking, walking, walking through the forest when something caught his eye. It was a strange moss-covered rock.

"How interesting!" Anansi said. "Isn't this a strange moss-covered rock!"

KPOM! Everything went black. Down fell Anansi, sense-less.

An hour later Anansi woke up. His head was spinning. He wondered what had happened.

"I was walking along the path when something caught my eye. I stopped and said, 'Isn't this a strange moss-covered rock.' "

KPOM! Down fell Anansi again. But this time, when he woke up an hour later, he knew what was happening.

"Aha!" said Anansi. "This is a magic rock. And whenever anyone comes along and says the magic words, 'Isn't this a strange hmm-hmmmmm hmm,' down he goes. This is a good thing to know," said Anansi. "And I know just how to use it."

So Anansi went walking, walking, walking through the forest until he came to Lion's house. Lion was sitting on his porch. At his feet was a great pile of yams. Anansi loved yams, but he was too lazy to dig them up himself. Anansi said to Lion, "Hello, Lion! It is very hot today. Don't you think so?"

"Yes, Anansi," said Lion. "It is terribly hot."

"I am going for a walk in the cool forest," said Anansi. "Would you like to come?"

"I certainly would," said Lion.

So Lion and Anansi went walking, walking, walking through the forest. After a while Anansi led Lion to a certain place.

"Lion! Do you see what I see?"

"Oh, yes, Anansi!" said Lion. "Isn't this a strange moss-covered rock!"

KPOM! Down fell Lion. Anansi ran back to Lion's house
and made off with Lion's yams.

An hour later Lion woke up. His head was spinning. Anansi was nowhere in sight. And when he got home, he found that every single one of his yams was gone. Lion was very sad.

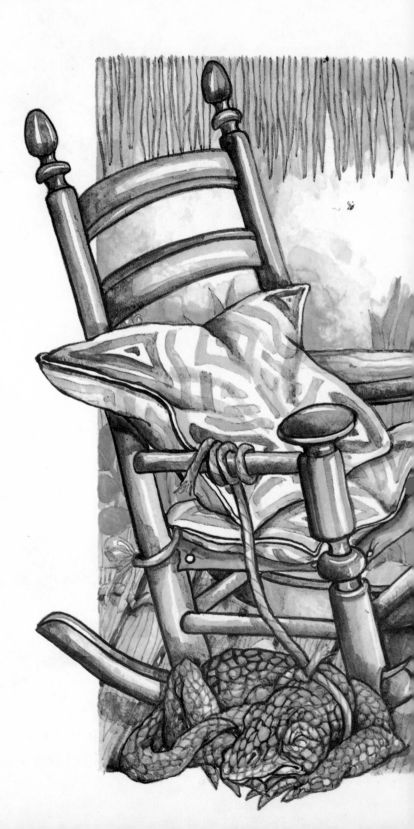

But Anansi was very happy. He couldn't wait to play his trick again.

Once more Anansi went walking, walking, walking through the forest. This time he stopped at Elephant's house. Elephant was sitting on his porch. At Elephant's feet was a great pile of bananas. Anansi loved bananas, but he was too lazy to pick them himself. So he said to Elephant, "Hello, Elephant! Isn't it hot today!"

"It is!" Elephant agreed.

"I am going for a walk in the cool forest," Anansi said. "Would you like to come?"

"That sounds nice," said Elephant. "Thank you for inviting me, Anansi."

So Anansi and Elephant went walking, walking, walking through the forest. After a while Anansi led Elephant to a certain place.

"Elephant! Look! Do you see what I see?"

Elephant looked. "Yes I do, Anansi. Isn't this a strange moss-covered rock!"

KPOM! Down fell Elephant. Anansi ran back to Elephant's house and made off with all the bananas.

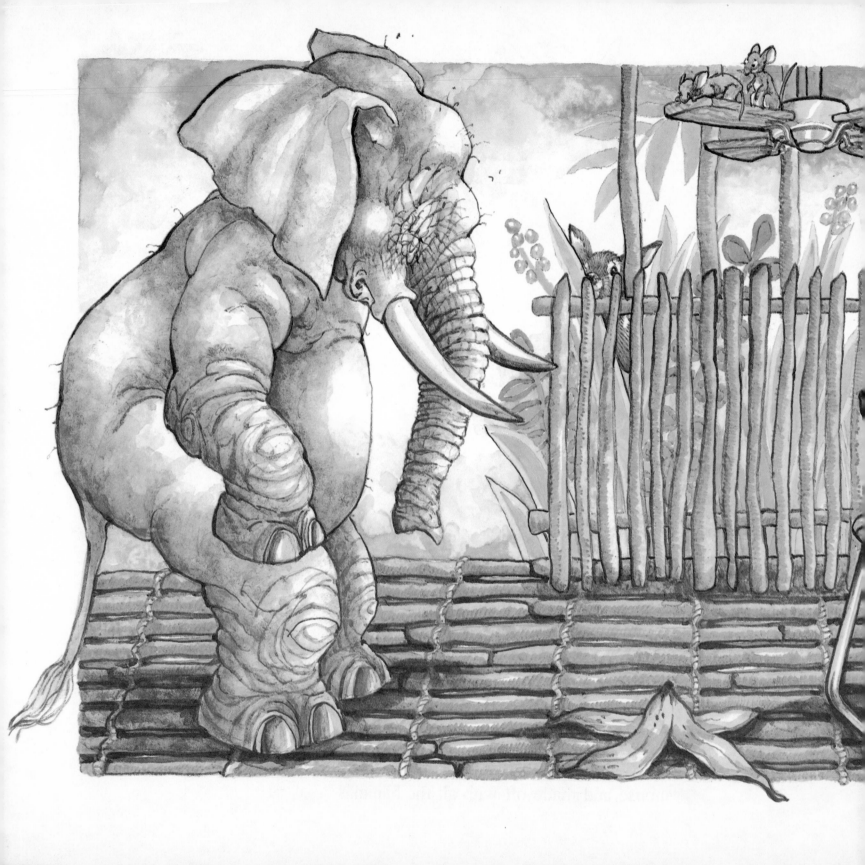

An hour later Elephant woke up. His head was spinning. Anansi was nowhere in sight. And when he got home, he found that every single one of his bananas was gone. Elephant was very sad.

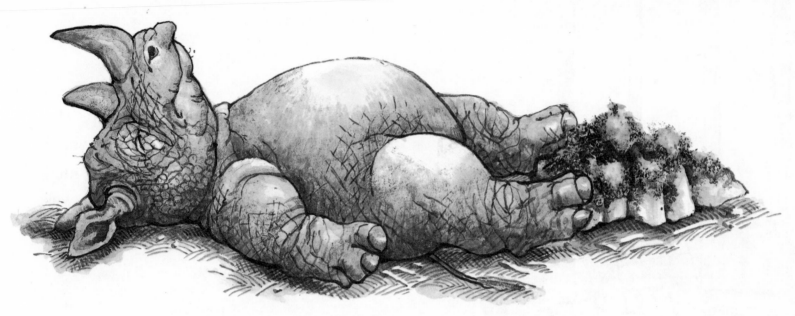

But Anansi was very happy. He couldn't wait to play his
trick again. He played it on Rhinoceros

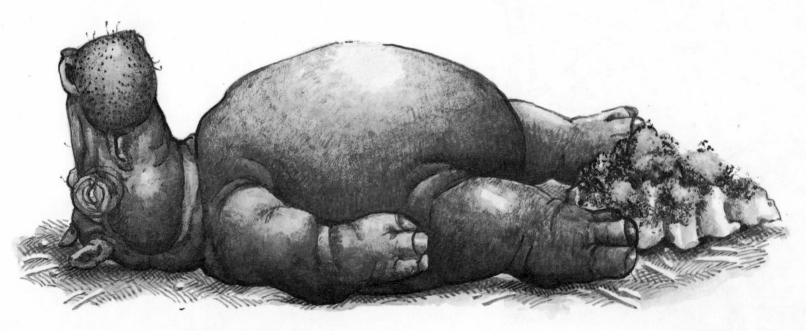

and Hippopotamus.

He played it on Giraffe

and Zebra. He played it on every single animal in the forest.

But all this time, watching from behind the leaves, was
Little Bush Deer. Little Bush Deer is small and shy, and very
hard to see. She watched Anansi play his wicked trick again
and again on all the other animals. Little Bush Deer decided
it was time for Anansi to learn a lesson.

So Little Bush Deer went deep into the forest to where the
coconut trees grow. She climbed a coconut tree and threw
down a great many coconuts. She carried the coconuts home
in a basket and set them on her porch. Then she sat down
beside them to wait.

In a little while along came Anansi. Anansi's eyes lit up when he saw Little Bush Deer's coconuts. Anansi loved coconuts. He loved to eat the tender white coconut meat and drink the sweet coconut milk inside. But he was much too lazy to gather coconuts himself.

Instead he said, "Hello, Little Bush Deer! It is so hot today!"

Little Bush Deer smiled. "It is very hot, Anansi."

"I am going for a walk in the cool forest. Would you like to come?"

"Yes, I would," said Little Bush Deer.

So Anansi and Little Bush Deer went walking, walking, walking in the cool forest. After a while Anansi led Little Bush Deer to a certain place.

"Little Bush Deer! Look over there! Do you see what I see?"

Little Bush Deer knew all about Anansi's trick. She looked. "No, Anansi. I don't see anything."

"You must see it. Look very carefully."

Little Bush Deer looked. "No. I still don't see anything," she said.

Anansi began to get angry. "You must see it. Look over here. Look right where I'm pointing. Do you see it now?"

"No, Anansi," said Little Bush Deer.

Anansi stamped his legs. "You see it. You just don't want to say it."

"Say what?" said Little Bush Deer.

"You know."

"Is that what I'm supposed to say?"

"Yes," said Anansi.

"All right. Then I will say it to make you happy. 'You know,' " said Little Bush Deer. "There! I said it. Are you satisfied?"

"No!" Anansi shouted. "You're not supposed to say 'You know!'"

"What am I supposed to say?"

"You're supposed to say, 'Isn't this a strange moss-covered rock!'"

KPOM! Down fell Anansi.

Little Bush Deer ran and got all the other animals. Together they went to Anansi's house and took back all the good things he had stolen from them.

An hour later Anansi woke up. His head was spinning.
Little Bush Deer was nowhere in sight. And when he got
home, he found his house as empty as it was before.

But if you think Anansi learned his lesson, you're mistaken.
Because he's still playing tricks to this very day.

Chemists' Guide
to Effective Teaching

VOLUME II

Chemists' Guide to Effective Teaching

VOLUME II

Edited by

Norbert J. Pienta
Department of Chemistry
University of Iowa

Melanie M. Cooper
Department of Chemistry
Clemson University

Thomas J. Greenbowe
Department of Chemistry
Iowa State University

PRENTICE HALL SERIES IN EDUCATIONAL INNOVATION

Prentice Hall
is an imprint of

Upper Saddle River, NJ 07458

CIP data available

Assistant Editor: *Carol G. DuPont*
Senior Acquisitions Editor: *Kent Porter Hamann*
Editor-In-Chief, Science: *Nicole Folchetti*
Marketing Manager: *Elizabeth Averbeck*
Managing Editor, Science: *Gina M. Cheselka*
Project Manager, Science: *Wendy A. Perez*
Cover Designer: *Margaret Kenselaar*
Art Director: *Jayne Conte*
Senior Operations Manager: *Alan Fischer*

Prentice Hall
is an imprint of

© 2009 by Pearson Education, Inc.
Pearson Prentice-Hall
Pearson Education, Inc.
Upper Saddle River, New Jersey 07458

The author and publisher of this book have used their best efforts in preparing this book. These efforts include the development, research, and testing of the theories and programs to determine their effectiveness. The author and publisher
make no warranty of any kind, expressed or implied, with regard to these programs or the documentation contained in
this book. The author and publisher shall not be liable in any event for incidental or consequential damages in connection with, or arising out of, the furnishing, performance, or use of these programs.

ISBN-13: 978-0-321-61195-6

ISBN-10:   0-321-61195-0

Printed in the United States of America
10 9 8 7 6 5 4 3 2 1

Pearson Education Ltd., *London*
Pearson Education Australia Pty., Limited, *Sydney*
Pearson Education Singapore, Pte. Ltd
Pearson Education North Asia Ltd., *Hong Kong*
Pearson Education Canada, Ltd., *Toronto*
Pearson Educación de Mexico, S.A. de C.V.
Pearson Education—Japan, *Tokyo*
Pearson Education Malaysia, Pte. Ltd

Titles in the Prentice Hall Series in Educational Innovation

Contents

Preface

Even before we started receiving positive feedback about the topics in Volume 1 of this book, we were committed to continuing the enterprise. The second volume starts with a contribution about the importance of chemical education written by Richard Zare (Department of Chemistry, Stanford University). I encourage you to share this 2nd volume with your colleagues and to point out Zare's first chapter to anyone who needs more help understanding many important facets of chemical education.

The remainder of this book contains contributions from a host of our talented colleagues and collaborators in the chemistry community. The intention was to continue covering new topics on the practical applications of learning theories and to further unravel those theories in language and examples that would be familiar to anyone teaching chemistry. To that end, this book is organized into three parts…

- Incorporating the Big Ideas in the Chemistry Classroom
- Implementing Specific Approaches to Teaching and Learning Chemistry
- Teaching and Learning Chemistry outside the Classroom

We believe that everyone can find information and inspiration in these 18 chapters. This book and its predecessor are as useful to novices like graduate students or newly appointed faculty as they are to more senior colleagues. Keeping up with the developments in teaching are just as important as in areas of one's scholarship. We encourage everyone to teach knowledgeably and confidently and to learn something new about your teaching.

Norbert J. Pienta
Melanie M. Cooper
Thomas J. Greenbowe

Part I

Incorporating the Big Ideas in the Chemistry Classroom

1

Introduction: Chemistry and the Role of Chemical Education

Richard N. Zare
Department of Chemistry
Stanford University,CA

Who can doubt that chemistry is more important than ever, occupying a central role in our understanding of new materials and life processes? And yet, who can dispute that chemistry departments are threatened with diminished importance in academia and in some cases with outright extinction? What has brought about this seemingly paradoxical state of affairs?

Applications of chemistry are ubiquitous – and they are growing all over the place. The language of molecules is widely spoken, describing phenomena that range from some of the most exciting aspects of astrophysics to the basis of new medicines to the latest technological advances. The world of the small, decorated with micro and nano prefixes, dominates so much of modern science today. Yet the spread of the language of chemistry does not mean survival of the discipline. After all, calculus and statistics are used nearly everywhere, but very few people call themselves mathematicians or statisticians. The number of people who call themselves chemists may also be declining.

It is possible for departments to disappear. For example, both rhetoric and geography were once leading activities at universities, with departments of their own, but today these topics are seldom even offered as advanced courses. Instead, rhetoric and geography have been subsumed into other departments, such as English, history, and political science. In similar ways departments of chemistry could also become absorbed into those of materials sciences, life sciences, bioengineering, molecular physics, etc. It is one thing to make a conscious decision for this to happen, quite another to find it happening because of some oversight or lack of attention.

I personally want to keep chemistry alive as its own discipline. Our field is already so diverse that even trained chemists find difficulties comprehending the full picture of its power to reveal the nature of matter and how matter can be transformed. If chemistry is only taught for what is needed by various other disciplines, I feel the loss would be a huge one. Universities continue to be parsed into departments, and it seems clear to many, including me, that without strong departments it is not possible to have strong interdisciplinary activities. Some of the most exciting research occurs at the interface between departments, but the people who do this work belong in general to one department or another. A department is the keeper of the truth for a discipline.

The importance of departments can be readily measured in terms of the breadth and depth of its effects on people? Often this measure can be made simply in terms of the number of student-hours taught in a department. Imagine then my horror to discover that at some major research universities teaching undergraduates is considered an activity that should be left to those individuals of less status, which is often described as those less gifted in doing research. Carried to its extreme, this idea seems a perfect recipe for the decline, if not demise, of a department, and hence its discipline. The trend toward hiring temporary faculty to teach introductory courses must be resisted and reversed. I assert that unless chemistry departments take seriously their responsibility to teach chemistry, particularly to beginners, they are doomed to decline and ultimately disappear.

It is well established that research and teaching do go together. It is my own belief that teaching is a secret weapon of the researcher in that it not only forces the teacher to relearn the material at a higher level of understanding than when the teacher was a student but it also causes the teacher to question deeply what is known. It is this questioning of how well something is really known that is a key to developing new research plans. In my opinion, some form of research pursuit including research into how we learn chemistry, no matter its degree of success, is an excellent complement to becoming an effective teacher. I have taught general chemistry in one form or another almost every year I have been a faculty member of MIT, the University of Colorado, Columbia University, and now Stanford University. I can personally attest to how useful teaching has been to me in sharpening my own research directions.

Excellence in teaching is not incompatible with first-rate research. As in so many other aspects of life, those who succeed best are those that can strike a happy balance between competing demands on time. My advice to a beginning faculty member is to work hard to find a way both to teach and do research without one of these activities completely overtaking the other. The rewards for finding this right balance are not only great personal satisfaction but also a much richer research program.

So the integration of teaching and research is not merely a nice idea, a mantra chanted by university administrators, but actually something whose success is coupled to the survival of the chemical sciences. Given its importance, you would think that more attention might be devoted to helping chemistry faculty members become effective teachers. Such, sadly, is often not the case. Instead, many of us learn how to teach the same way my father tried to teach me how to swim. One day he simply picked me up, threw me into a swimming pool, and said, "Go swim." His intentions were well meaning, but I never became a good swimmer. Often, we do no better with our beginning faculty, believing that if you understand a topic thoroughly, then, of course, you can readily teach it. Alas, for many of us, that is not so. Where can we turn for help?

As part of the Prentice Hall Series in Educational Innovation, Norb Pienta, Melanie Cooper, and Tom Greenbowe brought out in 2005 the paperback *Chemists' Guide to Effective Teaching*, an edited collection of chapters about how chemistry instruction can be most successfully done, written by experts in the field of learning. Few graduate students in chemistry receive any training in educational theories, pedagogy, and strategies for helping students of chemistry learn this discipline. The book has been warmly welcomed, and it provides a truly useful guide not only to the beginning chemistry teacher but also to those of us attempting to improve our teaching effectiveness and searching for ways of inspiring students to learn beyond the traditional large-lecture format. So it was with great pleasure that I received an invitation to write an introduction to the second volume of *Chemists' Guide to Effective Teaching*. Whereas the 2005 volume presented overviews of research in chemistry education, this second volume presents proven applications of that research, whose outcomes and successes have been, or are being, demonstrated by research results.

This volume shows the reader how much is gained when superb teachers collaborate with outstanding experts in learning to produce a collection of tips, hints, guidelines, and good advice for chemistry instruction. The volume is divided into three parts. Part 1 concerns big ideas for what to do in the classroom. Here you will find how different teaching styles affect outcomes. You will also learn about promoting cooperative learning, carrying out guided inquiry, utilizing visualization in learning, as well as making an assessment of what has been achieved. Part 2 presents specific approaches to teaching and learning chemistry, including POGIL (Process-Oriented Guided-Inquiry Learning) and PLTL (Peer-Led Teaching and Learning). You will also find detailed discussions on integrating laboratory and lecture material, and the MORE (Model-Observe-Reflect-Explain) Thinking Frame as an instructional tool designed to guide students' thinking in the laboratory and encourage students to reflect upon their ideas and how they fit with empirical evidence. Part 2 also addresses such a daunting topic as how to meet the challenge of mathematics in chemistry instruction, particularly, how a symbolic mathematics engine such as Mathcad can help students learn about models and explore the models as they build their understanding of chemical concepts. Part 3 concludes with how to teach and learn chemistry outside the classroom, from science museums to news articles. Of special interest is the last chapter on the fabulous resource: *The Journal of Chemical Education* Digital Library. Here the reader is introduced to a huge collection of on-line teaching tools, such as downloadable movie clips of various chemistry demonstrations – the type of material that can so enrich a lecture and, even more so, the same lecture demonstration done live before the class.

It is possible to get students to see the allure of science and experience the thrill of discovery. One consequence is that more students are drawn to careers in the sciences. The benefits not only involve invigorating the research enterprise but also producing a more scientifically literate society that supports such endeavors. Learning chemistry is a challenge, and effective teaching really does make a huge difference. Volume 2 of *Chemists' Guide to Effective Teaching* shares with the reader best practices that are known to yield results. It has taken a long time to sort out how to present the richness of chemistry in a manner that grabs the imagination of students. This task is not an easy one, but the most important aspect of teaching is not how information is conveyed but rather how students are stimulated to want to learn chemistry on their own. I consider the material presented in Volume 2 of *Chemists' Guide to Effective Teaching* to be essential reading for all of us who struggle to instruct others about the wonders of chemistry.

Exploring the Impact of Teaching Styles on Student Learning in both Traditional and Innovative Classes

Diane M. Bunce
Chemistry Department
The Catholic University of America

Abstract

Teachers don't actually teach "a class" of chemistry students; rather they teach 25, 100 or 200 individuals who each have a distinct learning style. The fit between the teacher's teaching style and the student's learning style may or may not be a good one. Research shows that when a significant mismatch occurs, student achievement in the course can be affected. Although it may not be possible to accommodate *all* the different learning styles within a single class, there are some things that can be done to accommodate a range of identifiable learning styles. Most of these approaches start with a realization of one's own teaching style and an understanding of possible student learning styles that may be present in one's classes. This understanding, together with the knowledge of which teaching approach will prove most useful for a specific group of learners, is essential to addressing the mismatch. Offering parallel choices of different approaches/activities for learning will require both a re-evaluation of the "lecture, three tests and a final" format of many large lecture courses and the incorporation of a "buffet" of alternative methods for learning a given topic along with a more diversified assessment strategy. The effect of the teacher on student learning does not disappear even when alternative teaching methods, such as POGIL (Process Orientated Guided Inquiry Learning), are used. Small changes in the way an innovation is implemented can have large implications for both the type of student helped and the depth of student learning that takes place in this setting. In the end, the role of the teacher is still one of the most important variables in student learning. This chapter will explore typical learning styles together with teaching practices that are most helpful for these different learning styles. Research results dealing with the mismatch between teaching and learning styles will be discussed and recommendations for more effective teaching will be proposed.

Biography

I earned a BS in chemistry from LeMoyne College, Syracuse NY in 1972 and a Masters of Arts in Teaching from Cornell University, Ithaca, NY in 1973. After six years of teaching high school chemistry in three states (New York, North Carolina and Maryland), I returned to the University of Maryland—College Park and earned a PhD in chemical education, graduating in 1984. While a graduate student at the University of Maryland, I served as a curriculum writer for the ACS ChemCom high school curriculum project. This affiliation continued for a year after graduation until I accepted a position in the chemistry department at The Catholic University of America in 1985. Since I began teaching at Catholic University, I have specialized in teaching the "chemistry-phobic" students in both nursing and non-science majors' courses. I have always attempted to adjust my teaching style to better serve my students and as a result have participated in the development of two other ACS curriculum projects (Chemistry in Context and Chemistry) along with doing research that investigates the variables involved in student learning. This research has led to additional studies of the mismatch between how we teach and the way students learn. My research interests in chemical education led to my efforts to create a chemical education research feature in the Journal of Chemical Education. I continue to serve as a chemical education research feature editor for the Journal.

Introduction

The basic underlying principle of analyzing learning and teaching styles is the belief that all students can learn chemistry. It is not sufficient to tell students who are experiencing problems that they just need to study more. Studying more, if it is in a way that doesn't match the student's learning style, may prove useless. If students talk to a teacher recounting all the ways they have tried to succeed in the course but still remain unsuccessful, the teacher must first ascertain if the students are doing all that they should to learn chemistry. If at this point the teacher is still at a loss to explain why the student's study plan of reading the text, studying class notes, doing the homework and attending study sessions has not worked, it may be time to consider the existence of a mismatch between the way the material is presented and the way this particular student learns best. Based upon students' responses to questions directed at characterizing their learning style, the teacher should be able to give more explicit advice to struggling students. This advice may involve using supports that exist in a "buffet" of options connected with the course such as the CD that accompanies the textbook, a programmed instruction unit, or making more deliberate use of a WebCT homework tool devised for the specific course. The teacher might also suggest the use of a tutor or help from a specific teaching assistant for students whose learning styles do not match the teaching style of the teacher. Suggestions on summarizing the notes each day, electronically recording the class, recording an audio version of a student's notes and replaying them for study, devising graphs or diagrams to summarize notes, writing out verbal descriptions of graphs or figures, using model kits, or computer simulations available online or in a chemistry learning center may be just the directed help the student needs to succeed. The important point here is that the help suggested by the teacher should not be a "shot gun" approach but rather, should be tailored to the specific learning style of the student. This means that the teacher must be knowledgeable of the different learning styles and become adept at matching the specific support available in the course from the "buffet" of alternatives to the student's specific style. This chapter will survey some typical learning styles and the course supports that might prove a better match for the specific learner than the main teaching approach used in the course.

Research Support for matching teaching and learning styles

Using the concept of learning and teaching styles, students' inability to succeed in chemistry may have less to do with innate intelligence and more to do with the students' inability to fully apply their learning strengths to the study of chemistry. Students who are not able to apply their learning styles to the study of a particular subject may experience difficulty. When learning and teaching strategies are compatible, students experience the largest learning gains (Vermunt & Verloop, 1999) and teachers report the highest degree of teaching satisfaction. Even with a good match between learning and teaching styles, friction between the two can occur. This friction is constructive if it presents a challenge to students to increase or diversify their learning strategies. It is destructive if it overwhelms the student and results in a decrease in learning. In some situations, a teacher can use a teaching style that doesn't quite match a student's learning style but one in which the student has some skill. With the teacher's guidance, the student should be able to succeed with this new teaching style. As the student becomes more familiar with a specific teaching style, the teacher's role changes from director (activator) of student leaning to that of supporter (monitor) (Vermunt & Verloop, 1999). It is helpful if the teacher can characterize the learning style that is needed for a particular concept and offer some guidance on what is expected of the student. For instance, if the material is being presented through the use of graphs, the teacher could explain that students are required to be able to interpret the material demonstrated by the graph. Students might not have to generate the graph, but they will need to be able to interpret and hypothesize using the graph. The teacher may suggest that if students have trouble with this type of interpretation, that they spend time writing out for themselves all the information that can be gleaned by the graph. If both the student and teacher monitor the effects of the "less than perfect" match between teaching and learning styles on this topic, the student may become more comfortable with a learning style different from his/her preferred style. Being cognizant of the effectiveness of different learning styles is a mark of a student taking charge of his/her own learning -- a necessary step on the road to becoming an independent learner. Further development along these lines could result in the student learning how to adapt to a wide array of teaching styles that may or may not be compatible with his/her preferred learning style.

It is not possible to deliver a teaching style that will be a perfect match with each of the individual learning styles of the students in our science classes. But the news is not all bad. By the time students get to college, they are a relatively select group that to some extent has learned to succeed with the traditional lecture teaching style. Therefore, the range of learning styles that the college teacher sees is a subset of all possible learning styles. Adult students also have a more developed ability to adapt to different teaching styles than do young children. The college teacher then, does not have to present a teaching style that matches all the individual learning styles in his/her classroom. Recognition of the range of learning styles present among students and the appropriateness of different teaching styles for specific learning styles is the first step. Helping students who are having difficulty learning science in a particular course become aware of the potential differences in their learning style and the teaching style used in the course is the next step. The third step is making accommodations for this mismatch between teaching and learning styles through the use of a variety of alternative materials geared to different learning styles that cover the material in question. Not all of these materials have to be created. Many already exist from published sources. The teacher's role may be to locate, review or make the materials available to students. The teacher can also make specific suggestions to students in class about ways to approach the material if they are having trouble. In some cases, the teacher may also want to consider a wider range of assessment tools in the course to accommodate the range of learning styles. This could be as simple as including open ended conceptual questions in addition to multiple choice or mathematically-based questions on tests. This way, students will be assessed on what they understand and not how well their learning style matches the teaching style used in the course. Forms of assessment other than the "three tests and a final" approach could include the embedding of formative assessment tools such as online quizzes, graded homeworks, and practice tests taken in a group format with instant feedback and support from instructors/computer programs.

Learning

Before the match between teaching and learning can be pursued, learning must be defined. For the purpose of this chapter, the constructivist definition of learning as an integration of new knowledge into the student's pre-existing knowledge structure will form the basis of the definition. In other words, if true learning has taken place, the student's knowledge base is now changed and the student should be able to apply this new or modified knowledge in novel applications or transfer problems. This definition rules out memorization without understanding as true learning.

True learning includes three types of activities, namely, cognitive, affective, and metacognitive (Vermunt & Verloop, 1999). The *cognitive* activities of learning are those that form the focus of most courses, i.e., the ability to apply knowledge to new situations through problem solving and the construction of logical essays. However, both affective and metacognitive activities lead indirectly to learning outcomes and sometimes it is these learning activities that cause our students trouble. *Affective* learning activities include both a willingness to learn and the ability to concentrate on the content for an extended period of time, persisting even when understanding becomes difficult. How a student judges his/her success or failure in the course can contribute to the affective domain in terms of the student's self image. *Metacognitive* activities involve the development of the student's plan on how to learn the content and then his/her monitoring of the success of this plan through reflection. In other words, metacognitive activities include the degree to which the student is aware of his/her own learning style and its effectiveness. All three types of learning activities (cognitive, affective and metacognitive) are part of a student's learning style. When all three work well, the student is perceived as a mature, self-directed learner who is willing to work hard to learn chemistry and will adjust the way he/she studies to meet the changing demands of the material.

Learning Styles—Cognitive Activities

One approach to understanding the learning process from the student's point of view depends on knowledge of learning styles. *Learning style* is a set of student behaviors with cognitive, affective and behavioral dimensions that are exhibited consistently over time and a range of tasks (Guild, 1994).

According to Felder (1993) there are five aspects of learning style including: 1) the *type of information* students prefer to receive (sensory vs. intuitive); (2) the preferred *modality* used to gain sensory information (visual, verbal, or kinesthetic); (3) the preferred *organization* of the information (inductive vs. deductive); (4) how the information is *processed* (active vs. reflective); and (5) the preferred *progression towards understanding* (sequential vs. global). This is only one approach to understanding learning styles. This way of looking at learning styles incorporates many of the variables included in alternate definitions but Felder explains them in a way that is more accessible to the non-specialist. A short discussion of these five aspects of learning style will help teachers better understand the range of students' learning styles.

Perception of new information: Sensory vs. Intuitive.   Students who prefer to learn information in a sensory fashion learn best when they are given facts and procedures. They are less comfortable with symbols including mathematical and chemical symbols. In order to understand symbols, sensors "translate" them into concrete mental images or devise verbal explanations. Since this process takes time and energy, sensors often run out of time on chemistry tests. Sensory students would benefit from longer time on tests or a more elaborate description of graphs or symbols in their notes and on test questions. Intuitive students, on the other hand, are bored with too much detail and like to work things out for themselves. They enjoy working out novel problems but are often careless with the details as they concentrate on the big picture. They enjoy thinking about abstract concepts and are more likely to be successful in chemistry courses than sensory students. Intuitive students, however, often lose points on details in mathematical calculations even though they gain points for correctly analyzing the problems.

Modality: Visual, Verbal or Kinesthetic.   Most, but not all students, are visual learners by the time they get to college. Visual learners prefer pictures, diagrams, graphs and demonstrations over verbal material. If they don't write down what is said in lecture, visual learners will most likely forget it. Verbal learners, on the other hand, process information as they hear or read it. They do not need to take detailed notes and learn well in a lecture format where the information is mostly verbal with an occasional diagram or chart written on the board. They are also adept at gaining understanding from reading the textbook. Frequently, the notes of verbal learners are incomplete and although they think they understand something fully from lecture, they may not be able to adequately address an application question on a test that requires deep understanding. Kinesthetic learners, which are included in theories other than Felder's, learn best from applications of theories to real situations or the use of analogies to explain chemical concepts. They also learn well from movement such as physically acting out what molecules do under certain conditions or by manipulating molecular models to better understand structure.

Organization: Inductive vs. Deductive. Inductive learners prefer to learn by examining the specifics of a situation through observations, experimental results, and numerical examples and use these to develop a hypothesis or theory. This approach is more easily handled within a group learning situation. Deductive learners prefer to begin with the general principle and then deduce the conclusions and applications. Deductive learning lends itself to an orderly progression from general to specific and thus these learners prefer the highly structured presentation of lecture. Since inductive students have developed the over arching principle from the data themselves, they have a better chance of retaining that knowledge than do deductive students who are presented with the logic worked out by others.

Processing: Active vs. reflective. Active learners learn while directly engaged in activities such as trying things out in lab, interacting in small groups, or discussing ideas with others. Active learners work best when they are interacting with someone or something. Reflective learners prefer to think things out before trying them. Reflective learners often choose to work alone or in pairs. They need time and quiet to put things together in their mind.

Progression towards Understanding: Sequential vs. Global. Sequential learners absorb information in small chunks. They can solve problems even if they don't fully understand the larger context by following algorithmic steps in the solution. Their work is usually orderly and easy to grade for partial credit. In contrast, global learners absorb information in a random, unconnected order and make sense of it in large leaps of understanding. It takes global learners longer to make the connections between new information and prior knowledge but once they make these connections, global learners generally understand the concept more fully than sequential learners. Global learners often do poorly on homework or tests until they have grasped the whole concept. They sometimes do not grasp a concept in time within the quick pace of a typical science course's presentation-assessment cycle to be considered successful. They need time to make connections between concepts. Global learners also tend to be the students who show an improvement in grades as the course proceeds.

Other learning style theories

Felder's approach to learning styles which encompasses several different theories of learning styles is written in a manner that is more easily accessible to the non-specialist. Others have proposed more elaborate schemes such as Dunn and Dunn's approach that encompasses 20 learning style variables including learning environment, lighting level, temperature, classroom layout, motivation, persistence and need for structure (R. Dunn & Griggs, 2000). Grasha and Riechman's approach to learning styles (in Jonassen & Grabowski, 1993) includes the dipolar scales of participant-avoidant, collaborative-competitive, and independent-dependent. Gregoric's definition of learning styles (in Jonassen & Grabowski, 1993) includes the four variables Concrete Sequential, Concrete Random, Abstract Sequential, and Abstract Random. An excellent survey of leaning styles including some of those described here, but written for the chemistry teacher, can be found in Bretz (2005).

Teaching styles

It has often been said that teachers teach the way they have been taught. On the surface, this seems to make sense. Teachers, who have learned science successfully through the use of lectures, tend to teach their current science classes using lecture. But this view of teaching preferences doesn't adequately explain why some teachers search for new teaching strategies that are very different from the way they were taught. For instance, some teachers who learned chemistry primarily through a lecture teaching style are drawn to the guided inquiry and other collaborative group teaching innovations that are prevalent today. A closer examination of this phenomenon leads to the idea that a teacher's choice of teaching style is one that best matches how he/she learns (R. S. Dunn & Dunn, 1979; Friedman & Alley, 1984). The teacher's own learning style, then, rather than the way they were taught, determines the teaching style he/she feels most comfortable with (Kuchinskas, 1979). After all, the teacher him/herself was successful learning science in a particular way and the teacher wants to provide students with the same advantage. The only problem is that the teacher's learning style may not match that of all the students in class. This situation helps explain why some teachers are successful with a certain type of student and other teachers are successful with a different type of student. In most cases, the teacher is most successful with students whose learning style is congruent with the teacher's learning style and subsequent teaching style.

Teaching has two components, namely, knowledge and thinking strategies. The role of the teacher is to stimulate learners to "construct, change and utilize their knowledge" (Vermunt & Verloop, 1999). This definition of teaching also involves the three aspects of learning, namely, cognitive, affective and metacognitive activities. The cognitive activities of teaching deal with the presentation of the course content through lecture, homework problems, lab activities, demonstrations, review sessions and tests.

Some types of knowledge predispose the teacher towards different teaching styles (Heikkinen *et al.*, 1985). For instance, chemistry and other physical sciences have historically used a lecture format to deliver "set" curricula where the topics are well defined and sequential as opposed to education courses that have more often employed a discussion format to deliver a teacher-determined set of topics (Hativa & Birenbaum, 2000). However specific topics in both chemistry and education courses may be better taught through a non-typical teaching style for that discipline, e.g., discussion format in chemistry to investigate the connections between molecular structure and functionality and lecture format in education courses to present the science standards.

The cognitive aspects of teaching styles are seen by experts to be parallel to learning styles (Vermunt & Verloop, 1999): Sensory vs. Intuitive; Visual, Verbal or Kinesthetic; Inductive vs. Deductive; Active vs. Reflective; and Sequential vs. Global. In addition to these variables, the communication attributes of the teacher in terms of the way the information is presented also have an effect on student learning. A description of these variables and how they impact teaching styles is included here (Felder, 1993).

Sensory vs. Intuitive. A sensory teaching style includes descriptions of physical phenomena from real or simulated experiments, use of demonstrations and presentation of problem solving algorithms. An intuitive teaching style uses theories, mathematical models and material that emphasize conceptual understanding over the use of algorithms.

Visual, Verbal, or Kinesthetic. A visual teaching style uses sketches, plots, vector diagrams, computer graphics and demonstrations extensively. A verbal teaching style relies on the teacher's verbal explanation of phenomena in class. Kinesthetic teaching makes use of applications of the chemical concepts to real world problems, uses analogies in class or laboratory experiences to promote understanding of abstract concepts. Some teachers who use kinesthetic teaching styles have students act out the motion of molecules or use molecular kits to help students understand chemical structure and change.

Inductive vs. Deductive. An inductive teaching style provides students with a set of data and some guiding questions that help students analyze the data to form a hypothesis. A deductive style of teaching presents students with the principle or law and then has students work on problems that are applications of this principle/law.

Active vs. Reflective. Providing time in class for students to work in groups to discuss or solve problems/questions is indicative of an active teaching style. A reflective teaching style makes provision for students to reflect on material presented through the use of ConcepTests during class (Ellis *et al.*, 2001) (conceptual questions presented in lecture and addressed by pairs of students who then vote on the best answer) or Minute Papers (Angelo & Cross, 1993) (students summarize and write down the most important point of the class or the remaining unanswered questions) before leaving class.

Sequential vs. Global. Sequential teaching involves students constructing a logical argument that addresses a specific question in class, on homework and tests. Both modeling this behavior in class and requiring students to practice it, will help support sequential thinking. A global teaching style is often used when a new topic introduced in class. This approach relates the new information to previously learned topics both verbally by the teacher and in homework problems solved by the students.

Affective activities of teaching appear difficult to promote but they center on the teacher's creating and maintaining a positive motivational and emotional climate for learners. Teachers can help promote a supportive atmosphere by being supportive of students, providing constructive feedback in a timely manner, reassuring learners and pointing out the relevance of specific tasks, assignments or tests to the learning of specific content (Vermunt & Verloop, 1999).

Typical metacognitive activities of teaching include the teacher's ability to make students aware of the different learning processes required by different topics in chemistry. For instance, it is helpful for teachers to point out that names and symbols of the elements must be memorized but that there is some rhyme and reason to it. Explaining the logic behind the symbols for Carbon(C), Calcium (Ca), and Cadmium (Cd) based upon the order in which they were discovered, helps the students understand the interplay between memorization and the use of logic to learn a large amount of material. Teachers can support students' metacognitive processes by informing students of the learning objectives and providing formative and summative feedback that students can use to modify the way they study (Vermunt & Verloop, 1999). Formative evaluation or checkpoint activities built into the course that help students and teachers become aware of deficiencies in student learning without penalizing the student, shifts the emphasis and responsibility for true learning to the student. These formative evaluations can be online quizzes or homework assignments with instant feedback and explanation of incorrect answers, use or analysis of sample questions/solutions in recitation sessions, and use of sample test questions or ConcepTests in lecture.

Communication attributes. Studies relating communication attributes to learner satisfaction suggest the following attributes for successful teaching: teacher organization and clarity; teacher knowledge; interaction and rapport with the class; and teacher enthusiasm and stimulation (Emanuel & Potter, 1992). The most important of these attributes appears to be teacher enthusiasm/expressiveness. Students of all learning styles react most positively to a teacher who is enthusiastic about his/her subject and is able to relate to the students across the formal structure of a lecture classroom.

A Teaching example—Equilibrium

Equilibrium is a topic taught in most general chemistry courses. Usually a definition is presented followed by factors that affect equilibrium (Le Chatelier's Principle) and mathematical problems on the topic. This approach represents a bare bones and direct approach in the mind of the teacher. It is an intuitive approach based on presentation of the concept using theories and mathematical models. Depending on the teacher, this presentation is primarily verbal (explanations of what is written on the board) with graphs of concentration vs. time changes in the concentration of reactants and products of a system as it achieves equilibrium (visual). This deductive approach presents the concept to students prior to assigning problems. It is neither active nor reflective. It is primarily a passive sequential presentation where students are not expected to interact but simply take notes on the written and verbal explanations of the concept which may or may not be connected to a prior concept. The teacher has done his/her job of picking the best examples and presenting an organized lecture. Now it is time for the students to do their job and learn the material by reading the textbook, attending class and taking notes, studying the notes and doing the homework problems. The teacher does not expect the students to have undue difficulty with the assignment unless the students don't do the work or are unprepared for the challenges of the course. The study of chemistry takes effort. The teacher is right! Chemistry does require effort on the part of the student but this typical way of presenting the concept of equilibrium favors students who, like the teacher, already understand the concept of equilibrium and for whom, the lecture is simply a review of material already learned. This approach may not match the background or learning styles of the average novice student in the class.

The presentation of equilibrium described above can be modified in lecture to provide access to other students enrolled in the class. Not all of the modifications described here may be necessary. Those chosen should match the needs of the particular student population being taught.

- At the beginning of class, the teacher could list on the board a simple outline of the concept and applications that will be presented in class. This outline, which should be visible to students throughout the entire lecture, is called an Advanced Organizer and helps students know where they are going and where they have been in a lecture. The approach is especially helpful to visual preference students and others who have trouble separating the global from the specific aspects of a concept (a common problem with novices in any field). The teacher should refer to the outline several times during the class so students will know where they are in the presentation, i.e., a basic component of the concept itself or an application of the concept.

- Before a definition of equilibrium is presented, students can "experience" what is meant by equilibrium in one of three ways—a chemical demonstration, a demonstration with balls, or by having students act out an equilibrium situation in the front of the room. A demonstration of equilibrium using tennis balls requires either a large demonstration table or floor space in the room that is visible to all students. Assuming that there is a large demonstration table available, volunteers from the class stand at either end of the demonstration table. The "reaction" starts with 7 tennis balls representing reactants at one end of the table. As the reaction proceeds, one tennis ball at a time is rolled over to the "product side" of the reaction. The reaction is stopped at several points so that the students can comment on the relative amounts of both reactants and products. When the "product" concentration reaches a reasonable level (three tennis balls), one product tennis ball reverses the reaction and returns to the "reactant" side. The reaction continues in both directions until two things occur, namely, 1) the number of tennis balls forming products equals the number of tennis balls reforming reactants as demonstrated by the same number of tennis balls passing each other in the middle of the table and 2) the number of tennis balls representing reactants and products remains stable even though the numbers are NOT equal to each other.

- A different version of the tennis ball demonstration can be acted out with 7 students in the front of the room taking the place of the tennis balls. At the start, all the students stand on the reactant side with no students on the product side of the room. The reaction starts with one student moving to the product side followed by another until there are three student "products". This critical concentration then starts the reverse reaction reforming reactants with the "product" students moving back to the reactant side of the room. Once again, the discussion with the class concentrates on the equal forward and reverse reaction rates and the resultant stable concentration of reactants and products.

- Both of the previous two demonstrations could be followed with the class being challenged to write how the words "static" and "dynamic" can both be applied simultaneously to the concept of equilibrium. This exercise will help students focus on two seemingly opposite terms used to describe the same concept.

- The kinesthetic and active presentations of equilibrium can be followed with a more traditional chemical demonstration of equilibrium with the students challenged to explain what they see in the chemical demonstration in terms of a molecular level explanation of equilibrium.

- A ConcepTest question presented to the class using a graph of concentration vs. time for a chemical system can be used. Peer discussion during the ConcepTest, as a formative evaluation, can help students make the transition from the demonstration of people and tennis balls to the more conventional representation of equilibrium in terms of graphs and symbols.

- The teacher can then present Le Chatelier's principle as the typical response of a system in equilibrium to the stresses of changes in concentration, temperature or volume. Students should be presented with the equation of a system in equilibrium and work in teams to predict how the system will respond to changes such as removal of reactants, addition of reactants, etc.

- The time spent on mathematical applications of equilibrium can follow with students working in groups or teams on problems in class followed by discussion of the logic behind the range of student answers.

This approach to teaching in lecture uses a sensory approach from real and/or simulated equilibrium experiments. It is both visual and kinesthetic because it uses a written outline of the class presentation and simulated molecular activity to explain the concept. It is an inductive approach because students "see" the simulation and make observations before the formal definition is presented. Students are active participants in the teaching/learning process. The students are presented with the material sequentially so that they can make sense of each part of the concept before it is formally summarized. Students are not as likely to "zone out" during this type of class. They are encouraged to make sense or "learn" the material while they are still in class and are likely to raise more questions as they attempt to integrate this new information with their previously held understanding of equilibrium. The students who already have a good understanding of equilibrium are no longer the only students who "learn". All students now, have a better chance of thinking about equilibrium on a new and deeper conceptual level.

Other visual, sensory, inductive, and active approaches to teaching do not need to be so radical or time consuming as the example presented here. Suggestions for ways to present the meaning of balanced equations (Bunce, 2004) and mathematical problem solving (Bunce, 2005) have been presented elsewhere.

Interaction of Learning and Teaching Styles

If students are not aware of their preference for a particular learning style with its advantages and disadvantages and if their preferred leaning style does not match the teaching style of the professor, students may not be able to effectively and efficiently learn the material. The traditional format used in most of our large chemistry course of "lecture, three tests and a final" may be helpful for learners who learn best from the presentation of problem solving algorithms (sensory) delivered through the use of organized notes written on the board or in Power Point (visual) and explained by the teacher (verbal), starting with the general principle followed by examples (deductive) presenting all aspects of a larger concept in turn with no presentation of the overall concept (sequential), followed by a 3 tests and a final. But there may be others in the class who do not learn well with this approach. The traditional lecture format in most cases is not helpful to either active or reflective learners since the active learners are not necessarily engaged in any activity during lecture and the pace of the material in a typical lecture may be too fast to provide reflective learners with the time they need to integrate new knowledge into their prior knowledge. Kinesthetic learners who learn best from applications of theory to the real world may miss the importance of the concept presented. When lectures are delivered by a teacher who is perceived as "distant" or "uncaring", the affective dimension of teaching can be unfulfilled. If the teacher does not believe it is his/her job to direct students in the best ways to study the material, nor offer any formative evaluation checkpoints in the course, the metacognitive dimension of teaching can likewise be unfulfilled. So what can a teacher do?

The answer to this question is multi-dimensional. The teacher can spend more time verbally explaining diagrams, graphs and symbols so that the verbal student has a better chance of understanding the significance of the figure. This verbal presentation can help decrease the intrinsic visual load of a typical chemistry class, thus making learning more accessible to students. The teacher can vary the presentation of concepts so that sometimes he/she presents data and allows the class to develop the principle rather than presenting the principle and using lab to verify it with the collection of data. This would help the inductive student grasp the meaning of the concept. Introducing a topic with a demonstration rather than with a mathematical formula would aid the sensory learner. Providing some time in lecture or discussion sections for students to discuss problems/questions in groups rather than in a lecture format would enable active learners to succeed more easily. Providing time for reflective learners to process information in lecture through the use of questions that each person in the class is expected to answer or work out would be helpful. Presenting an overview of a concept before the logical presentation of each factor of the concept would help both global and sequential learners. All of these approaches add up to varying the activities within a lecture so that students with different learning styles each have a chance of understanding the content in a way consistent with their approach to learning. Such diversity in presentation helps keep the class interesting. If the teacher takes the additional step of helping students understand that he/she is using a variety of teaching styles in an effort to help them learn the concepts of chemistry better, students will become more aware of different approaches to learning. Follow up discussions in one-on-one counseling of students can recall a particularly helpful approach and suggest the student employ it as a means of learning a current topic that he/she finds difficult.

Teachers can also utilize a variety of teaching styles within a course. Cooperative groups using Process Orientated Guided Inquiry Learning (POGIL) style (Moog & Farrell, 2002) activity sheets can help the active, deductive learner. Preparing the recorder's report in POGIL activities can also provide the reflective learner with the opportunity to review what has been learned. Another way to address the issue of active and reflective learners is to incorporate ConcepTests into lecture. These conceptual questions, inserted into the flow of lecture, offer students and teachers a chance to determine if concepts are being learned or if the use of another approach to the topic is warranted.

The key to successful teaching of a diverse learning strategies audience is threefold 1) Be clear about the particular teaching strategy being used to present a topic 2) Provide parallel learning paths through alternative learning activities outside of class for those students who are not able to grasp the concept using the chosen class teaching strategy and 3) Incorporate a variety of teaching styles into the course choosing the most appropriate style for the particular topic and students in your course (Henson & Borthwick, 1984).

Assessment-Both Formative and Summative

By analyzing student responses to test questions, teachers may find an indication of what is happening to students' affective abilities during the learning process. If students provide answers to test questions that are a literal recounting of the teacher's words or passages from the text, but which do not address the question asked, it may be that the student expects to fail. Students who are demoralized by their previous achievement on tests, in a last ditch effort to salvage their grade, will bypass any attempt to understand the material and instead opt for a literal recounting of what the expert (teacher or text) says (Schmeck, 1988). It doesn't seem to matter to the student that the answers they are providing do not match the questions asked. These students are likely to become even more frustrated if they are told they didn't answer the question properly. Their reliance on the words of the experts, in their minds, is the sure fire path to success. These students should be shown that they *do* have a reasonable chance of success in the course but that their preferred learning style (memorization) does not match the requirements of learning the topic. This approach, which acknowledges the quantity of work they have performed, but attempts to explain the need for a deeper level of understanding, is the first step towards addressing both the affective and metacognitive aspects of learning. Students should then be guided to pursue a deeper understanding of a topic and practice explaining it to peers or in an imaginary conversation with someone they know who is not in the course (Angelo & Cross, 1993). Being able to explain a chemistry concept to someone either in the course or not, forces the student to address gaps in his/her understanding. This approach should help students become aware of their own surface understanding of a topic that requires a deeper understanding for success in assessment situations. Students should also be encouraged to test their new understanding in a formative evaluation situation such as an online test embedded in a textbook CD or in a web-based homework tool that provides feedback.

Using formative assessments means providing opportunities for students to gauge how well they understand the material. In order for formative evaluations to be the most beneficial, they should not be used to *grade* student achievement. Instead, students should be able to use such evaluations as a way to judge how well they are learning chemistry. Formative evaluation should not be a stressful situation, but rather should provide a guidepost in an attempt to judge progress. There are several established ways to make such opportunities available to students. In lecture, ConcepTests can be used to help students see if they clearly understand what has just been taught. Teachers can use the percentage of students who succeed as an indication of whether additional teaching of a specific topic is warranted. ConcepTests can be administered in a low tech environment by asking for a show of hands for the suitability for each answer. ConcepTests can also be used in a high tech environment by using hand held personal response devices (clickers) to electronically send student responses to a central computer where class data regarding answer selection can be displayed.

Other formative evaluation opportunities involve using sample tests available on some commercially prepared CD's or websites that accompany standard chemistry textbooks. Here, students can test and correct their own understanding by using the immediate feedback provided by the CD or website. A teacher can also post test questions from previous exams in a WebCT format that would allow students to view a range of answers that the teacher considers reasonable. This activity can be used to sensitize students to the quality and depth the teacher is expecting in student essay answers. Since the same questions will not be used in the actual summative assessment, students can ascertain if they know the chemistry content to answer sample questions and use this information to guide their studying.

Research support for the learning-teaching style approach

Most of the research published follows a particular theory of learning and teaching styles. As a result, the categories used to describe the particular learning style being tested are described in terms of the theory used. The theory described in this chapter is one specific theory and therefore, may not exactly match the variables or categories tested in the research reported.

The following reports of research are summarized in Jonassen and Grabowiski (1993). Research on Cognitive mapping (Cafferty, 1980 in Jonassen and Grabowski, 1993) reports that the greater the degree of match between student and teacher cognitive maps (learning and teaching styles), the higher student grades. Matching based on even some of the teaching-learning variables such as symbolic orientation (visual learning), and modalities (deductive vs. inductive), also produced an increase in student grades. Zelazek's research on the Grasha-Riechmann learning styles (Zelazek, 1986 in Jonassen and Grabowski, 1993) reports a change in learning style with age as older learners become better able to adapt to different teaching styles and more willing to take part in cooperative activities. Other research shows that well organized instruction facilitates learning on topics that students had little previous knowledge of but this effect was not evident on topics with which students were familiar (Abramson & Kagen, 1975; Dyer & Kulhavy, 1974; Tobias, 1973 in Jonassen and Grabowski, 1993). This finding suggests that the more prior knowledge a student has, the less instructional support is needed and the less effect teaching style will have on achievement. In a study of concept mapping, students with a high verbal aptitude were able to use less structured techniques than low verbal aptitude students (Holley & Dansereau, 1984 in Jonassen and Grabowski, 1993). This finding relates to the learning strategy discussed here that visual (low verbal) students rely heavily on diagrams, maps, and schematics and in this case, concept maps, as part of their learning style. High verbal students' success may not be as closely linked to the particular teaching strategy used.

Spoon and Schell (1998) report that learning style changes with age and experience. This means that students who enter our chemistry courses with learning styles that are not easily matched with the preferred teaching styles of most chemistry professors, can with time and guidance (metacognitive activities) become more comfortable with these teaching styles. Dunn and Dunn (1987) report on research that shows that older students require less teacher motivation and structure in the learning environment. College freshman courses usually include some students who have achieved this independence, others who are in the middle of the transition and still others who have not yet faced this area of growth. Teachers of freshman general chemistry courses and sophomore organic chemistry courses may need to address the issue of learning-teaching styles more than teachers of upper level chemistry courses.

A qualitative study (Campbell *et al.*, 2001) that observed different teachers and the effect their teaching style had on the achievement of students, reports that in highly teacher-controlled classes (e.g. lecture) there was no difference in achievement between those students who were previously identified as surface learners vs. deep learners. Both categories of student learners in a lecture format focused on the superficial learning technique of memorization. Student evaluations of these courses included comments that the pace was too slow as well as comments that the pace was too fast. The teaching process was rated overall by the students as not very effective. In contrast, in classes where students' learning styles were taken into consideration and the teaching styles varied throughout the course to include other methods in addition to lecture, students with both surface and deep learning approaches reported being challenged to learn more. Student evaluations of these teachers included descriptions of active, interesting and effective learning presented in a supportive environment. It is crucial, however, that when varied teaching styles are used within a single course that students are explicitly taught how to learn from these different styles. The main conclusion of this study is that without attention paid to the range of learning styles within a class, all students may be reduced to the lowest common denominator of memorization as a means of success in the course.

Teaching evaluations and their reflection of learning-teaching styles approaches

In both Campbell et al (2001) and Hativa and Birenbaum (2000), students' evaluation of the course is correlated to the match between students' learning style and the teaching style used in the course. If there is not a good match, students tend to rate the course and the teacher lower than if there is a good match. This helps explain why a course evaluation by some students can be high (those whose learning styles match the teaching style used) and low for others in the same course (those whose learning styles do not match the teaching style). However when a range of teaching styles are incorporated in a course, along with a student-centered and supportive atmosphere (affective) and suggestions from the teacher on how to approach the learning of topics (metacognitive) by an engaged and enthusiastic teacher, evaluations are usually consistently high. Students of all disciplines rate the preferred/ideal professor as one who is clear, interesting and organized (Hativa & Birenbaum, 2000).

Effect of learning-teaching style approach on the implementation of new teaching innovations

Adopting a new teaching innovation that is very different from the traditional lecture style is not a complete answer to addressing student learning styles. Teachers' specific implementation of the innovation (teaching style) can have just as large an effect on student learning as deciding to implement the innovation in the first place. The POGIL (Process Orientated Guided Inquiry Learning) approach to teaching chemistry involves students working in cooperative groups that use ChemActivities worksheets to learn topics and concepts in chemistry. These ChemActivities worksheets use the concept-invention-application model (Farrell et al., 1999; Moog & Farrell, 2002; Spencer, 1999). Lecture is rarely used and if used, is limited to no more than 10 minutes of the teacher talking. In research conducted on the implementation of POGIL in a general chemistry courses by two different POGIL experts, differences in student achievement were measured (Daubenmire, 2004). Students in the POGIL classes experienced two slightly different teaching styles (Teachers A and B) within the POGIL framework. When implementing the ChemActivities worksheets in the small cooperative groups, both Teachers A and B circulated around the room. When asked questions by members of the groups, Teacher A often supplied direct answers. Teacher B, on the other hand, posed more questions of the groups and rarely supplied direct answers to student questions. On the daily summary report required of each group, Teacher A expected a listing of all the answers to the questions found within the activity sheets. In contrast, Teacher B required no direct answers but rather a summary of the important points covered in the activity sheets. Observation of the two classes over a semester, documented that students in Teacher A's class spent most of their time in class, checking answers to the questions on the activity sheets and discussing the discrepancies among answers within the group. Teacher B's class spent considerably more time discussing the logic of the answers to the questions on the activity sheets. In addition, students in Teacher B's class were more likely to offer help in understanding the problems to other students in the group who were confused but did not actively seek help. These relatively small changes in the teachers' behavior (or teaching styles) had some significant effects on student achievement in the two classes. On the American Chemical Society final exam (ACS Examination Institute, 1997), students in Teacher B's class scored significantly higher on the conceptual questions regardless of the students' level of logical reasoning ability. Students in Teacher A's class who were at the lowest level of logical reasoning ability scored higher on the traditional questions than the equivalent students in Teacher B's class. Thus, Teacher A's direct answering of questions in class benefited the lower logical reasoning ability students on traditional problems but did not help any ability group of students on conceptual understanding as measured by the ACS exam. Teacher B's style of challenging students with more questions rather than supplying a direct answer, helped all logical reasoning ability levels of students succeed on conceptual questions but did not necessarily help the low logical reasoning ability students solve traditional problems as measured by the ACS exam. This leads to the conclusion that how one implements a new innovation (or more specifically, the teaching style used) should be matched to the goals of the course (traditional or conceptual understanding) and the aptitude or learning style of the students (low logical reasoning vs. high logical reasoning).

Summary

No matter what the learning styles of the students in a particular class or whether traditional or innovative styles of teaching are used, the teacher is still the key to student success. This is as true today as it was over 25 years ago. "The teacher is key" when it comes to "a successful school program" (DeRose et al., 1979).. If the teacher chooses a style of teaching that is compatible with his/her own style of learning, then only the students who hold congruent learning styles will be reasonably assured of success in that course. Teachers who pay attention to the range of learning styles of their students and adjust their teaching styles to better match these learning styles, will have a better chance of helping more students be successful in their classes. Teaching style, with both its potential effect on students of differing learning styles and the potential match with a particular topic, should be considered in the very beginning stages of course planning. Once a teaching style or combination of teaching styles is determined, teachers can then make plans to address the other dimensions of teaching, i.e., the affective and metacognitive attributes. Students, who experience a motivating, enthusiastic, knowledgeable, and organized teacher who helps them understand how to address the learning necessary for understanding topics, are more likely to succeed than those students who do not. No computer program, Power Point set of notes, videotape of a Nobel Prize winner's lecture, viewing of an award winning animation, or programmed instruction module can take the place of a student-centered teacher who is both a content and teaching expert. All other support materials help students with different learning styles achieve meaningful learning but it is the teacher who selects or constructs these materials and helps different students choose to use them in a constructive manner. The teacher is still the key to effective learning for the vast majority of students in a course whether traditional or innovative approaches are utilized. Student learning can be more dependent on the variables connected with a specific teacher than with any other single support mechanism within a course.

The learning-teaching styles approach expands the role of the teacher from that of content knowledge expert to include that of a teaching expert. It acknowledges that knowing chemistry through a successful implementation of one's own learning style is not necessarily enough to assure success as a teacher. A teacher can be viewed as someone akin to a physician who observes symptoms of discord and based upon his/her up-to-date knowledge of how learning takes place, diagnoses the problem and prescribes treatment (in this case, alternative learning strategies). It isn't that some chemists are "born teachers" but rather that they have done the work necessary to become teaching as well as content experts. With both content and teaching expertise, teachers are able to use content knowledge and teaching expertise to help students understand both the content and the process of learning chemistry.

Suggested Further Reading

An easy-to-understand overview of the learning styles literature.

Bretz, S. L. (2005). All students are not created equal: Learning styles in the chemistry classroom. In N. J. Pienta, M. M. Cooper & T. J. Greenbowe (Eds.), *Chemists" guide to effective teaching* (Vol. 1, pp. 28-39). Upper Saddle River: Pearson Prentice Hall.

A summary of Felder's approach to learning and teaching styles written for the practitioner.

Felder, R. M. (1993). Reaching the second tier--learning and teaching styles in college science teaching. *Journal of College Science Teaching, 22*(5), 286-290.

A scholarly book summarizing many of the competing theories of learning and teaching styles along with reports on the research tied to each theory.

Jonassen, D. H., & Grabowski, B. L. (1993). *Handbook of individual differences: Learning and instruction.* Hillsdale, New Jersey: Lawrence Erlbaum Associates.

References

Abramson, R., & Kagen, E. (1975). Familiarization of content and different response modes in programmed instruction. *Journal of Educational Psychology, 67,* 83-88.

ACS Examination Institute. (1997). General Chemistry (2nd Term) 1997 Special Exam. Milwaukee, WI: ACS Examination Institute.

Angelo, T. A., & Cross, K. P. (1993). *Classroom Assessment Techniques: A Handbook for College Teachers* (Second Ed.). San Francisco: Jossey-Bass.

Bunce, D. M. (2004). Interpreting and Addressing Student Apprehension. In D. M. Bunce & C. M. Muzzi (Eds.), *Survival Handbook for the New Chemistry Instructor.* Upper Saddle Brook, N J: Pearson Prentice Hall.

Bunce, D. M. (2005). Solving Word Problems in Chemistry: Why Do Students Have Difficulty and What Can Be Done to Help? In N. J. Pienta, M. M. Cooper & T. J. Greenbowe (Eds.), *Chemists' Guide to Effective Teaching.* Upper Saddle Brook, N J: Pearson Prentice Hall.

Bretz, S. L. (2005). All students are not created equal: Learning styles in the chemistry classroom. In N. J. Pienta, M. M. Cooper & T. J. Greenbowe (Eds.), *Chemists' guide to effective teaching* (Vol. 1, pp. 28-39). Upper Saddle River: Pearson Prentice Hall.

Cafferty, E. L. (1980). *An analysis of student performance based on the degree of match between the educational cognitive style of the teacher and the educational cognitive style of the students.* University of Nebraska.

Campbell, J., Smith, D., Boulton-Lewis, G., Brownlee, J., Burnett, P. C., Carrington, S., et al. (2001). Students' perceptions of teaching and learning: The influence of students' approaches to learning and teachers' approaches to teaching. *Teachers and Teaching: theory and practice, 7*(2), 173-187.

Daubenmire, P. L. (2004). *A longitudinal investigation of student learning in general chemistry with the guided inquiry approach.* The Catholic University of America, Washington, D.C.

DeRose, J. V., Lockard, D., & Paldy, J. (1979). The teacher is the key: A report on three NSF studies. *The Science Teacher, 46*(4), 31-37.

Dunn, K., & Dunn, R. (1987). Dispelling outmoded beliefs about student learning. *Educational Leadership, 44*(6), 55-62.

Dunn, R., & Griggs, S. A. (Eds.). (2000). *Practical approaches to using learning styles in higher education.* Westport, CT: Bergin and Garvey.

Dunn, R. S., & Dunn, K. J. (1979). Learning styles/teaching styles: Should they. Can they be matched? *Educational Leadership, 36*(4), 238-244.

Dyer, J. W., & Kulhavy, R. W. (1974). Sequence effects and reading time in programmed learning. *Journal of Educational Psychology, 43,* 53-70.

Ellis, A. B., Landis, C. R., & Meeker, K. (2001, June 1). Classroom assessment techniques: Conceptests. Retrieved September 2, 2005, from http://www.wcer.wisc.edu/archive/cl1/flag/cat/contests/contests1.htm

Emanuel, R. C., & Potter, W. J. (1992). Do students' style preferences differ by grade level, orientation toward college, and academic major? *Research in Higher Education, 33*(3), 395-414.

Farrell, J. J., Moog, R. S., & Spencer, J. N. (1999). A guided inquiry chemistry course. *Journal of Chemical Education, 76*(570-574).

Felder, R. M. (1993). Reaching the second tier--learning and teaching styles in college science teaching. *Journal of College Science Teaching, 22*(5), 286-290.

Friedman, P., & Alley, R. (1984). Learning/teaching styles: Applying the principles. *Theory into Practice, XXIII* (1), 77-81.

Guild, P. (1994). Making sense of learning styles. *The School Administrator, 51*(1), 8-13.

Hativa, N., & Birenbaum, M. (2000). Who prefers what? Disciplinary differences in students' preferred approaches to teaching and learning styles. *Research in Higher Education, 41*(2), 209-236.

Heikkinen, M., Pettigrew, F., & Zakrajsek, D. (1985). Learning styles vs. teaching styles--studying the relationship. *NASSP Bulletin, 69*(478), 80-85.

Henson, K. T., & Borthwick, P. (1984). Matching styles: A historical look. *Theory into Practice, 23*(1).

Holley, C. D., & Dansereau, D. F. (1984). Networking: The technique3 and the empirical evidence. In C. D. Holley & D. F. Danserau (Eds.), *Spatial learning strategies: Techniques, applications and related issues*. New York: Academic.

Jonassen, D. H., & Grabowski, B. L. (1993). *Handbook of individual differences: Learning and instruction.* Hillsdale, New Jersey: Lawrence Erlbaum Associates.

Kuchinskas, G. (1979). Whose cognitive style makes the difference? *Educational Leadership, 36*(4), 269-271.

Moog, R. S., & Farrell, J. J. (2002). *Chemistry: A guided inquiry* (2 Ed.). Danvers, MA: John Wiley and Sons.

Schmeck, R. R. (1988). An introduction to strategies and styles of learning. In R. R. Schmeck (Ed.), *Learning strategies and learning styles* (pp. 3-19). New York: Plenum.

Spencer, J. N. (1999). New directions in teaching chemistry. *Journal of Chemical Education, 76*, 566-569.

Spoon, J. C., & Schell, J. W. (1998). Aligning student learning styles with instructor teaching styles. *Journal of Industrial Teacher Education, 35*(2), 41-56.

Tobias, S. (1973). Review of the response mode issues. *Review of Educational Research, 43*, 61-74.

Vermunt, J. D., & Verloop, N. (1999). Congruence and friction between learning and teaching. *Learning and Instruction, 9*, 257-280.

Zelazek, J. R. (1986). Learning styles, gender, and life change cycle stage: Relationships with respect to graduate students. *ERIC Document Reproduction Service No. ED 276 371.*

3

Guided Inquiry and the Learning Cycle

Mark S. Cracolice
Department of Chemistry
The University of Montana

Abstract

This chapter presents a guide to the implementation of the *learning cycle* instructional strategy, a five-phase method for science course delivery. Originally developed based on the psychology of how students learn, the learning cycle has been shown to be an effective instructional strategy for the development of conceptual understanding and enhancement students' thinking skills.

Biography

Mark S. Cracolice is Professor and Chair of the Department of Chemistry at The University of Montana, where he teaches general chemistry and graduate courses in chemical education. He directs a graduate program in chemical education that includes graduate-level preparation in traditional chemistry as well as coursework and research in cognitive science and chemical education research. His current central research interest is in acceleration and promotion of the development of higher-order thinking skills. Cracolice has conducted numerous workshops designed to enhance the professional development of instructors across the elementary, high school, and college spectrum. His professional publications include textbooks and papers in research and practitioner journals.

Introduction

A half century ago, an inspiring essay was published that should be required reading for all college chemistry instructors, but it still has not received the attention it deserves from the instructional community. Entitled *The Central Purpose of American Education,* this essay, written by a committee called the Educational Policies Commission, outlines an often neglected issue, namely, our duty to develop curricula that not only teach content, but also develop students' thinking skills (Educational Policies Commission, 1961).

There are two important points made in this essay. First, it asserts that the central purpose of American education is the *development of the ability to think.* This ability can be further defined as the development of the rational powers of a person: "These powers involves the processes of recalling and imagining, classifying and generalizing, comparing and evaluating, analyzing and synthesizing, and deducing and inferring. These processes enable one to apply logic and the available evidence to his ideas, attitudes, and actions, and to pursue better whatever goals he may have. This is not to say that the rational powers are all of life or all of the mind, but they are the essence of the ability to think." (p. 5).

The second important point in *The Central Purpose of American Education* is that, by providing an appropriate classroom environment that fosters the development of the ability to think, we provide our students with *freedom of the mind*. This freedom is constructed by the individual, and it not only frees the individual, but it also preserves the society in which he or she lives: "Freedom of the mind is a condition which each individual must develop for himself. In this sense, no man is born free. A free society has the obligation to create circumstances in which all individuals may have opportunity and encouragements to attain freedom of the mind." (p. 3). One circumstance in which our society has a unique opportunity to fulfill this obligation is in its science classrooms.

To accomplish these goals, the development of students' ability to think and freedom of their minds, we must design chemistry courses based on something other than the discipline itself. We must design courses based on knowledge of how curricula can have a positive effect on thinking skills. We can simultaneously effectively teach chemistry content knowledge *and* develop our students' thinking skills. In fact, the two are inexorably linked. According to the Educational Policies Commission, "The ability to think cannot be developed or applied without subject matter." (pp. 18-19).

How do we Facilitate the Development of the Ability to Think?

If we accept the responsibility to do more than just teach chemistry content, and also design our courses so that we promote the development students' thinking skills, most chemistry instructors must change their curricula. Which of the following approaches is most similar to what you do now? Which looks the best for promotion of thinking skills?

Strategy 1
You spend hours preparing presentation slides that are complete with high-quality multi-colored graphics that include fades, dissolves, wipes, etc. The slides are also illustrated with photographs, art, molecular-level animations, and video clips. Students attend this lecture on acids and bases, which is initiated with a spectacular demonstration. Students electronically vote on their answers to sample questions during the lecture and see whole-class response data. After lecture, students do on-line homework that gives them immediate feedback. They then perform a lab exercise about acid–base properties.

Strategy 2
Students attend lab, where they are first asked the question, "What are acids and bases?" They reflect on the question and write individual answers. They then perform a laboratory exercise where, among other things, they investigate the chemical properties of various substances, such as strong acids and bases (unknowns to the students), and their reactions with substances such as phenolphthalein, magnesium metal, and magnesium nitrate solution. Students are then asked to identify the patterns in their data, draw conclusions, and justify their decisions. In place of lecture, students use their laboratory data and data collected and reported by others as the basis from which they build their conceptual understanding. Your preparation time is mostly spent in building exercises for students to work. Your primary in-class role is to provide leading questions and hints to small groups of students as they work on their data-based problems. After-class work is largely based on application questions and activities that challenge students to propose hypotheses and use data to evaluate their validity.

A cornucopia of evidence exists that indicates that Strategy 2—a guided inquiry approach—is more conducive to the development of students' thinking skills and conceptual understanding (e.g., Abraham & Renner, 1986; Berg, Bergendahl, & Lundberg, 2003; Farrell, Moog, & Spencer, 1999; Hake, 1998; Johnson & Lawson, 1998; Lawson, 1985; Lawson, 1990; Lawson et al., 2002; Renner, Abraham, & Birnie, 1988; Renner et al., 1973; Saunders & Shepardson, 1987; White & Frederiksen, 1998). It is certainly wise for educators to be cautious about avoiding educational fads and to avoid curricula that will result in decreased student performance. However, inquiry curricula are neither a fad nor lacking in rigor. The studies listed here, and many other similar research efforts over the past four decades, clearly demonstrate that inquiry-based curricula are superior to "traditional" expository curricula.

In terms of measuring the effects of an interactive engagement instructional strategy, the Hake (1998) study is most impressive. Introductory physics courses were compared on the basis of whether they were designed to facilitate active in-class engagement or not. Interactive engagement was defined as "methods as those designed at least in part to promote conceptual understanding through interactive engagement of students in heads-on (always) and hands-on (usually) activities which yield immediate feedback through discussion with peers and/or instructors." (p. 65). The average gain in conceptual understanding of the 4,458 students in interactive engagement courses was almost two standard deviations above that of the 2,084 students in traditional courses. A two-standard-deviation gain is a huge effect, essentially equal to the gain seen when comparing individual tutorial instruction with group instruction (Bloom, 1984).

How People Learn

If we want to design curricula that teach chemistry concepts and promote the development of students' thinking skills, we must first know something about how people learn. Among the more accessible recent summaries of research on how students learn is *How Students Learn: Science in the Classroom* (2005) from the National Research Council. In this book, three core research-based learning principles are described:

1. Students come to the classroom with preconceptions about how the world works. If their initial understanding is not engaged, they may fail to grasp the new concepts and information, or they may learn them for purposes of a test by revert to their preconceptions outside the classroom.

2. To develop competence in an area of inquiry, students must (a) have a deep foundation of factual knowledge, (b) understand facts and ideas in the context of a conceptual framework, and (c) organize knowledge in ways that facilitate retrieval and application.

3. A "metacognitive" approach to instruction can help students learn to take control of their own learning by defining learning goals and monitoring their progress in achieving them.

These principles, implications for teaching, and their application to the chemistry classroom are summarized in Table 1.

Learning and Implications and Applications

Core Learning Principle	Implication for Teaching	Application to the Chemistry Classroom
People often hold ideas about how the natural world works that are inconsistent with generally accepted scientific principles.	The first step in teaching a scientific concept is to help students become aware of their current thinking about that concept.	Instructors must be aware of common preconceptions and integrate these into the curriculum. Alternatively, our courses must be structured to elicit these preconceptions.
Knowledge of factual information is necessary but not sufficient for a person to be able to solve problems. Knowledge must also be mentally organized into useful frameworks.	Coverage of some concepts by working with applications from multiple contexts is a better approach than a lighter treatment of many concepts.	Chemistry textbooks usually are written to include many more topics than are needed in a course. Instructors should select a few central topics to cover in depth, selecting multiple contexts in which to illustrate the concept.
Expert problem solvers carefully monitor their progress as they think. Novices often do not use this self-monitoring strategy, but it is a teachable skill.	Instructors should explicitly teach students how to have an "internal conversation" while solving problems.	Instructional materials should incorporate programmed examples to help students learn to monitor their learning. Tutorials should incorporate instruction on monitoring strategies.

Table 3.1 Research-based findings about learning and implications and applications. Adapted from National Research Council (2005).

Guided Inquiry

If we are to design a chemistry classroom based upon principles of how people learn, it is apparent that most courses are not aligned with the Application to the Chemistry Classroom from Table 1. We never ask students what they think before we begin instruction on a topic, we tend to teach a large number of topics in a superficial manner, and we rarely, if ever, listen to students as they think out loud while solving a problem. Fortunately, there is a well-established instructional strategy that is based on how people learn. The mental functioning model of Jean Piaget (1963) serves as the basis of the *inquiry* strategy.

The term *inquiry* literally means "a search for knowledge." The most well known advocate of inquiry curricula from the early history of education is John Dewey. A century ago Dewey (1910/1978) wrote, "science has been taught too much as accumulation of ready-made material with which students are to be familiar, not enough as a method of thinking, an attitude of mind, after the pattern of which mental habits are to be transformed." Alas, this remains as true today as it did 100 years ago. Instead of presenting chemistry as a quest for knowledge, many instructors only hope that students will become familiar with some of the material so that it can be more easily be recalled at some later date. The term *guided inquiry* likely found its origin in a 1962 paper by Atkin and Karplus in which they described a guided discovery approach to science teaching.

The key difference between an inquiry and a non-inquiry approach is the sequence in which instruction occurs. In general, most college chemistry courses include three phases per major concept: (1) inform students about the concept, usually through lecture and/or textbook readings, (2) verify that the concept is indeed true, sometimes through a laboratory exercise, but almost always through information transmitted via lecture and/or the textbook, and (3) practice answering questions about the concept, usually through end-of-chapter homework problems. This "traditional" sequence is usually called inform–verify–practice.

An inquiry approach reverses the sequence of the first two phases described above. The laboratory comes first. Students collect data before they are told about the concept. If a lab is impractical, data can be provided to the students, ideally with a description of the instrumentation used to collect the data and information about the conditions under which the data were collected. Students then use the data to construct their own knowledge of the concept. That concept is then refined through practice. In essence, an inquiry strategy follows a verify–inform–practice sequence, but the verification phase is a "consider the data" phase and the inform phase is a "construct the concept in your own mind" phase.

The Learning Cycle

The learning cycle instructional strategy provides the most practical way to implement a guided inquiry curriculum in a college chemistry course. Abraham (2005) described an instructional strategy as "the arrangement, combination, and form of learning activities, materials, and instructional tactics designed to meet educational objectives." Thus, the learning cycle is a framework upon which a variety of activities and materials can be built.

The learning cycle had it origin in the Science Curriculum Improvement Study (SCIS), a post-Sputnik era National Science Foundation-funded project (Karplus & Their, 1967). Robert Karplus, a University of California Berkeley physicist-turned-science-educator, was the key person driving the SCIS project. Karplus and co-workers developed a complete elementary science curriculum in the 1960s, and he did pioneering work in researching the development of students' thinking skills in the 1970s (Fuller, 2003). The three central phases of the learning cycle were distinctly described by Karplus and others in 1977 (Karplus et al., 1977).

To implement the learning cycle instructional strategy, the essential concepts appropriate for the course must first be chosen. For each essential concept, instruction proceeds in a series of five phases. These phases must be followed in sequence for the maximum benefits for the promotion of students' conceptual knowledge and improvement in their thinking skills (Abraham & Renner, 1986). The five-phase sequence is repeated multiple times, preferably building on one another, many times throughout the typical course.

Engage

The first phase of the learning cycle is called engage. It has two primary purposes: (1) to promote students' curiosity and engage their attention and (2) to elicit their preconceptions. Human senses are continually bombarded with stimuli. At this very moment, you are seeing the words on the page, hearing the sounds in the room, smelling the airborne scents, feeling the sensations associated with what you are touching, etc. Because of the huge quantity of sensory information available to us at any given moment, we must be selective about what we pay attention to. The same issue with attention is also true on a larger scale. We make choices about what we will read in the newspaper, what we will watch on television, etc., and we choose a level of attention. We may skim a magazine article, read it word-for-word, or critically analyze it, pausing in reflective thought every few paragraphs. Students must make similar choices about learning. To bring students past the "skim" attention level for learning in our classrooms, each learning cycle should start with a question that piques students' interest. Many chemistry instructors use a demonstration for this purpose. Demonstrations work best when students are asked to predict the outcome of the demonstration in advance. This is one method of eliciting preconceptions.

Explore

The explore phase is second in the sequence. Its primary purpose is to guide students to collect and process the meaning of information or data. Marek and Covallo (1997) recommend that this phase include what they call six essential experiences: observing, measuring, interpreting, experimenting, model building, and predicting. Students need experiences in observing nature; what is seen by an individual is a function of their past knowledge, and thus observation is the critical first step in learning about natural phenomena. Measuring is a logical extension of observing. All chemists understand the need to incorporate measuring into a course curriculum, and understanding the function and manipulation of the appropriate measurement instruments is an associated skill that should be developed in the explore phase. After data have been collected, whether qualitative (observed), quantitative (measured), or both, they must be interpreted. Instructors must be cautious not to provide too much guidance in the interpretation of data; students should be provided with hints about identifying flaws in interpretation rather than being told directly that they are right or wrong so that they can learn to rely on the data themselves rather than the opinion of an authority.

The interpretation experience leads to the next three experiences, experimenting, model building, and predicting, which, in turn, often leads back to additional interpretation. Experimenting refers to making additional observations and measurements, but under controlled conditions. This process will generate more data that students will use to construct the underlying scientific concept. Model building follows from experimenting. This is the point at which a hypothesis—a proposed explanation for the observed phenomenon or pattern—is developed. The hypothesis is usually in the form of a model (Justi & Gilbert, 2002). It has been suggested that models are the essence of scientific thinking (Harrison & Treagust, 2000), although it is also unfortunately true that model building is rarely incorporated into college chemistry curricula (Bodner, Gardner, & Briggs, 2005). After a hypothesis or model is constructed, it can be used to make predictions, and predicting is the last of the six essential experiences. Predicting is particularly useful when patterns in the data lead to multiple working hypotheses because it will help to support or contradict the hypotheses posed, leading to a process of recognizing when none of the hypotheses have reasonable support or when multiple causes underlie the observed phenomena.

Explain

After students have had the opportunity to explore the concept, they must be given the opportunity to explain what they have learned. The explain phase provides this opportunity. Note in particular that it is the *students* who are supposed to do the explaining, not the instructor! The instructor has two primary roles in this phase: (1) providing hints, guiding questions, and Socratic argumentation, all in an attempt to help students construct their knowledge, and (2) proving the appropriate terminology and vocabulary commonly shared in the scientific community when discussing the concept. When students demonstrate a sound understanding after the engage and explore phases, there is little for an instructor to do in the explain phase other than to provide terminology.

Students who do not have a proficient understanding of the concept by the time the explain phase occurs should not be told "the correct conclusion" in an attempt to keep them moving along through the curriculum. This type of approach will teach the student that they will be allowed to memorize the "right answer" as long as they wait out the instructor, and they will not develop the type of meaningful understanding that comes from a data-to-concepts approach. Instead, tactics such as providing hints, probing for understanding of prerequisite knowledge, focusing the student on the critical data, questioning, and asking the student to explain his or her reasoning must be used until the student is able to invent his or her own understanding. This type of tutoring may be provided by the instructor or a more knowledgeable peer.

Elaborate

Understanding a concept in isolation from its relationships to other concepts is essentially useless. The elaborate phase gives students the opportunity to reorganize their newly learned knowledge in the context of what they already understand. The theoretical importance of the elaborate phase was emphasized by both Vygotsky and Ausubel. Vygotsky (1986) noted that conceptual reorganization is the key event in the transition between an intuitive understanding of a concept and the more powerful ability to consciously perform intellectual operations with the concept—in other words, to use the conceptual understanding to solve novel problems. Ausubel (1963) also described the importance of mentally reorganizing newly learned concepts with those that were previously learned so that meaningful learning can occur.

Thus, the elaborate phase of the learning cycle should focus, as much as possible, on helping students see the relationship between the concept just learned and concepts that were learned earlier in the course or in prerequisite courses. This is usually conducted with additional data-to-concept activities. For example, one learning cycle activity we use in high school chemistry begins with students inventing a new personalized length unit. The explore and explain phases end when students understanding the relationships between their system of measurement and the metric system. The elaborate phase is designed to extend that relationship to any system of measurement and ultimately to a very generalized understanding of proportional reasoning. In general, we always attempt to use the elaborate phase to extend students' understanding to the thinking skill underlying the concept. Thus, the thinking skill becomes the most general organizational structure, and all subordinate concepts are ultimately organized as an application of the skill.

Evaluate

The final phase of a learning cycle is evaluation of students' learning. In general, students should be given an opportunity for self-assessment before they encounter a more formal evaluation. Traditionally, most chemistry courses have provided self-assessment in the form of homework problems that are followed by an exam that consists of homework-like questions. Lab exercises are traditionally followed by a lab report or a research-like poster session. These types of traditional activities will fit into a learning cycle curriculum, although the emphasis on exams should change from lower-order and algorithmic questions to higher-order and conceptual questions as students gain experience with learning via a learning cycle approach. We also suggest that students' thinking skills be evaluated. This is not needed with each cycle, but rather their development should be tracked over a longer time period, such as a semester or academic year. Instruments such as the Classroom Test of Formal Reasoning (Lawson, 1978; Lawson, 1992) or the Group Assessment of Logical Thinking (Bunce & Hutchinson, 1993; Roadrangka, Yeany, & Padilla, 1982) can be used for this purpose.

Table 2 lists appropriate and inappropriate instructor actions for each phase of the learning cycle. These should provide a different perspective on the preceding explanations of the phases.

Implementing the 5E Learning Cycle

Learning Cycle Phase	What To Do	What *Not* To Do
Engage	• Ask a question about the natural world • Elicit students' preconceptions about the targeted concept • Provoke students' curiosity about the concept via a demonstration, illustration of a relevant application, etc.	• Give a definition of what students are about to learn • Encourage students to read ahead or preview the textbook material
Explore	• Provide students with instructions about how to collect data, or, if a laboratory approach is not possible, provide students with an explanation of how data was collected and the data themselves • Ask students to analyze the data and draw conclusions based on those data	• Answer the question • Introduce a verbal statement of the concept • Immediately verify that a student's data analysis is "correct"
Explain	• Provide vocabulary that scientists use when discussing the concept • Encourage students to compare their explanations with others while explaining their thought processes	• Give students terminology before they understand the concept
Elaborate	• Assign homework problems to help students see applications of the same concept in different contexts • Additional laboratory exploration of the same concept in different contexts • Assign problems designed to help students organize their new knowledge and its relationship with their preexisting knowledge	• Assume that exposure to a concept in one context is sufficient for meaningful learning • Assume that students will spontaneously revise their prior knowledge
Evaluate	• Assess students' content knowledge and improvement in thinking skills through written and oral examinations • Assess students' declarative and procedural knowledge through laboratory reports and presentations	• Overemphasize exam questions that encourage students to learn algorithms

Table 3.2 Implementing the 5E Learning Cycle. Adapted from Trowbridge, L. W., & Bybee, R. W. (1990).

An impressive body of work over the past 30 years by Lawson and colleagues supports the effectiveness of the learning cycle model (e.g., Lawson, 2003; Lawson, Abraham, & Renner, 1989). Research shows that the core three phases of the learning cycle, (1) exploration of a pattern in nature, (2) discussion of the pattern and introduction to its associated vocabulary, and (3) application of that pattern in new situations, are each necessary and work best when sequenced in this order. Additionally, learning cycle classrooms are the best-known curriculum models for fostering the development of students' ability to think. Researchers from the *Cognitive Acceleration through Science Education* and *Centre for the Advancement of Thinking* groups have conducted numerous experiments that demonstrate the effectiveness of inquiry curricula based on the theories of Piaget and Vygotsky (Adey & Shayer, 1994; Shayer & Adey, 2002). Their work demonstrates that an appropriately-designed science curriculum can have a positive effect on improving components of a student's content knowledge *and general intelligence*.

Similarly, Schneider and Renner (1980) compared traditional teaching to a learning cycle approach with 48 ninth-grade students in a physical science course over a semester, finding that the students in the learning cycle group outperformed those in the traditional group in content knowledge on immediate and delayed posttests. Additionally, students in the learning cycle group outperformed the traditional group on measures of formal reasoning on immediate and delayed posttests. The learning cycle students also showed greater gains on an IQ test.

Chemistry Applications

A college chemistry instructor who wishes to begin to use a guided inquiry and/or learning cycle approach to instructional design will most likely find that the best first step is to revise the laboratory curriculum. A number of inquiry-oriented laboratory manuals for college chemistry have been developed. Abraham and Pavelich's (1999) *Inquiries Into Chemistry,* Bauer, Birk, and Sawyer's (2005) *Laboratory Inquiry in Chemistry,* Cooper's (2006) *Cooperative Chemistry Laboratory Manual,* and Peck and Williamson's (2005) *Experiences in Chemistry I and II: Inquiry and Skill Building* are good examples of inquiry lab curriculum materials. A key idea is to sequence the lab to occur before the concept is discussed in lecture. Thus, the lab would be the explore phase in the 5E learning cycle. We suggest that you begin to get your feet wet in implementing inquiry instruction simply by choosing one or more of the exercises from one of these books and following the guidance in the Instructor's Manual. For example, if you are now doing a verification-style acid–base lab, you can find your favorite closest match in one of the commercially-available lab manuals, and substitute it the next time you teach the course.

A more intensive change in lab can be accomplished by implementing a technique such as the Model-Observe-Reflect-Explain (MORE) Thinking Frame, a guided inquiry lab format that places an emphasis on the promotion of metacognition (Rickey & Stacy, 2000; Tien, Rickey, & Stacy, 1999). Students begin a lab exercise by expressing their representation of their initial model of the experimental system. After experiment in a series, students are required to reflect on the relationship between their data and their model, prompting modification of their initial model. Research on this format indicated that the curriculum did indeed improve students' metacognitive abilities, as well as their content understanding.

Another more intensive change in the lab can be accomplished by combining a guided inquiry format with the Science Writing Heuristic (SWH). In this context, the term *heuristic* refers to an educational method in which learning takes place through discoveries that result from investigations made by the student—in other words, in a data-to-concepts inquiry sequence. The SWH provides students with a method for writing lab reports that helps to encourage deep thinking and promote conceptual understanding (Greenbowe & Hand, 2005; Rudd, Greenbowe, & Hand, 2001/2002). The essence of the SWH is to change the traditional laboratory report into an exercise that consists of questions such as "What are my questions about this experiment? What did I see when I completed my tests and procedures? What evidence do I have for my claims?" This type of structure helps students to make the appropriate connections between their data and the target concept much more effectively than does a traditional lab report.

A more advanced integration of guided inquiry into a course would involve both the lab and the lecture portions of the course. One of the more impressive and well-developed efforts to implement an inquiry approach in the entire general chemistry course has been undertaken by Farrell, Moog, and Spencer (1999) at Franklin and Marshall College. Their approach is lecture-free, where students work in small groups during the traditional lecture time with worksheets while the instructor primarily observes. Their lab is also based upon a guided inquiry curriculum. When compared with historic success rates, students in the guided inquiry general chemistry course are more likely to earn a passing grade.

Moog and Farrell (2006) have published a series of 62 activities for guided inquiry in the "lecture" part of the general chemistry course. This is an excellent starting point for general chemistry instructors who want to implement a guided inquiry approach instead of the traditional lecture. The same author team has also produced two textbooks to support a guided inquiry approach to physical chemistry (Moog, Spencer, & Farrell, 2004; Spencer, Moog, and Farrell, 2004).

Lewis and co-workers (Lewis & Lewis, 2005) at the University of South Florida have blended the Farrell, Moog, and Spencer (1999) guided inquiry approach with that of the Peer-Led Team Learning (PLTL) project (Gosser et al., 2001). They call this blended approach peer-led guided inquiry. Their strategy is to use the Moog and Farrell (2006) guided inquiry activities to introduce each topic to small groups of students, as guided with the assistance of a peer leader, as in the PLTL approach. They reduced the amount of lecture time to accommodate the peer-led guided inquiry sessions. Even with this reduction in lecture time, students in the peer-led guided inquiry course slightly outperformed a control group who had more lecture time.

Barriers to Inquiry

Given the preponderance of evidence that shows that an inquiry approach to teaching chemistry is superior to a lecture–verification lab–recitation approach, it is remarkable that a survey from more than a decade ago indicated that only 8% of U.S. colleges and universities with chemistry programs approved by the American Chemical Society used inquiry laboratories (Abraham et al., 1997). Our experience with professional development of practicing college and high school instructors indicates five major reasons for not using inquiry-oriented curricula.

1. Too much work

All of the major textbook publishers provide beautifully illustrated, well written four-color textbooks for all high-enrollment chemistry courses, complete with instructor support packages that include lecture presentation slides, test banks, online homework and course management systems, and many other convenient ancillaries. No such package is currently available for an inquiry approach to a college chemistry course. It is certainly true that these packages make teaching easy, but the easiest choice does not necessarily correspond with the best choice. As with physicians, our duty as instructors is to provide the best known practice in our profession. Given that an inquiry-oriented approach is the best practice, it is our obligation to devote the time and energy necessary to employ the strategy.

Our experience indicates that the transition from expository instruction can be made easier by (a) gradually implementing an inquiry-based curriculum and (b) obtaining guidance from an instructor with experience in inquiry teaching. Additionally, if you have the opportunity to work with a colleague in changing your curriculum, sharing the work and having someone to talk with helps in making the transition. As noted previously, the best place to start the change is in the laboratory. A variety of materials are available, and the laboratory is a natural place to do inquiry-oriented chemistry instruction.

2. Cannot cover the ACS-recommended content and implement an inquiry approach (pace is too slow)

Numerous studies have shown that what we may perceive as examination-based evidence of student learning actually reflects little or no meaningful conceptual understanding (Mason, Shell, & Crawley, 1997; Nakhleh, Lowrey, & Mitchell, 1996; Nurrenbern & Pickering, 1987; Sanger, 2005; Zoller et al., 1995). Thus, "covering" the standard content in a course is not necessarily related to students' learning that material. Given that the national average percentage correct on the 2003 American Chemical Society Division of Chemical Education General Chemistry Exam is 59%, it is readily apparent that the average student is not learning content at the level of expectation of the committee who constructed the exam; this level of expectation is likely parallel to most college general chemistry instructors. There is much to gain and relatively little to lose by implementing an inquiry approach. It is important to consider that covering less content in more detail may result in net increased student achievement. However, our experience with implementation of intensive inquiry curricula in high schools has shown that even though the pace of an inquiry-oriented course at the beginning of the academic year is often slower than the curriculum it replaced, once students become comfortable with a data-to-concepts approach, they eventually cover content more quickly with the inquiry approach. The net effect of switching from a lecture to inquiry typically is that content coverage is approximately the same, but student declarative and procedural knowledge increases.

3. Discomfort and teaching habits

Almost all of today's faculty learned their undergraduate chemistry in a lecture-dominated course. Additionally, many faculty begin teaching a new course by adapting the course of their predecessor, and that is usually a lecture course. For faculty who are experienced teachers, the years of development of a series of lectures is often too much of an investment to easily abandon. Therefore, it is a major change to implement an inquiry-oriented approach, and it is uncomfortable to change. This is largely fear of the unknown, however, because we have never known an instructor to regret the transition to an inquiry curriculum. Professional development opportunities such as the workshops that are part of the Biennial Conferences on Chemical Education and the Chautauqua Short Courses for College Teachers are available to help instructors gain confidence and receive support in making the transition.

4. Alternative conceptions about inquiry

The term *inquiry* has evolved into an educational buzzword that has many interpretations. Some instructors believe that they are already implementing an inquiry approach when a subjective examination of their classrooms would reveal that they are not. Abraham (1982) developed an instrument that reveals students' view of the nature of the laboratory portion of a course. When this instrument is used to measure students' perceptions of the laboratory, it is sometimes seen that what an instructor may describe as an inquiry laboratory actually is not. A similar disconnect was also seen the Third International Mathematics and Science Study (TIMSS), which compared mathematics and science achievement of U.S. students with students from other countries. The TIMMS researchers found that seventy percent of U.S. teachers claimed to be implementing best-practices methods for teaching, but videotaped analysis of their lessons revealed that they were only implementing surface features of the model curriculum. U.S. teachers failed to focus their lessons on the key point of promoting high-level thinking (Stigler et al., 1999). Our experience with science teachers reveals a similar trend where many say that they are teaching by inquiry, but they are, in fact, only implementing some of the less important features while neglecting the key elements needed to allow students to construct their own knowledge, proceeding from data to concepts. This problem can be avoided by investing the time necessary to develop a meaningful understanding of the nature of scientific inquiry. The suggested readings at the end of this chapter provide sources for development of such an understanding.

5. Inadequate infrastructure and/or too many students

Another barrier to implementation of an inquiry-oriented curriculum is the awkward infrastructure that accompanies most large college chemistry courses. Students in such courses often perform any given laboratory in a time frame that may be spread over an entire week. This makes a data-to-concepts approach difficult if the data are collected in the lab and the concepts are formulated in the lecture. Some students will have collected the data a week before others, so the temporal relationships in the course do not flow well. One of the more radical (but ingenious!) approaches to overcoming this barrier was formulated and described by Williamson and Abraham (1992). Their course was structured so that students always alternated between lab and lecture every other class meeting. Thus, the data collected in the lab were pooled and always analyzed in the subsequent lecture and before the next lab.

Even with a conventional large-course structure, this barrier can be overcome by choosing larger-scale and smaller-scale learning cycles that fit within the course format. On the larger scale, a whole-course approach to data analysis can be accomplished, even if data are collected over a week. A brief refresher is usually sufficient to help students recall the laboratory exercise. Many small-scale approaches allow a course to be inquiry-oriented, as described through this chapter and in the references cited. For example, with appropriate teaching assistant training, each laboratory section in a large course can do their own learning cycles, pooling only the data collected in their section. Of course, laboratory collection of data is not a requirement of a learning cycle approach. Data can be provided for students, and they can work toward constructing conceptual understanding as an in-class, discussion section, or homework exercise (Deming & Cracolice, 2004). Thus, any given lecture can become a learning cycle, as long as you start by presenting data and working toward the concept.

Conclusions

It has been more than a decade since Bodner (1992) suggested that simply changing the topics taught in chemistry courses without changing the curriculum delivery method would be insufficient to resolve our present well-known problems with chemical education. Unfortunately, most chemistry instructors who have involved in reform projects over the last decade (or more) have an all-too-keen understanding that such projects have had too little of a lasting effect. Even students who are "successful" in a typical general chemistry course tend to have an algorithmic, lower-order cognitive skills understanding of chemistry, as opposed to the conceptual, higher-order cognitive skills understanding needed to be a successful problem solver (Zoller et al., 1995).

The learning cycle instructional strategy provides a theory-based, research-proven approach to curriculum delivery that will accommodate any science curriculum. Materials are beginning to be developed for chemistry courses that will allow instructors to at least implement pieces of a guided inquiry learning cycle in their courses. This type of gradual implementation is highly recommended.

Acknowledgements

I sincerely appreciate Norb Pienta, Melanie Cooper, and Tom Greenbowe for their vision and their tireless efforts in seeing this project to its completion and their helpful reviews of earlier versions of the chapter. I also wish to express my appreciation to Robin Shropshire of The University of Montana–Helena College of Technology for a critique of the first draft of this chapter and to John Deming of Winona State University for his contributions in the form of many valuable discussions over many of the topics in this chapter.

Suggested Readings

Lawson, A.E., Abraham, M.R., & Renner, J.W. (1989). *A theory of instruction: Using the learning cycle to teach science concepts and thinking skills.* Cincinnati, OH: National Association for Research in Science Teaching.

Marek, E.A., & Cavallo, A.M.L. (1997). *The learning cycle: Elementary science and beyond.* (Rev. ed.) Portsmouth, NH: Heinemann.

The following Internet resources may also be helpful:

The process of the Science Writing Heuristic homepage:
http://avogadro.chem.iastate.edu/SWH/homepage.htm

The Process Oriented Guided Inquiry Learning (POGIL) website:
http://www.pogil.org/

References

Abraham, M.R. (1982). A descriptive instrument for use in investigating science laboratories. *Journal of Research in Science Teaching, 19*(2), 155-165.

Abraham, M.R. (2005). Inquiry and the learning cycle approach. In N.J. Pienta, M.M. Cooper, & T.J. Greenbowe (Eds.), *Chemists' guide to effective teaching* (pp. 41-52). Upper Saddle River, NJ: Pearson Prentice Hall.

Abraham, M.R., Cracolice, M.S., Graves, A.P., Aldhamash, A.H., Kihega, J.G., Palma Gil, J.G., & Varghese, V. (1997). The nature and state of general chemistry laboratory courses offered by colleges and universities in the United States. *Journal of Chemical Education, 74*(5), 591–594.

Abraham, M.R., & Pavelich, M.J. (1999). *Inquiries into chemistry* (3rd ed.). Prospect Heights, IL: Waveland Press.

Abraham, M.R., & Renner, J.W. (1986). The sequence of learning cycle activities in high school chemistry. *Journal of Research in Science Teaching, 23*(2), 121–143.

Abraham, M.R., & Williamson, V.M. (1992). Integrating the laboratory and lecture with computers. In W.J. McIntosh & M. W. Caprio (Eds.), Successful approaches to teaching introductory science courses (pp. 21-28). Cedar City, UT: Society for College Science Teachers.

Adey, P., & Shayer, M. (1994). *Really raising standards: Cognitive intervention and academic achievement.* London: Routledge.

Atkin, J.M., & Karplus, R. (1962). Discovery or invention? *Science Teacher, 29*(5), 45.

Ausubel, D.P. (1963). *The psychology of meaningful verbal learning*. New York: Grune and Stratton.

Bauer, R.C., Birk, J.P., & Sawyer, D.J. (2005). *Laboratory inquiry in chemistry* (2nd ed.). Belmont, CA: Brooks/Cole.

Berg, C.A.R., Bergendahl, V.C.B., & Lundberg, B.K.S. (2003). Benefiting from an open-ended experiment? A comparison of attitudes to, and outcomes of, an expository versus an open-inquiry version of the same experiment. *International Journal of Science Education, 25*(3), 351–372.

Bloom, B.S. (1984). The search for methods of group instruction as effective as one-to-one tutoring. *Educational Leadership, 41*(8), 4–17.

Bodner, G.M. (1992). Why changing the curriculum may not be enough. *Journal of Chemical Education, 69*(3), 186–190.

Bodner, G.M., Gardner, D.E., & Briggs, M.W. (2005). Models and model building. In N.J. Pienta, M.M. Cooper, & T.J. Greenbowe (Eds.), *Chemists' guide to effective teaching* (pp. 67–76). Upper Saddle River, NJ: Pearson Prentice Hall.

Bunce, D.M., & Hutchinson, K.D. (1993). The use of the GALT (group assessment of logical thinking) as a predictor of academic success in college chemistry. *Journal of Chemical Education, 70*(3), 179–187.

Cooper, M.M. (2006). *Cooperative chemistry laboratory manual* (3rd ed.). New York: McGraw-Hill.

Deming, J.C., & Cracolice, M.S. (2004). Learning how to think. *The Science Teacher, 71*(3), 42–47.

Dewey, J. (1910/1978). Science as a subject-matter and as method. In J.A. Boydston (Ed.), *John Dewey: The Middle Works* (Vol. 6, pp. 179–356). Carbondale, IL: Southern Illinois University Press.

Educational Policies Commission (1961). *The Central Purpose of American Education*. Washington, DC: National Educational Association.

Farrell, J.J., Moog, R.S., & Spencer, J.N. (1999). A guided inquiry general chemistry course. *Journal of Chemical Education, 76*(4), 570–574.

Fuller, R.G. (2003). "Don't tell me, I'll find out." Robert Karplus—A science education pioneer. *Journal of Science Education and Technology, 12*(4), 359–362.

Greenbowe, T.J., & Hand, B. (2005). Introduction to the science writing heuristic. In N.J. Pienta, M.M. Cooper, & T.J. Greenbowe (Eds.), *Chemists' guide to effective teaching* (pp. 140-154). Upper Saddle River, NJ: Pearson Prentice Hall.

Gosser, D.K., Cracolice, M.S., Kampmeier, J.A., Roth, V., Strozak, V.S., & Varma-Nelson, P. (2001). *Peer-led team learning: A guidebook*. Upper Saddle River, NJ: Prentice-Hall.

Hake, R.R. (1998). Interactive-engagement versus traditional methods: A six-thousand-student survey of mechanics test data for introductory physics courses. *American Journal of Physics, 66*(1), 64–74.

Harrison, A.G., & Treagust, D.F. (2000). A typology of school science models. *International Journal of Science Education, 22*(9), 1011–1026.

Johnson, M.A., & Lawson, A.E. (1998). What are the relative effects of reasoning ability and prior knowledge on biology achievement in expository and inquiry classes? *Journal of Research in Science Teaching, 35*(1), 89–103.

Justi, R., & Gilbert, J. (2002). Models and modeling in chemical education. In J.K. Gilbert, O. De Jong, R. Justi, D.F. Treagust, & J.H. Van Driel (Eds.), *Chemical education: Towards research-based practice* (pp. 47-68). Dordrecht, The Netherlands: Kluwer Academic Publishers.

Karplus, R., & Their, H.D. (1967). *A new look at elementary school science.* Chicago: Rand McNally.

Lawson, A.E. (1978). The development and validation of a classroom test of formal reasoning. *Journal of Research in Science Teaching, 15*(1), 11–24.

Lawson, A.E. (1985). A review of research on formal reasoning and science teaching. *Journal of Research in Science Teaching, 22*(7), 569–617.

Lawson, A.E. (1990). Science education in Japan and the United States: Are the Japanese beating us at our own game? *Science Education, 74*(4), 495–501.

Lawson, A.E. (1992). What do tests of "formal" reasoning actually measure? *Journal of Research in Science Teaching, 29*(9), 965–983.

Lawson, A.E. (2003). *The neurological basis of learning, development and discovery: Implications for science and mathematics instruction.* Dordrecht, The Netherlands: Kluwer Academic Publishers.

Lawson, A.E., Abraham, M.R., & Renner, J.W. (1989). *A theory of instruction: Using the learning cycle to teach science concepts and thinking skills.* Cincinnati, OH: National Association for Research in Science Teaching.

Lawson, A., Benford, R., Bloom, I., Carlson, M., Falconer, K., Hestenes, D., Judson, E., Piburn, M., Sawada, D., Turley, J., & Wyckoff, S. (2002). Evaluating college science and mathematics instruction: A reform effort that improves teaching skills. *Journal of College Science Teaching, 31*(6), 388–393.

Lewis, S.E., & Lewis, J.E. (2005). Departing from lectures: An evaluation of a peer-led guided inquiry alternative. *Journal of Chemical Education, 82*(1), 135–139.

Marek, E.A., & Cavallo, A.M.L. (1997). *The learning cycle: Elementary science and beyond.* (Rev. ed.) Portsmouth, NH: Heinemann.

Mason, D.S., Shell, D.F., & Crawley, F.E. (1997). Differences in problem solving by nonscience majors in introductory chemistry on paired algorithmic-conceptual problems. *Journal of Research in Science Teaching, 34*(9), 905–923.

Moog, R.S., & Farrell, J.J. (2006). *Chemistry: A guided inquiry* (3rd ed.). Hoboken, NJ: John Wiley & Sons.

Moog, R.S., Spencer, J.N., & Farrell, J.J. (2004). *Physical chemistry, a guided inquiry: Atoms, molecules, and spectroscopy.* Boston: Houghton Mifflin.

Nakhleh, M.B., Lowrey, K.A., & Mitchell, R.C. (1996). Narrowing the gap between concepts and algorithms in freshman chemistry. *Journal of Chemical Education, 73*(8), 758–762.

National Research Council (2005). *How students learn: Science in the classroom.* Committee on How People Learn, A targeted report for teachers, M. S. Donovan and J. D. Bransford, Editors. Division of Behavioral and Social Sciences and Education. Washington, DC: The National Academies Press.

Nurrenbern, S.C., & Pickering, M. (1987). Concept learning versus problem solving: Is there a difference? *Journal of Chemical Education, 64*(6), 508–510.

Peck, M.L, & Williamson, V.M. (2005). *Experiences in Chemistry I and II: Inquiry and Skill Building* (2nd ed.). Plymouth, MI: Hayden-McNeil.

Piaget, J. (1963). *Psychology of intelligence.* Paterson, NJ: Littlefield and Adams.

Rickey, D., & Stacy, A.M. (2000). The role of metacognition in learning chemistry. *Journal of Chemical Education, 77*(7), 915-920.

Renner, J.W., Abraham, M.R., & Birnie, H.H. (1988). The necessity of each phase of the learning cycle in teaching high school physics. *Journal of Research in Science Teaching, 25*(1), 39–58.

Renner, J.W., Stafford, D.G., Coffia, W.J., Kellogg, D.H., & Weber, M.C. (1973). An evaluation of the science curriculum improvement study. *School Science and Mathematics, 73*(4), 291–318.

Roadrangka, V., Yeany, R.H., & Padilla, M.J. (1982). *Group test of logical thinking.* Unpublished manuscript, University of Georgia.

Rudd, J.A., II., Greenbowe, T.J., & Hand, B. (2001/2002). Recrafting the general chemistry lab report. *Journal of College Science Teaching, 31*(4), 230–234.

Sanger, M.J. (2005). Evaluating students' conceptual understanding of balanced equations and stoichiometric ratios using a particulate drawing. *Journal of Chemical Education, 82*(1), 131–134.

Saunders, W.L., & Shepardson, D. (1987). A comparison of concrete and formal science instruction upon science achievement and reasoning ability of sixth-grade students. *Journal of Research in Science Teaching, 24*(1), 39–51.

Schneider, L.S., & Renner, J.W. (1980). Concrete and formal teaching. *Journal of Research in Science Teaching, 17*(6), 503–517.

Shayer, M., & Adey, P. (Eds.) (2002). *Learning intelligence: Cognitive acceleration across the curriculum from 5 to 15 years.* Buckingham, UK: Open University Press.

Spencer, J.N., Moog, R.S., & Farrell, J.J. (2004). *Physical chemistry, a guided inquiry: Thermodynamics.* Boston: Houghton Mifflin.

Stigler, J.W., Gonzales, P., Kawanaka, T., Knoll, S., & Seranno, A. (1999). The TIMSS videotape classroom study: Methods and findings from an exploratory research project on eight-grade mathematics instruction in Germany, Japan, and the United States. U.S. Department of Education National Center for Education Statistics Report Number 99-074.

Tien, L.T., Rickey, D., & Stacy, A.M. (1999). The MORE thinking frame: Guiding students' thinking in the laboratory. *Journal of College Science Teaching, 28*(5), 318–324.

Trowbridge, L. W., & Bybee, R. W. (1990). *Becoming a secondary school science teacher* (5th ed.). Columbus, OH: Merrill Publishing.

Vygotsky, L.S. (1986). *Thought and language.* Cambridge, MA: The MIT Press.

White, B.Y., & Frederiksen, J.R. (1998). Inquiry, modeling, and metacognition: Making science accessible to all students. *Cognition and Instruction, 16*(1), 3–118.

Zoller, U., Lubezky, A., Nakhleh, M.B., Tessier, B., & Dori, Y.J. (1995). Success on algorithmic and LOCS vs. conceptual chemistry exam questions. *Journal of Chemical Education, 72*(11), 987–989.

Teaching to Achieve Conceptual Change

Gabriela C. Weaver
Purdue University
Department of Chemistry

Abstract

There is substantial evidence indicating that students can have deeply held misconceptions about scientific phenomena. They may learn to succeed in a class by memorizing information given to them without actually changing their fundamental understanding of a concept. Conceptual change theory elucidates the process by which learners can modify their held conceptions. The conditions of intelligibility, plausibility, and fruitfulness must be met for new ideas to be incorporated by the learner. Various teaching strategies can be employed that are compatible with this theory and encourage students' concepts to be changed.

Biography

Gabriela Weaver is currently Associate Professor of Chemistry and of Curriculum and Instruction. She received her B.S. in Chemistry from the California Institute of Technology and her Ph.D. in Chemical Physics from the University of Colorado at Boulder. She was a member of the faculty at the University of Colorado at Denver where she taught chemistry and carried out research in chemical education before moving to Purdue in 2001.

She has been the principle investigator on numerous NSF-funded projects to develop improved approaches to chemistry and science teaching at the K-12 and university levels. She has been actively involved in the development and assessment of instructional technologies, including web-based tools, DVD's and computer games. She is currently the director of the Center for Authentic Science Practice in Education, which serves to develop and implement research-based laboratory curricula for the 1st and 2nd years of chemistry.

Introduction

In 1987 the Harvard-Smithsonian Center for Astrophysics produced a short video documentary that stunned educators and non-educators alike and caused many to question the quality of our educational system. The documentary, *A Private Universe*, begins with an unforgettable sequence of interviews with Harvard students on their graduation day. They are asked to explain the reason that seasons occur on Earth and the large majority of them are unable to do so. While this introduction is entertaining, albeit sad, the body of the documentary is a more serious examination of the ineffectiveness of teaching, delving deeply into the roots of these adults' misconceptions. The story follows the efforts of a dedicated teacher to help a very bright ninth-grader understand the existence of seasons. The student appears to progress from a relatively naïve and misguided set of ideas to an understanding that is in agreement with the scientifically acceptable explanations for the phenomenon in question. What is particularly striking is that, upon probing by the interviewer, the student demonstrates that she is clearly still holding onto her original incorrect conceptions, while having simply added the new explanations and terminology onto them to successfully answer the current set of questions.

The revelations of *A Private Universe* were rather frustrating to science educators. The goals of science education include helping students learn scientific explanations and processes and rid themselves of misconceptions. But simply getting students to the point where they can answer test and homework questions correctly apparently does not guarantee that they actually have dismissed flawed mental constructs in favor of valid ones.   Indeed, research in science education has documented the existence of pervasive student misconceptions in a variety of chemistry content areas (eg. Birk and Kurtz, 1999; Chiu, et al., 2002; Furio, et al., 2000; McKenna and McKenna, 1984; Mulford and Robinson, 2002; Sanger and Greenbowe, 1997).   For example, researchers have provided evidence that students use a variety of inappropriate reasoning strategies for determining a limiting reagent, such as assuming that the reagent with the lowest stoichiometric coefficient will always be the limiting reagent (Huddle and Phillay, 1996).

To make teaching more effective it is necessary to address students' own conceptions and to provide a learning experience that can motivate change in those conceptions when they are inappropriate.   This is not fundamentally a new idea, since the act of teaching will often arise spontaneously in response to someone demonstrating a conception that is not in agreement with accepted views.   Take as an example a parent teaching a young child that it is not necessary to blow on all foods before eating them, only on "hot" foods.   The difference between this example and what is needed to achieve teaching for conceptual change in an academic setting is a level of awareness by the educator regarding the learners.   It is necessary to understand how students learn and what they believe about the subject at hand if one is to construct a learning experience that will achieve the desired ends.

Theories of Conceptual Change

In order to develop teaching strategies that assist students in changing misconceptions, it is important to consider how concepts develop initially.   There is a vast body of literature detailing theories of concept development.   From these works we can extract some foundational ideas that contribute to an understanding of how concepts change.   Constructivist theories of learning assert that learners construct their own knowledge, rather than simply absorbing completely formed concepts from others (Bodner, 1986; Cracolice, 2005)   The construction process, the learning, takes place within the framework of concepts that the learner has already developed or begun to develop (Ausubel, Novak and Hanesian, 1978).   This means that what a student already knows is what this person brings to the learning environment as the building blocks for further cognitive development.   The student relies on held conceptions in order to interpret and organize new information.   Therefore, if a student believes that electrons orbit the nucleus in a series of constrained circular orbits of increasing radius they will build their understanding of the interaction of radiation with matter on that conception.

The combination of held concepts and a person's understanding of the relationships between them can be thought of as a conceptual ecology.   Depending on the particular conceptual ecology of a learner, a new observation or experience may lead to interpretations that are different from those held by others.   For example, a study on students' understanding of thermodynamics concepts found that some of them believe aluminum foil will be more effective than a wool wrapper at keeping a soda cold (Lewis, 1996).   The students based their explanations on the use of aluminum foil for items in a refrigerator, and the use of wool for warm winter clothing.   When students develop explanations that are not in agreement with the generally accepted understanding for a phenomenon, those concepts are referred to as misconceptions, or sometimes as alternate conceptions.

Whether their ideas are in keeping with accepted scientific truths or not, the important thing for educators to keep in mind is that learners *do* have conceptions that will affect how they perceive and interpret information (Ausubel, Novak and Hanesian, 1978; Cracolice, 2005).   Samarapungavan and Nakhleh (1999) have contributed to a growing body of work about students' understanding of the particulate nature of matter.   An important conclusion of their work is that children have theories about the natural world.   Scientific theories develop as explanations for experimental data, and the early theories of children similarly develop as explanations that are consistent with sets of "experiments," their realm of observation and experience of the world around them.   Among the children in their study, Samarapungavan and Nakhleh observed a range of explanations for the behavior of materials that spanned from a continuous view of matter to a particulate view, and included a transitional view for some students.   For example, some students would describe water as being composed of "small pieces" but copper wire as "one big piece", which was consistent with their observation that water flows but copper wire does not.

The knowledge that a learner constructs will continually be tested and can be modified.   New information can result in *assimilation* if it represents a concept that simply fits within frameworks that the learner already holds (Bodner, 1986;

Yager, 1991). However, when new information cannot be reconciled with the learner's existing cognitive structures, some level of *accommodation* of those structures must take place. An example would be the conception of light as a wave. Many observations of the behavior of electromagnetic radiation can be explained using a wave conception, such as color (frequency), intensity, refraction and others (Figure 1).

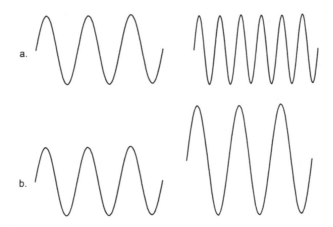

Figure 1. A wave conception of light. In *a*, the two light pulses would have the same intensity but different color. In *b*, the two light pulses would have the same color, but different intensity.

But there are classic examples of light behavior that cannot be explained with a wave conception, such as the photoelectric effect in which electrons are emitted from a conducting surface when light of a certain minimum frequency is used, with the onset of electric current being independent of the light intensity. This observation led to an accommodation of the conception of light to include a particle picture. In fact, this example represents an important conceptual change event for the scientific community as a whole, though the components of this combined wave-particle picture needed to emerge from individuals.

Conceptual change theory specifies the conditions that are necessary for existing cognitive structures to be modified in order to incorporate new information (Hewson & Hewson, 1984; Posner, et al.,1982). The four conditions that are generally accepted as necessary for conceptual change to occur are *dissatisfaction, intelligibility, plausibility* and *fruitfulness*. Initially, there must be a condition to cause *dissatisfaction* with an existing concept. For example, this can be an observation that is contradictory to the expected outcomes that the existing concept would predict (Hewson & Hewson, 1984; Posner, et al.,1982; Tyson, et al. 1997). This process is referred to as cognitive conflict (Mischel, 1971). In the example above of the wave-particle nature of light, the condition of dissatisfaction was a result of experiments that could not be explained by the wave conception alone.

Once dissatisfaction has occurred, a learner is open to considering new concepts to replace or modify the existing ones. The new concepts will be tested and will only be accepted if they are found to be *intelligible, plausible* and *fruitful*. Intelligibility implies that the learner is able to understand the new concept and represent that concept to others. If the concept is plausible to the learner, it can be used to explain observations or solve problems that the original concept could not, usually beginning with the observation that led to dissatisfaction with the original concept. In the example of the use of different materials for insulating purposes, students carried out simple experiments in which they collected temperature data for objects wrapped in sleeves made of different materials and exposed to different environmental conditions (Layman, et al., 1996). The concept that materials that can conduct heat are *poor* insulators was quickly found to be consistent with these observations while the students' original concept (aluminum – a thermal conductor – will keep an object cold) could not explain the data.

The final condition for conceptual change, *fruitfulness*, suggests that in order to be accepted and lead to accommodation, the new concept must be one that is consistent not only with an experience that led to conceptual dissatisfaction, but also with other knowledge and life experiences of the student. That is, the new concept must be extendable to additional phenomena in varied contexts. In essence, this extendibility serves as a final confirmatory phase as the learner explores the new concept in relation to ones previously held. Students exploring the heat conducting properties of different materials would be able to extend their concept by discussing the insulating walls around a refrigerator and, for a more advanced group, to discuss the heat exchange process that takes place through the coils that are made of a thermally conducting material.

Early work on conceptual change theory (Hewson & Hewson, 1984; Posner, et al.,1982) presents a view of relatively radical conceptual change. That is, the process is described as one in which a new conception will lead to immediate accommodation of existing frameworks once it is deemed to be acceptable. Later work (Tyson, et al., 1997; Vosniadou and Ioannides, 1998) provided an expanded description of how conceptual change takes place, taking into account learners' natural tendencies to hold on to familiar ideas with which they are already comfortable. These later developments of conceptual change theory describe a process that is gradual and dynamic, one in which the existing conceptual frameworks are continually being reformulated and tested. As this occurs, the old conceptions are not abandoned in an outright manner but substantial fragments of these are maintained while new ideas are tested and incorporated. The case study in *A Private Universe* described at the beginning of this chapter provides a clear example of the evolutionary way in which conceptual change takes place. Because components of the original conceptions can coexist with new ones, it is possible that students will be at a level where they are juggling both their original misconception and a newly developing conception while grappling with a learning experience.

An example of this coexistence of conceptions commonly arises in general chemistry courses when students are learning about chemical equilibrium. Student misconceptions about chemical equilibrium have been extensively studied (eg. Banerjee, 1991; Furio, et al., 2000; Huddle and Pillay, 1996; Niaz, 1998; Piquette and Heikkinen, 2005; Thomas and Schwenz, 1998) because it is a concept for which misconceptions appear to be prevalent and quite persistent. An example of students' misconceptions is that a reaction stops completely once it reaches equilibrium. In solving mathematical problems associated with simple equilibrium systems, students may continue to believe that the no further reaction is taking place, thus preserving their initial belief while still being able to provide correct numerical answers for typical equilibrium questions. Only an examination of the system at the molecular level, and conceptual questions targeted at these ideas, would address the misconception of a system that is at a standstill. Another typical misconception is that a reaction at equilibrium is one in which all components are present in equal quantity. If traditional instruction proceeds primarily by an algorithmic approach to solving equilibrium problems, students may be unable to understand the meaning of the equilibrium constant if they are starting with the misconception that equilibrium leads to equal quantities.

Such a situation puts students in a cognitive transition state, where a carefully applied learning experience can move them seamlessly toward full integration of the target concept. The classroom environment as a whole can play a role in this, because conceptual change can be initiated and facilitated by social contexts, such as those of a laboratory or cooperative learning experience. In one study specifically designed to examine the effect of conceptual change strategies on students' understanding of chemical equilibrium (Canpolat, et al., 2006), the authors found a significant improvement for students who were taught using approaches consistent with conceptual change conditions.

Barriers to Conceptual Change

Dudley J. Herron talks about the "principle of least cognitive effort" (1996) which, as a rule of thumb, allows us to understand why students will sometimes avoid conceptual change. In essence, if a simpler cognitive task appears to be sufficient, it will preferentially be employed over a more complex one. Because conceptual change takes some amount of mental work, there are numerous tactics that learners might employ instead (Chinn & Brewer, 1993; Strike and Posner, 1985), though usually subconsciously. One rather dramatic alternative to assimilating or accommodating a new conception is simply *rejecting* it. Rejection can occur when the new experience is so apparently disparate from a held conception that it does not register at all with the learner. It is not seen as an experience that has any connection or relevance and may not even be recalled by the learner later. A dramatic example of rejection was used by Mazur (2004) when he showed a video to an audience and asked them to count the number of times a ball was passed from a person wearing a white shirt to another person wearing a white shirt. The 2 to 3-minute video was produced by Daniel Simons (Viscog, 2003) and consisted of approximately six people standing in a circle bouncing several balls between them. The video is part of a group of videos that have been used by Simons in studies about visual awareness (Simons and Levin, 2003). Because of the number of people and balls involved, the audience members focus a great deal of attention on counting the correct number of passes. The majority of people in the audience never notice that a person wearing a gorilla suit steps into the middle of the circle at one point, bangs its chest, and then leaves. When the audience is told of this occurrence, many do not believe it. Only on viewing the video a second time do those people see the plainly visible gorilla. This same cognitive rejection effect can occur with students in a classroom or during a learning task, particularly if the seemingly anomalous event, or data, is embedded in a task that requires a great deal of cognitive effort already.

Rejection of a concept takes the least amount of cognitive effort. Rejection is different from the act of *ignoring* a new conception, which requires the learner to actively make the decision that it is not relevant to current conceptions and therefore of no concern. Students commonly do this when they are collecting laboratory data and have some data that do not fit an expected trend. Many times, students will decide that these points are the result of some unspecified "error" and ignore them in the overall analysis. *Exclusion* of a concept is the act of compartmentalizing it as a separate category, to be used in specific cases but not to be integrated with conceptions that already exist. Science educators commonly see this approach to learning topics in science, where it appears that students separate their "classroom knowledge" from what they consider to be "real knowledge" (Soudani, et al., 2000). A simple example of this is the belief exhibited by some students that the bubbles in boiling water are composed of hydrogen and oxygen gasses, in spite of their ability in class to describe the change of state of water as one in which the molecules remain intact.

A final avoidance tactic to conceptual change is *reinterpretation*. In this case, the learner constructs an understanding of the new conception by forcing it to fit within conceptions that are already firmly held. This avoidance approach requires the largest amount of cognitive effort. To consider an example of reinterpretation, we can return to the topic of chemical equilibrium. A study by Chiu, et al., (2002) looked at students' understanding of various chemical systems, including the aqueous equilibrium between iron(III) ion and the iron thiocyanate ion:

$$Fe^{3+} + SCN^{-} \rightleftharpoons FeSCN^{2+}$$

In this reaction, the aqueous iron solution is yellow, the thiocyanate solution is colorless and the iron thiocyanate product is a reddish color, making it simple to visually determine shifts in the equilibrium position of the system. The Chiu study observed that some students hold the general misconception that a system reaches equilibrium when one or both of the reactants are completely consumed. When asked about the iron thiocyanate reaction, some students stated that the iron ion was consumed at equilibrium. However, addition of thiocyanate ion to the system at equilibrium results in the system becoming distinctly redder. In a case of reinterpretation, a student may respond that the thiocyanate ion itself, not due to reaction with iron, makes the solution redder (even though it is colorless on its own). The student justification for this could be that the thiocyanate is "the piece that gives the compound its red color." In this case, the student feels that an explanation exists for the shift in color, without conflicting with their belief that all of the iron has been consumed.

It is possible that students may appear to demonstrate an understanding of concepts presented in the classroom, even though they are employing various cognitive avoidance tactics. In fact, work by Bunce (2001) has demonstrated that successful students may not actually understand the material but may succeed by knowing how to apply algorithmic knowledge, knowing how to follow a sequence of steps to achieve the answer that they perceive is required by their professor. As in the example that was so plainly brought to life in *A Private Universe*, learners may not actually be letting go of their held misconceptions while still being able to provide "correct" responses to questions.

A key to conceptual change avoidance lies in the fact that held conceptual frameworks form the basis on which to judge new ideas. When a learner is in the process of deciding if a new conception is intelligible, plausible and fruitful, a comparison is necessarily drawn between the new and old conceptions. However, this can only occur if the learner is able to connect the new concept in some way to the old. Clement (1993) describes the need to use intuitive anchors and bridging analogies as a way to start from an idea that the learner already understands well and then form a stepwise link to a new concept, through a bridging concept that is easily plausible to the learner. This is closely related to Vygotsky's idea of teaching within a zone of proximal development, ZPD (Cracolice, 2005; Vygotsky, 1986). A new concept that is too large a step for the student, too far outside the students' ZPD, will not be intelligible to the student, and thus will lead down the path of cognitive avoidance. As was pointed out by Dreyfus, et al., (1990) "the basic problem appears to be the ability of pupils to reach a state of *meaningful conflict*." Outright confusion is not a state of cognitive conflict that will lead a student towards comparison and testing of a new conception. This is more likely to result in rejection, exclusion or other avoidance.

Traditional classroom strategies can fail in numerous ways to provide an environment that promotes conceptual change. First, the students may not be aware initially of their held conceptions. If students are not aware of their held conceptions, then new conceptions that are in conflict with these may not be recognized as contradictory. For example, in some lecture situations students are simply told the definition of equilibrium. Students will be able to write the equations and even use them, but they have not had to provide their own explanation of the concept. As such, they will not be in a position to examine the given definition of equilibrium on a conceptual level in comparison to their own conceptions. Instead, a concept that is presented to the students can easily be excluded or reinterpreted. In a passive student environment, as is often the case in a traditional lecture-based classroom, there would be little or no opportunity to undergo a process of comparison by which students would make judgments about the fruitfulness or plausibility of new ideas.

Strategies for Conceptual Change

Teaching for conceptual change is not a one-size-fits-all endeavor. A search of the literature will quickly reveal that researchers and educators are attempting numerous types of conceptual change teaching implementations (eg. Cakir, et al., 2002; Chiu, et al., 2002; Sanger and Greenbowe, 2000; Piquette and Heikkinen, 2005). The goal in this monograph is to present several possible strategies as examples. It is possible to modify these, combine them in different ways, and select the options that are best suited to the particular learning environment where they will be used. However, successful conceptual change teaching strategies share some structural elements that are at the core of conceptual change teaching. First, an opportunity must exist for students to become aware of their held conceptions. Students need to know what they believe initially. In fact, it is also useful for the instructors to be aware of what students believe. The learning experience must then provide a situation in which the held belief needs to be examined, questioned and modified if necessary. Through this process, a new conception can possibly take its place. Ultimately, there must be an opportunity for students to test the new conception, being able to judge its intelligibility, plausibility and fruitfulness.

Discrepant Events. A discrepant event is an experience that is overtly counterintuitive and directly challenges students' held conceptions. An example of a discrepant event involves an experiment in which a candle is placed into an Erlenmeyer flask or jar that is inverted over a shallow pan of water. The candle goes out in a short while and the water level rises in the flask (Figure 2).

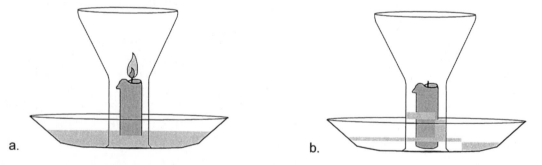

a.   b.

Figure 2. The enclosed candle experiment. The Erlenmeyer flask is inverted over a lit candle that sits in a shallow pan of water (*a*). After a short time (*b*), the water rises and the candle goes out.

A common explanation for the observation is that the candle has consumed the oxygen in the flask, causing the combustion process to end and the water level to rise to fill the volume which was previously occupied by that gas. The discrepant event occurs when a candle and a mouse are put into a bell jar together (Birk, 1999). The candle is extinguished a short time after the bell jar is sealed, but the mouse continues to be active. The presence of the mouse as an "oxygen detector" that is showing no evidence of a lack of oxygen causes the observer to rethink their understanding of the system. This example can work well as a discussion and teaching tool if students are brought through the process with a conceptual change approach: first they observe the system with the candle and they propose an explanation, then they observe a system that does not support their explanation and requires a new one to be proposed and tested.

For some topics, it may be useful to include some instruction on the subject before students are asked to commit to their own explanations. This is obviously true for concepts with which students have little familiarity. However, it can also be true for concepts that students are so familiar with that they may have developed very firmly held misconceptions. For example, a study by Ashkenazi and Weaver (2007) examines the use of discrepant events to probe the behavior of different types of intermolecular interactions. In this study, students made predictions about the miscibility of various liquids in a demonstration that compared four different systems (Figure 3.) The liquids were initially poured very carefully into graduated cylinders such that they would form separate layers. Although all of the liquids are colorless, different coloring agents (blue food coloring for water and iodine for pentane) were used to allow the different liquids to be distinguished. Students were told the name, molecular structure and dipole moment of each substance. Students were then asked to predict what would happen when each cylinder was agitated to mix the liquids: remain as separate layers or mix, and which layers would mix.

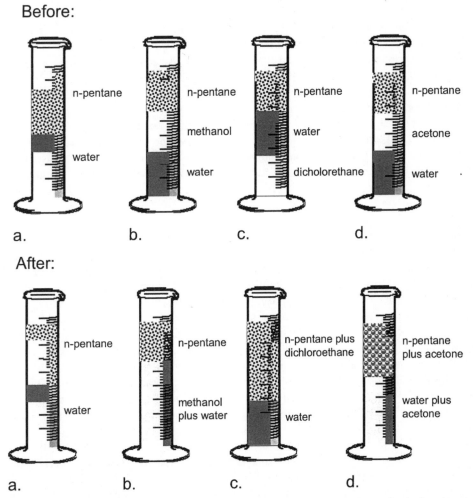

Figure 3. Set-up for a discrepant event demo involving miscibility of liquids and results after each tube is agitated and allowed to settle.

Students are asked to predict each system, which is then agitated, and a discussion about the results follows before moving to the next system. The majority of students generally predict the behavior of the first system (Figure 3a) correctly. If students have internalized the statement that "like dissolves like" they will recognize that the nonpolar pentane and the polar water will be immiscible. The second system further supports the expectations of most students. The discussion of this system may expose some students questions about the possible mixing of methanol with pentane, based on the presence of the $-CH_3$ group, which becomes an important point for understanding the fourth system (Figure 3d). The discussion of the second system may also expose the issue of whether the molecular polarity or hydrogen bonding is responsible for the miscibility of methanol and water.

The third system (Figure 3c) provides the first potential cognitive conflict opportunity because 1,1-dichloroethane has a dipole moment of 2.06 D, whereas pentane has no dipole moment and water has a dipole moment of 1.85 D. Most students will incorrectly predict that the dichloroethane will mix with the water. The discussion that either follows or precedes this demonstration can focus on the difference between a compound simply being polar or having the ability to form hydrogen bonds. The discrepant result of system three highlights the unique nature of the hydrogen bond. The final system (Figure 3d) further develops the concept of miscibility through hydrogen bonding, but also adds the concept of partitioning, because acetone is miscible in both pentane and water to different degrees. Depending on the success of the discussions associated with the preceding systems the final system will either be a major discrepant event or serve to confirm students' refinement of the concepts behind the "like dissolves like" rule. The methyl groups and the lone pair electrons on the oxygen atom each play a role in this partitioning effect.

The use of discrepant events can occur either as part of the lecture or as part of the laboratory, where students have the opportunity to carry out the particular activity themselves. In either case, it is important for students to commit to an idea of how the system will behave and what they will observe *before* they observe it. This key step will allow dissatisfaction with existing conceptions to take place when the discrepant event occurs, promoting the subsequent comparison steps necessary for a new conception to be accommodated.

Classroom Discourse. In their work detailing possible avoidance strategies for conceptual change, Chinn and Brewer (1993) also point out that students must have the opportunity to carry out *deep processing* of their conceptions and of new ones that need to be assimilated. This implies that students need to confront why they hold particular beliefs and what evidence supports these beliefs. This metacognitive process can be facilitated by the social interactions that can take place during classroom discourse (Beeth and Hewson, 1999). Research in physics education has shown that classroom discourse can help students be actively involved in the learning process and learn more effectively (Hake, 1998).

The discourse must be guided such that students' held conceptions are the main subject of discourse. A key to doing this is to ensure that conceptual change is explicitly stated to be a learning goal of the class. This creates an environment where self-knowledge of concepts is accepted as important. The discourse will consist of three main components: exposure, justification and exploration. In the exposure phase, students explain what their held conceptions are. This can be prompted by requiring a prediction by students before a demo of what they will see or having them explain to other students a question or problem of a conceptual nature. A useful framework for this is the peer instruction approach (Mazur, 1997) in which students answer a problem on their own and then attempt to explain to one another what their understanding is of the answer. After this, the students can work on the problem again. The explanation phase that is incorporated in this approach is particularly important because it allows students to deeply explore their held conceptions, and helps them clarify their own ideas (Lemke, 1990). This clarification allows students to become more aware of the potential limitations of their held conceptions, thus making them more available for comparison to new conceptions that may be more plausible and fruitful under other circumstances.

Concept Mapping. The detailed mechanics of using and evaluating concept maps have been described in detail elsewhere (Nakhleh, 2005). However, their use specifically for promoting conceptual change (Gravett, Swart, 1997; Sen, 2002) is of interest here. Concept maps consist of topics or concepts that are joined by linking words that are often verbs. Concept mapping is a teaching method through which students ideas' and the connections between them can be raised to a conscious level. This achieves a similar goal to the peer teaching approach discussed above, but it can take place on an individual basis. Concept maps provide a visual or graphical method for students to clarify and explore their conceptual frameworks, rather than a verbal one. For some students this can be more effective than the verbal approach, depending on their particular learning styles. In addition to allowing students to explore their conceptions of a topic, concept maps can be a useful study aid to help students remember ideas. Figure 4 is an example of a very simple concept map.

The concept maps themselves can also allow an instructor to explore the existence of possible misconceptions held by students and determine the extent of these misconceptions within the class. Consequent instruction can be specifically targeted to address these, thus helping to promote conceptual change (Wallace, 1990). For example, in the concept map shown in Figure 4, the student may hold the misconception that energy level is the only defining parameter of orbitals. This can serve as a point for further exploration of quantum numbers and types of orbitals.

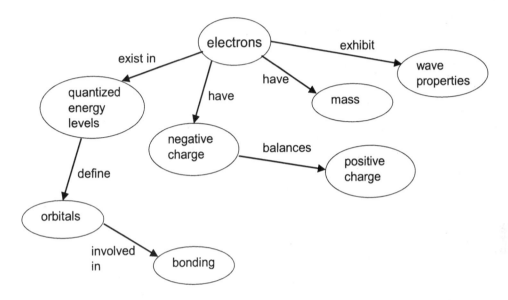

Figure 4. A simple concept map about electrons.

Context as Cognitive Anchor. Previous work has shown that instruction that is situated in authentic contexts can be more effective at engaging students (Nieswandt, 2001; Weaver, 1998). Situating learning in contexts that are familiar to students can serve to provide them with a "cognitive anchor" as they begin to explore new conceptions and branch out from their own. This can simplify the process for some students, as compared to situations where they must consider settings that are completely alien to them, such as "consider a massless, frictionless piston." Such an example may be so inconceivably to students that they are not able to build a concept beginning from that point, causing the remainder of the instruction on that topic to likely be fruitless. The suggestion by Clement (1993) that bridging analogies be employed to help students make connections to ideas they already understand is particularly useful when those analogies are put into a larger context. An example of an authentic context would be the use of greenhouses gases and global warming as a context to present information about the interaction of light with matter (Eubanks, et al., 2005). By placing the chemical topic within the bigger picture of an application, the process for comparison and judging the merit of new conceptions is given a relational setting against which specific questions of intelligibility, plausibility and fruitfulness can be answered concretely.

An extension of using context that is presented to students is to create a learning experience that is task-oriented (Schnotz and Preuss, 1997). A task-based activity, if designed appropriately, should allow students to propose outcomes and then test the actual outcomes against the conceptions that they hold. This is a way for learners to verify and commit to their own knowledge, or find it insufficient thus requiring that a new conception be assimilated. Task-oriented context is a natural fit for a laboratory course. However, not all laboratory experiments will engender concept evaluation. The critical step that allows students to become aware of their held conceptions must be present in order for a proposal about the task to be created by the student, and subsequent comparison to actual outcome or behavior of the system.

The tasks themselves will be more effective at promoting conceptual change if they are authentic in nature. As Brown, Collins and Duguid (1989) point out, many of the activities students undertake in traditional classrooms are not the activities of the practitioners, but abstract, isolated activities. The truth of this statement can be seen, for example, when one compares the common 3-hour "cookbook" lab to the act of carrying out experimental scientific research. Brown, Collins and Duguid argue that concepts are highly dependent on the community within which they are developed, requiring negotiation with other practitioners and with the environment. They propose a cognitive apprenticeship approach for the learning environment, where content, process and social interactions are all important components. Within the framework of conceptual change learning, authentic activity provides the problem solver a means to evaluate the adequacy of a solution, a necessary step when testing both the validity of a held conception and the plausibility of a new one. When situated in an authentic task, Brown, Collins and Duguid assert that new information is more likely to be meaningful to the learner, allowing for intelligibility, plausibility and fruitfulness to be judged. The cognitive apprenticeship approach for teaching in the sciences is, in fact, the model we predominantly employ in this country for graduate education. In this case, the learning occurs via authentic research. Evidence exists to suggest that the use of research and cognitive apprenticeship as a component of undergraduate education can lead to improved performance and academic success (Chiu, et al., 2002; Nagda, 1998).

Technology-based approaches can be useful for various forms of conceptual change teaching. With respect to context and situated cognition, computer-based environments can be created that function as *macrocontexts* (CTGV, 1990,1993; Sherwood, et al., 1987). A particularly flexible virtual environment that has recently been developed (Woodfield, et al., 2004, 2005) that allows users to carry out experiments in organic or inorganic chemistry in a laboratory environment. The environment is "stocked" with a variety of reagents and instruments allowing tremendous variety in the types of experiments that can be carried out. With such virtual environments, rich problem spaces can be created that can effectively provide multiple scenarios in which existing and proposed conceptions can be tested for validity. This multiplicity of tests is important because "conceptual deficits can be detected if the [mental] models are used in a sufficiently variable way, whereas they can remain unnoticed if used in a limited manner," (Sherwood, et al., 1987). The macrocontext approach, while an approximation of reality, can serve as an effective facsimile of our daily "informal" learning environments ("what is the best time of day to take the highway versus the back roads route?") and to the type of cognitive apprenticeship environments we employ in graduate programs. Various studies that used technology to provide "situated" experiences as macrocontexts found that learning was facilitated via the advantages common to informal learning environments (CTGV, 1990,1993; Kozma, 1994; Sherwood, et al., 1987)

In Summary

In order to teach for conceptual change there are several conditions that must be attended to. The first and foremost is that students' held conceptions must be brought to a conscious level. It is important for the students themselves to be aware of their beliefs and to understand the details of their beliefs: why do they hold them, when do they apply and how are they connected to one another. It is also important for the instructor to be aware of the students' conceptions. Effective instruction can be formulated to change a conception if there is some idea of what is being changed. Methods for exploring the existence and characteristics of held conceptions can include student discourse, concept mapping or the use of conceptual test items.

Once students' conceptions have been unearthed, the learning environment should provide opportunities for students to test their conceptions and decide if those conceptions are inadequate (the condition of dissatisfaction.) New conceptions can be proposed either through instruction or through discovery processes. However, in all cases it is necessary to provide students the opportunity to test these new conceptions. Students must be able to understand and explain them, they must find them plausible for explaining the phenomena where their original conceptions failed, and they must find the new conceptions useful for explaining additional phenomena under different sets of circumstances. Situated learning, task-dependent learning, and macrocontexts are examples of how the fruitfulness of new conceptions can be tested. As students begin to explore new conceptions, instructors must be cognizant that conceptual change will be most effective if students have some cognitive anchors, concepts that they feel are stable and can be trusted before they take steps in a new direction.

Suggested Reading

Limón, M. and Mason, L. (Eds.) *Reconsidering Conceptual Change: Issues in Theory and Practice.* Dordrecht: Kluwer, 2002.

Posner, G.T., Strike, K.A., Hewson, P.W., & Gertzog, W.A. (1982). Accommodation of a scientific conception: Toward a theory of conceptual change. *Science Education*, **66,** 211-227.

Stepans, J. *Targeting Students' Science Misconceptions: Physical Science Concepts Using the Conceptual Change Model*, 2nd ed. Riverview, FL: Idea Factory. 2003.

Schnotz, W., Vosniadou, S., Carretero, M. *New Perspectives on Conceptual Change*. Oxford, UK: Elsevier Science, 1999.

References

Ashkenazi, G. and Weaver, G. C. (2007). Interactive lecture demonstrations as a context for classroom discussion: Effective design and presentation. Submitted to *Chemical Education Research and Practice*.

Ausubel, D. P., Novak, J. D., and Hanesian, H. (1978). *Educational psychology: A cognitive view.* New York: Holt, Rinehart, and Winston.

Banerjee, A. C. (1991). Misconceptions of students and teachers in chemical equilibrium. *International Journal of Science Education*, **13**, 487-494.

Beeth, M. E., Hewson, P. W. (1999). Learning goals in an exemplary science teacher's practice: Cognitive and social factors in teaching for conceptual change. *Science Education*, **83**, 738-760.

Birk, J. P. and Kurtz, M. J. (1999). Effect of experience on retention and elimination of misconceptions about molecular structure and bonding. *Journal of Chemical Education*, **76**, 124-128.

Birk, J. P. and Lawson, A. E. (1999). The persistence of the candle-and-cylinder misconception. *Journal of Chemical Education*, **76**, 914-916.

Bodner, G. M. (1986). Consructivism: A theory of knowledge. *Journal of Chemical Education*, **63**, 873-878.

Brown, J. S., Collins, A. and Duguid, P. (1989). Situated cognition and the culture of learning. *Educational Researcher*, **18**(1), 32-41.

Bunce, D. M. (2001). Does Piaget still have anything to say to chemists? *Journal of Chemical Education*. **78**. 1107.

Cakir, O. S., Uzuntiryaki, E., and Geban, O. (2002). Contribution of conceptual change texts and concept mapping to students' understanding of acids and bases. Paper presented at the annual meeting of NARST (New Orleans).

Canpolat, N., Pinarbasi, T., Bayrakceken, S., Geban, O. (2006). The conceptual change approach to teaching chemical equilibrium. *Research in Science and Technological Education*. **24**, 217-235.

Chinn, C. A. and Brewer, W. F. (1993). The role of anomalous data in knowledge acquisition: A theoretical framework and implications for science instruction. *Review of Educational Research*, **63**, 1-49.

Chiu, M-H, Chou, C-C, and Liu, C-J. (2002). Dynamic processes of conceptual change: Analysis of constructing mental models of chemical equilibrium. *Journal of Research in Science Teaching*. **39**, 688-712.

Clement, J. (1993). Using bridging analogies and anchoring intuitions to deal with students' preconceptions in physics. *Journal of Research in Science Teaching*. **30**(10). 1241-1257.

CTGV (The Cognition and Technology Group at Vanderbilt). (1990). Anchored instruction and its relationship to situated cognition. *Educational Researcher*, **19**(6), 2-10.

CTGV (The Cognition and Technology Group at Vanderbilt). (1993). Anchored instruction and situated cognition revisited. *Educational Technology*, **33**(3), 52-70.

Cracolice, M. S. (2005). How students learn: Knowledge construction in college chemistry courses. In N. J. Pienta, M. M. Cooper, and Greenbowe (Eds.) *Chemists' Guide to Effective Teaching*. 12-27. Upper Saddle River, NJ: Pearson Prentice Hall.

Dreyfus, A., Jungwirth, E., & Eliovitch, R. (1990). Applying the "cognitive conflict" strategy for conceptual change – some implications, difficulties and problems. *Science Education*, **74**, 555-569.

Eubanks, L. P., Middlecamp, C. H., Pienta, N. J., Heltzel, C. E., Weaver, G. C. (2005). *Chemistry in Context* (6 Ed.) Washington, D.C.: American Chemical Society.

Furio, C., Calatayud, M. L., Barcenas, S. L., Padilla, O. M. (2000). Functional fixedness and functional reduction as common sense reasoning in chemical equilibrium and in geometry and polarity of molecules. *Science Education*. **84**, 545-565.

Gravett, S. J., Swart, E. (1997). Concept mapping: A tool for promoting and assessing conceptual change.

Hake, R.R. (1998). Interactive engagement versus traditional methods: A six thousand student survey of mechanics test data from introductory physics courses. *American J. Physics*, **66**, 64-74.

Herron, J. D. (1996). *The Chemistry Classroom: Formulas for successful teaching.* DC:ACS Press.

Hewson, P.W. and Hewson, M.G. (1984). The role of conceptual conflict in conceptual change and the design of science instruction. *Instructional Science*, **13**, 1-13.

Huddle, P. A. and Pillay, A. E. (1996). An in-depth study of misconceptions in stoichiometry and chemical equilibrium at a South African university. *Journal of Research in Science Teaching*, **33**(1), 65-77.

Kozma, R. (1994). Will media influence learning: Reformulating the debate? *Educational Technology Research and Development*, **42**, 7-19.

Layman, J. W., Ochoa, G. and Heikkinen, H. (1996). *Inquiry and Learning: Realizing Science Standards in the Classroom.* New York: College Entrance Examination Board.

Lemke, J. L. (1990). *Talking Science: Language, Learning and Values.* Norwood, NJ: Ablex.

Lewis, E. L. (1996). Conceptual change among middle school students studying elementary thermodynamics. *Journal of Science Education and Technology*. **5**, 3-31.

Mazur, E. (1997). *Peer instruction: A user's manual.* Upper Saddle River, NJ: Prentice Hall.

Mazur, E. (2004). Confessions of a converted lecturer. Plenary presentation at *Invention and Impact: A Conference of the CCLI Program.* (Crystal City, VA).

Mulford, D. R. and Robinson, W. R. (2002). An inventory for alternate conceptions among first-semester General Chemistry students. *Journal of Chemical Education*, **79**, 739-744.

Nagda, B. A., Gregerman, S. R., Jonides, J., von Hippel, W., and Lerner, J. S. (1998). Undergraduate student-faculty research partnerships affect student retention. *Review of Higher Education*, **22**, 55-72.

Nakhleh, M. B. (2005). Using concept maps to figure out what your students are really learning. In N. J. Pienta, M. M. Cooper, and Greenbowe (Eds.) *Chemists' Guide to Effective Teaching*. 12-27. Upper Saddle River, NJ: Pearson Prentice Hall.

Nakhleh, M. B. and Samarapungavan, A. (1999). Elementary school children's beliefs about matter. *Journal of Research in Science Teaching.* **36**, 777-805.

Niaz, M. (1998). A lakatosian conceptual change teaching strategy based on student ability to build models with varying degrees of conceptual understanding of chemical equilibrium. *Science Education*, **7**, 107-127.

Nieswandt, M. (2001). Problems and possibilities for learning in an introductory chemistry course from a conceptual change perspective. *Science Education*, **85**(2), 158-179.

Piquette, J. S. and Heikkinen, H. W. (2005). Strategies reported used by instructors to address student alternate conceptions in chemical equilibrium. *Journal of Research in Science Teaching,* **42**, 1112-1134.

Posner, G.T., Strike, K.A., Hewson, P.W., & Gertzog, W.A. (1982). Accommodation of a scientific conception: Toward a theory of conceptual change. *Science Education*, **66,** 211-227.

Sanger, M. J. and Greenbowe, T. J. (1997). Common student misconceptions in electrochemistry: galvanic, electrolytic, and concentration cells. *Journal of Research in Science Teaching*, **34**, 377-398.

Sanger, M. J. and Greenbowe, T. J. (2000). Addressing student misconceptions concerning electron flow in aqueous solutions with instruction including computer animations and conceptual change strategies. *International Journal of Science Education.* **22**, 521-537.

Sen, A. I. (2002). Concept Maps as a Research and Evaluation Tool to Assess Conceptual Change in Quantum Physics. *Science Education International*, **13**(4), 14-24.

Sherwood, R. D., Kinzer, C. K., Hasselbring, S., and Bransford, J. D. (1987). Macro-contexts for learning: Initial findings and issues. *Applied Cognitive Psychology*, **1**, 93-108.

Simons, D. & Levin, D. (2003). What makes change blindness interesting? In D.E. Irwin & B.H. Ross (Eds.), *The psychology of learning and motivation, Vol. 42.* (pp. 295-322) San Diego, CA: Academic Press.

Schnotz, W. and Preuss, A. (1997). Task-dependent construction of mental models as a basis for conceptual change. *European J. of Psychology of Education*, **12**(2), 185-211.

Soudani, M., Sivade, A., Cros, D., Medimagh, M. S. (2000). Transferring knowledge from the classroom to the real world: Redox concepts. *School Science Review*, **82**, 65-72.

Strike K. A. and Posner, G. J. (1985) A conceptual change view of learning and understanding. In L. H. T. West and A. L. Pines (Eds.), *Cognitive structure and conceptual change* (pp. 211-231). Orlando, FL; Academic Press.

Thomas, P. L. and Schwenz, R. W. (1998). College physical chemistry students' conceptions of equilibrium and fundamental thermodynamics. *Journal of Research in Science Teaching.* **35**, 1151-1160.

Tyson, L. M., Venville, G. J., Harrison, A. G., Treagust, D. F. (1997). Multidimensional Framework for Interpreting Conceptual Change Events in the Classroom. *Sci. Ed.*, **81**, 387-404.

Vosniadou, S. and Ioannides, C. (1998). From conceptual development to science education: a psychological point of view. *Intl. J. Sci. Educ.*, **20**(10), 1213-1230.

Viscog Productions (2003). Surprising studies of visual awareness. http://www.viscog.com/surprising_studies.html. Accessed October 10, 2006.

Vygotsky, L. S. (1986). *Thought and Language (Revised Edition)*. Cambridge, MA: The MIT Press.

Wallace, J. D. (1990). The concept map as a research tool: Exploring conceptual change in biology. *Journal of Research in Science Teaching*, **27**, 1033-1052.

Weaver, G. C. (1998). Strategies in K-12 science instruction to promote conceptual change. *Sci. Ed.*, **82**, 455-472.

Whitehead, A. N. (1929). *The aims of education*. New York: MacMillan.

Woodfield, B. F., Andrus, M. B., Waddoups, G. L., Moore, M. S. Swan, R., Allen, R., Bodily, G., Andersen, T., Miller, J., Simmons, B. and Stanger, R. (2004). The *Virtual Chemlab* project: A realistic and sophisticated simulation of organic synthesis and organic qualitative analysis. *Journal of Chemical Education*, **82**, 1728-1735.

Woodfield, B. F., Catlin, H. R., Waddoups, G. L., Moore, M. S., Swan, R., Allen, R. and Bodily, G. (2004). The *Virtual Chemlab* project: A realistic and sophisticated simulation of inorganic qualitative analysis. *Journal of Chemical Education*, **81**, 1672-1678.

5

Transforming Lecture Halls with Cooperative Learning

Lynn Geiger
Department of Chemistry
University of Colorado at Boulder

Loretta Jones
School of Chemistry, Earth Sciences, and Physics
University of Northern Colorado

Idahlynn Karre
The Chair Academy
Mesa, AZ

Abstract

Many instructors are interested in experimenting with innovations in the teaching of chemistry but feel hampered by large class sizes and a lecture hall environment. Cooperative learning techniques can be adapted for lecture halls of any size and can be used by instructors with little training. Thus they can serve as a first means of experimentation with innovation in teaching. The techniques can be incorporated gradually into a class or can become the primary mode of instruction. In this chapter the basic elements that lead to success in the use of cooperative learning in a lecture hall are presented. An array of tools is presented along with guidelines for individual accountability in cooperative learning. Some personal experiences of the authors are used to illustrate the techniques and as a guide to getting started. The results of several studies of cooperative learning methods in a lecture hall are summarized.

Biographies

Lynn Geiger (Ph.D., Northwestern University) is Academic Advisor and Instructor in the Department of Chemistry and Biochemistry, University of Colorado at Boulder. She has a theoretical physical chemistry background and has led a number of innovative projects in chemical education, including a program that takes chemistry graduate and undergraduate students into middle and high school classrooms. She has been developing and refining cooperative learning methods for lecture courses in general and physical chemistry since 1993.

Loretta Jones (Ph.D. and D.A., University of Illinois at Chicago) is Professor of Chemistry at the University of Northern Colorado. Her research area is in chemical education, particularly the active involvement of students in their learning, the applications of advanced technologies, and visual learning. She is a principal developer of a number of award-winning multimedia chemistry courses and has helped to lead large undergraduate chemistry reform projects. She has taught chemistry at the college level for 26 years and first became interested in cooperative learning while teaching general chemistry at the University of Illinois at Urbana-Champaign.

Idahlynn Karre (Ph.D., University of Colorado) is a retired professor who is a consultant, leader of educational innovation, and active promoter of cooperative learning methods in higher education. She was National Teacher of the Year (1992) and 2000 recipient of the Paul Elsner International Leadership Award. She is a facilitator and major contributor to the Academy for Leadership Training and Development training manuals. Her column on Tips and Tools for College Teaching appears regularly in the Chair Academy's journal, *Academic Leadership*.

Introduction: The Story of an Awakening

Our growing understanding of teaching and learning processes in higher education has led us to value student-centered instructional strategies. One way to accomplish this is to use cooperative learning. Many of us have made the mental transition from being "sage on the stage" to the "guide on the side". However, many of us are still teaching in the traditional lecture format, reluctant to change the way we actually teach. We may be concerned that changing our teaching methods will change the teaching and learning outcomes of our courses. Common concerns are, What if I try and I fail? What if I cannot cover all the material? What if the students hate it and my teaching evaluations suffer? What if it takes too much of my time to prepare? What if the weaker students just copy from the stronger ones? A lecture hall setting may exacerbate the concerns, because the architecture of the room is often designed to inhibit group learning. We would like to begin this chapter by addressing some of these concerns through an account of our personal experiences.

In January 1993 the three of us began working together as university instructors concerned about our teaching and our students' learning. We were each in different stages of our teaching careers. Each of us was experiencing different successes and challenges in our classrooms. We came together as a team—a cooperative team of colleagues dedicated to improving our teaching and our students' learning successes. During bi-monthly conversations devoted to investigating and applying cooperative learning teaching strategies, we discussed, debated, shared, and supported. We challenged one another's thinking, supported one another's efforts for innovation, and celebrated when we found success for our students. This chapter chronicles our understanding of cooperative learning in the context of the personal teaching journey of one of us.

In the spring of 1993, one of us (Lynn), a relatively new instructor, decided to try cooperative learning in her general chemistry I class room of about 60 students. This decision was reached after half of the semester had already gone by, as it took this long for the others in our cooperative learning discussion group to convince Lynn to try. Lynn was very reluctant to do this. She had many of the concerns listed above, but decided to try anyway. She kept a journal of her experiences during her initial experiences with cooperative learning. Here is her story.

Lynn's Journal:

Once a week I devoted a day in my general chemistry course solely to problem solving. I decided that instead of solving problems for the students on the blackboard, I would ask them to form groups and solve the problems themselves. Only after the students attempted their own solutions would we share and discuss solutions as a class. This seemed like a fairly safe way to get started with cooperative learning. So, I went to class and explained all of this to my students. Many of my students got up and left. This was slightly upsetting, but I decided to proceed with my plan. The remaining students stayed and worked well in the groups. I decided to reward these students with some extra credit points for being so cooperative. Word got out about the extra points and later in the semester as I experimented with other cooperative learning activities, the students stayed for class. That semester was an experiment for me. As I tried very simple and informal activities, I learned how to manage my classroom and how to address my concerns about cooperative learning. The following fall I taught the same course and continued to use cooperative learning techniques, many of which will be described in this chapter. I am so comfortable with this method of teaching that I now incorporate it into my teaching at all levels (general chemistry as well as undergraduate and graduate physical chemistry courses).

When I first started teaching this way I kept a teaching journal. I found that the journal helped me to organize my thoughts and keep track of my progress. It helped me to reflect on what I was doing. I have also found it to be a useful tool for helping others get started using cooperative learning. I will be sharing some excerpts from this journal with you in this chapter.

Why Cooperative Learning?

Cooperative Learning offers an opportunity to transform college chemistry classrooms, even lecture halls, into active learning environments (Cooper, 1995 and 2004). Effective cooperative learning focuses on carefully designed classroom experiences that emphasize **individual student responsibility** within a framework of student-to-student **positive interdependence** (Karre, 1994; Johnson & Johnson, 2004). Cooperative learning is a learner-centered instructional process in which small, intentionally selected groups of three to five students work together on a well-defined learning task to improve their mastery of course content. The purpose of cooperative learning groups in chemistry is to make each member a stronger individual in his or her own right. Effective cooperative learning in the chemistry classroom is characterized by four key components:

- Heterogeneous teams

- Positive interdependence

- Individual accountability

- Development of group processing and social skills

The first key component of cooperative learning in college chemistry classrooms is assigning, building, and maintaining classroom teams. Students are assigned to **Heterogeneous Teams**. Teams include student learners who engage in face-to-face interaction on a well-designed learning task suitable for small group work. Face-to-face *promotive interaction* occurs on cooperative learning chemistry teams. Students promote each other's learning by helping, sharing, and encouraging efforts to learn. Students explain, discuss, and teach what they know to classmates. Chemistry instructors can structure learning groups so that students sit together and talk through each aspect of an assignment, check each other's understanding and comprehension of lecture materials, or work together to apply, integrate, or deepen individual and collective understanding of concepts studied.

The second key component of cooperative learning in the college chemistry classroom is **Positive Interdependence.** In this chapter we show how Positive Interdependence can be structured into students' learning tasks. Chemistry students need to be encouraged to see the value of cooperation in science. Through positive interdependence they learn that the quality of their individual achievement increases when they work with others. Cooperative learning groups provide students with learning situations in which they need each other in order to complete the group's task (Fig. 1). Chemistry instructors can structure positive interdependence by establishing mutual goals—"Learn the key concepts of this unit and make sure that all other group members learn them as well." Joint rewards are helpful in encouraging positive interdependence—"If all group members score above a given criteria, each member of the team will receive a bonus." Likewise, sharing resources contributes to positive interdependence—"Each learning team will receive one folder for all the team's resources." Or, "The key components of the lesson have been divided into four sections so that each member of your team will be responsible for sharing the information in their part with the rest of the team." Chemistry students can also be asked to perform team roles such as leader, recorder, reporter, and encourager. These roles can rotate among students during the term so that each student gets the opportunity to learn and practice the important skills of these roles.

Sample Cooperative Learning Activity 1

Assign the following as homework:

Draw a Lewis dot structure for each of the following molecules. Use your Lewis dot structure or predict the electronic and molecular geometries for each molecule.

CO_2, HCN, BF_3, CH_2O, SO_2, CH_4, CH_3Cl, CH_2Cl_2, NH_3, H_2O.

Have the students complete the following in class. It may be helpful to bring molecular model kits for the students to work with.

Exchange papers within your group and correct each other's homework. Agree as a group about the correct Lewis structures and geometries for each molecule. Which of the molecules are polar? You may want to build molecular models to help you decide. Use your homework and your group discussions to generate a table relating molecular shapes to molecular polarity.

Figure 1. A group activity for general chemistry that encourages positive interdependence

The third key component is absolutely essential for the success of cooperative learning in chemistry: **Individual Accountability**. Instructors must ensure that students are responsible to their team and to their learning. Only when students feel that all members of the team are contributing to the group task and to each other's learning can chemistry instructors truly feel that cooperative learning is reaching its positive potential as a teaching and learning strategy. To do this, instructors can make sure that each student's performance is frequently assessed through checks for comprehension by the team and instructor during class discussions and learning tasks. Students can be required to arrive at class ready to learn, having completed an individual assignment that will contribute to the group's discussion or learning task. Individual tests also demonstrate individual accountability and learning, because after participating in a cooperative activity, group members should be better prepared to complete similar tasks by themselves. To ensure that each student is individually responsible and accountable for doing his or her fair share of the group's work, chemistry instructors need to assess how much effort each member of the team is contributing to the group's work, provide feedback to groups and individual students, and ensure that every member is responsible for the quality of the final outcome. Figure 2 provides an example of how individual accountability can be built into a group activity. Additional suggestions are listed in the Cooperative Learning Tools section of this chapter.

Sample Cooperative Learning Activity II
Building individual accountability into a group/class problem

Traditional problem:

a) Using the table of pKa's and pKb's in your textbook, pick a conjugate acid/base pair that you could use to prepare a buffer of pH 4.5. Find the ratio of acid-conjugate base concentration that will give you the exact pH desired.

b) Use the conjugate acid/base pair that you selected in part a, and assume that the concentration of the acid in your buffer is 0.10 mol/L. Calculate the pH of your buffer after the following amounts of acid and base are added to 100.0 mL of buffer solution: 10.0 mL of 0.100 molar HCl, 5.00 mL of 0.100 molar NaOH

Revised problem including individual accountability:

1   a) You need to prepare a buffer solution with a certain pH. Using the table of pKa's and pKb's in your textbook, decide with weak acid and base to use. The pH of your buffer should be:

           (even-numbered groups) 4.5
           (odd-numbered groups) 10.0

       b) Find the ratio of conjugate acid-base concentrations that will give you the exact pH desired. Compare your results with your neighbors. Even- and odd-numbered groups should find a group consensus and write it on the chalkboard.

2 Use the conjugate acid/base pair that you selected in part a, and assume that the concentration of the acid in your buffer is 0.10 mol/L. Calculate the pH of your buffer after the following amounts of acid and base are added to 100.0 mL of buffer solution:

       Person A: 10.0 mL of 0.100 molar HCl
       Person B: 10.0 mL of 0.100 molar NaOH
       Person C: 5.00 mL of 0.100 molar HCl
       Person D: 5.00 mL of 0.100 molar NaOH

Figure 2. An example of how a traditional general chemistry problem can be converted into a group activity that emphasizes individual accountability. Students work together to develop a strategy to solve the problem, but each must solve an individual problem using that strategy.

The final key component of cooperative learning in the chemistry classroom is the development of **Group processing and social skills**. In order to coordinate efforts to achieve mutual goals students must get to know and trust each other. We are not necessarily born instinctively knowing how to interact effectively with others. Opportunities to work together, communicate ideas, accept and support one another, and resolve conflicts constructively are all key social skills that chemistry students learn in cooperative group processes when chemistry instructors provide structured learning tasks, feedback on team progress, and opportunities to practice social and group processing in a safe learning environment. College students face professional careers with increasing demands for collaboration (Jones, Stillings, & Jordan, 2005). Collaborative skills such as leadership, decision-making, trust building, communication, and conflict management are part of the important personal and professional social and group skills that students learn in the chemistry classroom. Groups can be provided with opportunities to discuss how well they are achieving their learning goals and maintaining effective working relationships among members. Instructors can also monitor groups and give feedback on how well the groups are working together.

Cooperative Learning is important for our students' future success—The SCANS Report (Secretary's Commission, 1991), Work Force 2000 (Judy & D'Amico, 1997), and the report from an industrial roundtable sponsored by the American Chemical Society Committee on Professional Training (ACS, 1996) all affirm the need for chemistry students to be prepared not only with knowledge and skill in their discipline, but also with knowledge, skill, and attitudes appropriate for teamwork, collaboration, leadership, communication, negotiation. We no longer have the luxury of advancing only the academic agenda of our chemistry classrooms; teamwork will be at the heart of future careers for our students. Effective communication, group processing skills, complex issues of power and influence, and division of labor characterize most real-life work settings

Cooperative learning can take on many forms in the classroom and students can be assigned to formal or informal groups. We believe that cooperative learning tools or strategies can be adapted for use with both traditional and innovative teaching pedagogies. The cooperative groups can allow students to work together in the chemistry classroom for the purposes of cognitive processing, critical thinking, and group processing and teambuilding.

Cooperative learning tools in the chemistry classroom offers many learning advantages for students. The highly structured cooperative learning tools provide opportunities for students to clarify, reinforce, and extend the academic lesson. Critical thinking, reflective thought, and team decision-making become important dimensions of the academic lesson. The opportunity to discuss the strategies being used during problem-solving can help to build metacognition, the awareness of how one is learning, in students (Rickey and Stacy, 2000). Cooperative learning tools "break-up" a lecture and provide chemistry students with important attention breaks and opportunities to make the lesson their own by discussing critical problems or key concepts with cooperative learning team members. When the instructor carefully monitors for individual student accountability on cooperative learning teams, students learn valuable lessons about individual responsibility. Students value the life-long lessons they learn about cooperation, positive interdependence, and acceptance when they work together (Falvo and Pastore, 2005).

A personalized portfolio of cooperative learning tools provides chemistry instructors with the opportunity to use specific, engaging, active learning strategies while simultaneously using other strategies of college instruction like interactive discussions, performance assessments, classroom assessment, and lectures. They help college chemistry instructors and students ease in transition from lecture to active learning. Cooperative learning tools engage students more actively in their own learning and provide break points in the lecture that instructors can use to assess student comprehension of content in incremental stages.

Cooperative Learning Tools for the Chemistry Classroom

Tools that can be quickly adapted and used allow faculty to connect students with content in meaningful ways while using classroom time effectively. They provide checks for comprehension, application, and integration—qualities often missing in a traditional lecture class. Good cooperative learning tools provide accessibility and personal contact between the instructor and students—individuals and groups. The following cooperative learning teaching strategies provide for highly structured team learning opportunities within the large chemistry classroom.

A. Good tools: the secret to successful cooperative learning

Because the lecture hall environment is not ideal for cooperative learning, successful use of cooperative learning methods in a lecture hall depends on the instructor having at hand a set of easy-to-use tools that can be readily adapted to the learning of chemistry. In the first volume of this series, Melanie Cooper offered some good suggestions on how to get started using cooperative learning in the classroom (Cooper, 2004). An article by Orzechowski (1995) offers additional help for those new to cooperative learning. In this chapter we provide a set of tools that can be used by the novice instructor as well as by one having experience with cooperative learning groups. Any class can make use of cooperative learning methods.

This approach to cooperative learning uses carefully designed classroom cooperative learning tools. Each cooperative learning tool is a framework that can be implemented in "traditional" chemistry classrooms along with the instructor's current text, assignments, and evaluation procedures. The tool approach to cooperative learning provides chemistry instructors with a repertoire of educational strategies and helps faculty and students adopt active learning pedagogies in chemistry classrooms, while simultaneously continuing to rely on some traditional methods of chemistry instruction.

Cooperative learning tools in the chemistry classroom are highly structured tools that allow instructors to monitor students' time on task, individual accountability and other aspects of group work in the classroom. Each of the following tools facilitates active learning within the classroom and advances students' academic achievement. These cooperative learning tools offer chemistry students opportunities to clarify understanding, verbalize new concepts, think critically about academic ideas, personalize the lesson, and evaluate their learning. The tools are engaging and provide chemistry students with meaningful lessons on social skill development, group processing, and teambuilding.

Each tool can be implemented within the lecture-discussion format of the traditional chemistry classroom to help college students master their learning. Chemistry instructors can decide which tools best facilitate their academic goals. We have provided examples of our applications of the cooperative learning tools to illustrate their usefulness in the chemistry classroom. Table 1 summarizes the tools and their classroom applications.

Summary of Cooperative Learning Tools

FUNCTION	Assessment	Classroom Management	Content Mastery	Review	Team Building
	End-of-Meeting Evaluation Jigsaw	All-in-One Folder/Teams	Book-Ends	Five on Friday	All-in-One Folders
			Five on Friday	Muddiest Point	End-of-Meeting Evaluation
			Jigsaw	Roundrobin	Goodnews
	Magic Moment		Muddiest Point	Team Concept Web	
	Minute Paper		Prairie Fire	Three-Step Interview	
	Review Panel		Review Panel		
			Roundrobin		
			Team Concept Web		
			Think-Pair share		
			Three-Step Interview		
			Traveling File		

Table 1. Summary of Cooperative Learning Tools

B. Setting up and managing a cooperative classroom

The First Day

It is important for students to experience cooperative learning groups on the very first day, before they become settled into a familiar passive learning mode. The activity should be fun and relaxing, but have an outcome that students turn in. It should also serve as an introduction to your approach to teaching. Examples include having groups interpret the results of a demonstration or work out how they would go about finding a part-time job. Various strategies worked out by the groups can then be shared and elements of the scientific method they employed in these strategies pointed out. Other assignments might involve solving diagnostic review problems or discussing study strategies for the course. A Think Pair Share activity (see below) is an excellent tool for the first day, because it can be quickly and easily implemented in an unstructured setting.

Setting up Groups

Cooperative learning can be used in any size lecture hall. In very large classes it is often most efficient to have informal groupings where students merely turn to the students next to them to work on an activity and usually nothing is turned in for credit. However, when groups can be kept together throughout the semester, students have more opportunities to build team skills and assessment of the group work is easier.

In a very large classroom technology now allows intact groups to function and even be assessed through the use of electronic personal response systems, or "clickers" (Judson & Sawada, 2002). Students can purchase these devices in bookstores and use them in groups or individually to answer questions posed by the instructor. A number of chemistry "ConcepTests" have been created for use in large lectures at all levels of chemistry either with groups who "vote" on preferred answers to instructor questions either by the use of cards or personal response systems (Landis, Ellis, Lisensky, Lorenz, Meeker, & Wamser (2001). A limitation of the personal response systems is that the student is limited to a multiple choice response.

Although effective groups can vary in size from three to five, groups of four function well in a classroom because they are small enough for everyone to participate, but large enough to continue to function as a group if a member is absent.

Students in the second semester of a course sequence may want to select their partners. The advantage of this method is that students who are friends may also continue their groups outside of class as study groups. The disadvantage is that some dependencies may have already been established and the work may not be shared equally. Setting up groups so that they are intentionally diverse helps to ensure that students meet other students they might not otherwise know and build important team-building skills.

To ensure that the groups are diverse, one of the following procedures can be used:

1) Students fill out demographics forms; groups are created so that each includes a diversity of majors.

2) If the size of the class and room allow, have the students break up into four sections by a criterion such as birthdate or major, and go to the four corners of the room. The groups of four are formed by distributing the same set of group number cards to the students in each corner so that each group includes one student from each corner.

3) Give a mathematics or other diagnostic test and put students in groups that are heterogeneous by student ability, as determined by the test scores.

Journal entry

August 30

Today we set up our all-in-one folders. The students were given an incentive to come, 5 points of the 100 points set aside for in-class activities, for getting into groups. I set up 22 groups using majors. Each group contained one student from each of the following major groups:
> chemistry, physics, math (and math related)
> premed, and health,
> biology and earth sciences
> miscellaneous and undeclared majors.

> In class we got into groups using the overhead projector, with students going to the parts of the room corresponding to the position of the group on the overhead. After everyone found their group members we did a "get to know" one another exercise:
>
> Answer the following two questions;
> 1. List your anxieties about taking chemistry.
> 2. Why are you taking chemistry?
> We took 10 minutes to get acquainted.
>
> The students worked on two problems in their groups. The students thought the day's group activities were fun, and were looking forward to doing this again. I was surprised at how well this worked.

All-in-one teams

Communication with intact groups can easily be managed by means of a two-pocket folder, the "all-in-one folder." The folder is labeled with the group number and students pick up the folders each day when they enter the classroom. Homework and student questions and suggestions are collected, exams are returned, notes are sent to students, and group assignments are transmitted by means of the folders (Fig. 3). The folders greatly reduce the amount of class time needed for paperwork distribution and collection. It is a good idea to use color-coded folders. For example, in a class with 30 groups, groups 1-5 can be red, groups 6-10 blue, etc., for a total of six colors. The folders for a large class can then be easily assembled into stacks in which a student can quickly find the folder for a specific group.

Figure 3. The all-in-one folder helps to structure group work. It holds all student assignments and serves as a means of communication between student and instructor.

Some things that we have found useful to keep in the folders are:

- Letter from the instructor describing cooperative learning and its benefits
- A sheet with the group member's names, group roles, initial group tam-building activity and group contract.

- Some sort of chart or grid to keep track of students' scores on group assignments.

- Name of the group, if students have chosen one, and a photograph of the group, if desired and students agree.

These handouts can be inserted into the all-one folders before they are initially passed out in class. They should remain in the folder during your course. Continue to bring the folders to class each day your class meets.

First team activity

On the day on which the all-in-one folder is first used, students meet their teammates, the students with whom they will be working for the rest of the semester. Inside the folder they find a form on which they list their names, backgrounds, and the unique characteristics each student brings to the group. The first activity might include naming the group, discussing how their group will function most effectively, listing fears concerning the course, and discussing why they are taking chemistry. When students earn points for completing group assignments collected in the folders, attendance increases significantly. Students tend to sit with their group members and develop a commitment to the group.

Rotating roles

In order for the cooperative learning experience to help students build individual responsibility and to reduce the incidence of one student dominating a group, it is important to have the students select a role to play and to switch roles with other students. Roles can be swithched each time the group meets for class, or at several points during the semester, as long as each student in the group has at least one chance to play each role in the group. Various types of roles are possible. A good set of four roles for beginning the semester are:

- Leader: organizes the other students in performing the activity and checks that everyone is doing his or her job.

- Recorder: records all student work and discussion and submits the written consensus of the group.

- Reporter: reports the results of the group's work to the class orally or on the chalkboard.

- Encourager: keeps up group morale and makes sure that everyone participates.

For larger groups an additional role, that of the Critical Thinker, can be assigned. The Critical Thinker asks the others to explain what they are doing to the group, questions their work when appropriate, and suggests alternatives.

C. Some Useful Cooperative Learning Activities

Activities that build content mastery and problem-solving skills

Think-pair-share: This is a very easy tool to use that can be used in any lecture hall even if students have never worked in groups before. Stop after presenting a topic and ask the students a related question. Give them a minute to think through the answer on their own, then a few minutes to talk with their neighbors or teammates and arrive at a solution. Ask volunteer pairs or groups to share their solution with the class.

Example: This tool can be used as a way to get the students to formulate strategies for solving problems. A problem can be presented to the class on the board or overhead projector. After the students think about the problem and compare their ideas with their neighbors they share with the class different ways of solving the problem. Because students do not share immediately everyone has a chance to consider their own solution before an eager shouts out an answer.

Goals: Reflection, self-assessment, peer feedback, skill building.

Journal entry

September 14

For exam review I brought a series of example problems. I did the problems on the blackboard using a think-pair-share format with the students. I presented the problem and asked them to work out a strategy for solving the problem with their neighbor but not to work out a solution. We then worked the problems together on the board with suggestions from the groups.

Bookends: Tie together a class discussion by asking students to observe a lecture demonstration or animation at the beginning of class or to record their thoughts and questions about the day's topic at the beginning of class. Ask several of the groups to share their questions with the class. At the end of class students return to their groups and explain the lecture demonstration or animation to each other or answer their questions using what was learned in class.

Example: At the start of a class on weak acids students watch a demonstration showing that magnesium reacts more vigorously with a solution of hydrochloric acid than with a solution of acetic acid of the same concentration. The students are asked to record their observations of the demonstration and to discuss possible hypotheses to explain the behavior. At the end of class, students revisit and revise their explanations.

Goals: Engagement, reinforcement, concept mastery

Journal entry

October 1

Today we started class with the voice activated reaction as a lecture demonstration (Summerlin & Ealy, 1985). Two flasks went around the classroom, and the students were instructed to say nice things into the flask. They then interrupted class when they noticed any change. The blue flask turned pale yellow and the purple one changed yellow-green. The students were given time to discuss the lecture demonstration at the end of class and assigned to write a minute paper to hand in at the beginning of the next class meeting.

Review Panel: Assign a problem at the end of class for the students to complete individually as homework. Each student brings a solution and the groups then correct/modify the individual papers or use the individual responses to answer a more complicated problem together. This tool works well for both conceptual problems and numerical problems.

Example: Assign each student in the group to draw a different Lewis structure. On the next day students correct and report out the four Lewis structures and decide which structures are resonance structures.

Goals: Review and reinforcement, peer evaluation, feedback on understanding

Prairie fire: Write short-answer questions on an overhead transparency, each with a group number. Each group can have its own question or several groups can be assigned to each question. Give the groups a few minutes to come up with an answer to their questions. Have each group report their answer as you call out the group numbers. Record answers and ask the class if they agree with each answer. With this approach, students consider a relatively large number of related problems in a short period of time.

Example: Review of chemical nomenclature, definitions, identification of types of possible intermolecular forces, and predicting solubility or the products of chemical reactions.

Goals: Reinforcement, practice, peer evaluation

Journal entry

September 13

Today we did a naming lesson. After reviewing the rules I placed 22 names/formulas on the overhead. The groups had 2 minutes to decide on their name or formula. We then went around the classroom and each group called out their name, as I recorded them. After this the class corrected any mistakes. This worked well. There were only 3 mistakes.

Jigsaw: Each team member is assigned a different calculation or portion of a lesson to master for the following class. In class each member shares his or her expert knowledge with the others.

Example: Each student calculates a point on a pH curve. In class the points are then plotted, along with points from other groups, to form the curve.

Goals: Content mastery

Team Concept Web: Each team is given a large piece of newsprint paper on which they create a team concept map on a topic, once you give them a central concept such as thermochemistry, bonding, or acids. These concept maps are called "webs" since they are jointly created (Regis, Albertazzi, & Roletto, 1996).

Example: You can distribute colored pens so that each team member can use a different color to identify their individual contributions. The concept web is a good capstone for a topic or it can be an ongoing one, with students adding to it during each class.

Goals: Concept mastery

Traveling File: "Files" or folders, each containing one or more questions, are distributed to the teams. Each team discusses and prepares a written answer to the question, which they add to the file. The file is then exchanged with another team that had a different question. The second team may read the first team's answer, but must also create their own response. After teams have responded two or three times, the questions can be discussed by the class as a whole. Alternatively, teams phrase their own question about some concept they are struggling with learning. The file containing the question is exchanged with another team. The second team attempts to answer the question. The file is then sent to a third team, which checks the answer, correcting it if necessary. The file is then returned to the first team, which must indicate whether or not they feel their question has been answered.

Example: Groups are asked to write a question they have about the topic being discussed. Group-generated questions are often conceptual or relate to problem-solving strategies. They might be along the lines of, "How can I tell if a molecule is polar?" or "How do you find the pH of a solution of ammonium chloride?"

Goals: Critical thinking, concept mastery, building problem-solving strategies, peer evaluation

Three-step Interview: Teams of four split into two and one person of each pair interviews the other on a topic in the course. Then they switch roles. In the third step, the team members take turns sharing what they learned with the others in their team or the class.

Example: This technique works well after a demonstration, when students share their interpretations of their observations. It can also be used to allow students to share what they have learned in laboratory, computer, or homework assignments.

Goals: Concept mastery

Muddiest Point: At the end of a class or a topic, give the students a few minutes for each to write down questions that they still have about the topic, being as specific as possible. Teammates then share their questions and attempt to clarify the Muddiest Points of their team members. Any Muddiest Points that have not been clarified in the group are placed in the all-in-one folders for the instructor. The questions can then serve as the basis of the review on the following day.

Example: This technique can be used as the basis of a feedback session after returning scored examinations.

Goals: Critical thinking, feedback on learning for the instructor

Minute paper: Assign a problem at the end of class for the students to take home and work individually as home work. Each student brings a solution or a part of the solution to the next class meeting. Groups then correct/modify the individual papers to formulate a group response.

Example: Assign a summary problem and ask the student to write individual answers as homework. At the beginning of the next class period give the students time to compare/correct their answers.

Goals: Mastery, Application. Classroom Assessment, Performance Assessment

---

Journal entries

October 23

Today I ended class with a minute paper assignment of a simple heat transfer problem. The students will compare answers and hand it in to be graded on Monday.

October 26

The class came in as usual and started working right away to check their specific heat problem with their neighbors. We took about four minutes for them to check and prepare a group response to hand in. I also had them hand in their individual papers. Anyone who did not attempt the problem over the weekend did not get credit.

Roundrobin: Assign groups an issue to discuss. Each person on the team suggests their point of view in a structured order. When a student feels that he or she has no more to add to the discussion he or she can "pass" but rejoin again on the next round. The recorder notes key phrases and summarizes the discussion at the end of the discussion.

Example: Pose a question for the students that will encourage them to think more deeply than usual about a topic, such as, "Are ionic and covalent bonds completely different types of bonding or just the extremes of a continuum?" "Would acetic acid be a strong or weak acid in liquid ammonia?" When showing a simulation of molecular processes, students can learn better to interpret the animation when you ask, "What in this simulation is real and what is not real?"

Goals: Concept mastery

Five on Friday: During the final five minutes of class on Fridays, students are asked to write individually what they feel they learned during the week and to include remaining questions. The writings are shared with team members and included in the folder for the instructor to review.

Example: Students are asked to provide positive feedback to one another about their group activities and to write about topics that they found confusing or difficult in the current unit. This cooperative learning tool can also be used on any day of the week to gather feedback from the students. It is a good tool to use to collect topics/questions for an exam review or general problem-solving day.

Goals: Reflection, peer evaluation, instructor feedback

Journal entries
September 20
Tomorrow is problem day. We took requests for group problems at the end of lecture today.
September 21
I prepared problems covering all requested topics on overheads and the students worked these problems out in their groups for the entire lecture. . . . At the end of each problem I called on groups to report their final answers/solutions and instructed the class to check their work against the reported answers.

Team-building activities

Good News: Ask the students to bring some news to share with the class. Select several students at random to share their news with their groups or the entire class.

Example: Ask the students to bring a news item to class that is related to chemistry, along with a one paragraph review.

Goals: Engagement, appreciation of role of chemistry in society

TENS! is an acronym for Touch, Establish Eye Contact, Use the Person's Name, and Smile! This is a greeting activity that is very useful in building team spirit and a sense of community. It also gets students started off with a smile and positive attitude.

Example: Use this activity often toward the beginning of the semester to assist teams in building good team rapport. Asking students from different cultural backgrounds to share their greeting rituals helps them to feel welcome.

Goals: Engagement, team building

Evaluation activities (also see the assessment section below)
Magic moment: Allow the students some time to discuss the answer to a quiz question with their group members. Stop the discussion after a few minutes and have the students write individual answers.

Example: When the class does poorly on an exam allow them to "buy" their curve. One way to do this is to bring to class a problem similar to one that most students had trouble with on the exam and give it as a quiz to add as much as 10% to their exam score. The students have 3 - 4 minutes to discuss a solution with their group. Then they write individual solutions. Any group that does not stop discussion when they are told loses the opportunity to gain points on their exam.

Goals: Content mastery

End-of-Meeting Evaluation: Give each student a 3x5 card on which they write their names. At the end of class, the students within a team place their cards together face down and shuffle them. Students each pick a card, then write "honest and constructive" feedback for the team member whose name appears on the reverse. Team members return the cards to each other and engage in a discussion about their progress, needs and successes.

Example: Use end-of-meeting evaluations after the teams have worked together a while. This activity provides an opportunity for students to reward one another for their contributions and to discuss better approaches to working together. The activity is a powerful builder of community and team responsibility.

Goals: Peer assessment. The instructor need never know what was written, although in a small class students may enjoy sharing their feedback with everyone.

D. Tools for Building Individual Accountability in Cooperative Learning Teams

The goals of interdependence with individual accountability is critical for encouraging every student to be an active participant in cooperative learning classrooms. A number of methods can be used to build individual accountability into cooperative learning activities. Some methods are intrinsic to certain activities, such as the jigsaw. Other activities can be designed for individual accountability. Some examples follow:

- In a group problem each student has the same question, but different conditions. For example, each student may have to calculate the pH of a buffer, but the concentrations or the identity of the weak acid may vary. Students begin with a group discussion of what strategies to use to solve the problem, then apply the strategies individually to their assigned calculations.

- Each student may have a different calculation to perform before coming to class. The results of each calculation are necessary to complete the assignment. Common examples include students in calculating points that are used to set a curve.

- Jigsaw the "homework" problems at the end of a chapter, asking each student to complete one question. At the beginning of class for which the "homework" has been assigned provide time for students to discuss their solutions and receive feedback on their work from their team. Collect the "homework" problems and team comments in the All In One Folder. Assess the individual work from each student as a check for Individual Accountability. Provide "bonus" points for teams that successfully complete *all* "homework" problems.

- The group proposes the percentage of the score that should go to each team member for an activity, unit, project, or quiz. The score is then divided accordingly.

- In a jigsaw or traveling file activity students can be asked to sign their contributions.

- Five on Friday can be used as a team assessment strategy. Ask students to take 5 minutes during the last class period of the week to return to their team ground rules and assess their functioning as a team. Students can submit a brief summary of their team successes and challenges and set a goal for continuing to work successfully together.

- For Team Projects require Individual Accountability Benchmarks throughout the term. For example, ask student teams to select a research topic. Provide one week for all members of the team to research the key components and sub-categories of the topic. Provide team time in class for students to share their understanding of the research topic. Ask students to report for which part of the research topic they are going to be individually accountable. Provide two weeks of research time for students to research their individual sub-topic. Provide class time for each student to teach their team their sub-topic and thereby become a team of individual experts on a broad topic area. Ask students to determine a format for sharing their research—oral presentation, paper, etc. Ask students to work together—as a team of experts—on the overall presentation or paper.

E. Assessment

When students learn together they also need to know that they will be assessed individually. That knowledge encourages students to use the group experience as a means of mastering the material individually. However, group assessment is also useful for providing feedback to the group with little time required of the instructor and for assigning credit for contributing to a group assignment.

Not all group work is graded or even collected. For example, some one-minute papers may simply be shared within the groups. However, typically, students turn in their work in their all-in-one folder; the total score for group work and group quizzes can account for 5-10% of the course grade. The work turned in by groups can be assessed in various ways, as outlined below.

- Collect all the individual student papers for credit. This is the most common mode of assessment. Group members self-correct their work during the class discussion of the results. Typically a few points are awarded for showing up and contributing to the group work (more points are awarded for activities that are graded). Because credit is awarded for participation, class attendance is encouraged.

- Students assess each other. In many activities students work on a problem individually, then trade or share papers for discussion and feedback.

- Members of each team sign their contributions and indicate the percentage of the score that should go to each team member.

- The individual responses are all graded.

- Group members collaborate on one paper that is scored for credit.

- Each group member submits the solution to a problem, but only one paper, selected at random, is scored. This strategy encourages groups to ensure that every team member has mastered the problem.

- Longer-term projects are collected and scored. For example, concept webs are collected and evaluated for comprehensiveness and logical connectivity.

- Bonus points can be awarded if each group member scores above a certain level on an individual quiz.

- Group quizzes can have a higher level of difficulty and may require more time than regular quizzes. A group quiz can be submitted on one paper for a single score or, where the members of a group have related, but slightly different questions, the score can be a combination of the individual and average group scores.

- Group quiz papers can be traded with another group, each group scoring the other paper. The papers are then graded by the instructor, both for the work on the original paper and for the scoring of the other team's paper.

- Group final exam. This can be a complicated (marathon) problem that ties together several units from the semester as a group exercise to count for 25% of the final exam score. Announce a maximum amount that the student's final exam score can be raised by the group problem, such as 5-10%. Prior to the group final exam, state which units (chapters) the question will cover and suggest that each group member become the group expert on one of the topics. Hand out the problem on the last day of class and give the groups the entire time to work the problem. If the score on a student's individual section of the final exam is higher than the score on the group problem, the student's score is only that earned on the individual section. If the group problem will help the student, combine the two scores according to the posted ratio.

Outcomes

Despite various difficulties, including outraged students during the first implementation, we have continued to use cooperative learning groups for a substantial portion of class time. Although the lecture hall environment is not ideal for cooperative learning, the benefits outweigh any additional effort that may be required at first. Once the instructor is comfortable with cooperative learning groups, the time required is minimal and much effort is saved through the use of the all-in-one folders. Instructors who have incorporated cooperative groups into their teaching report a number of benefits, such as increased attendance, increased awareness of student learning difficulties, and a stronger connection with students (Johnson & Johnson, 2003; Falvo and Pastore, 2005). Commonly, instructors say that their relations with students have improved and that the atmosphere in the lecture hall becomes more like that of a small classroom (Bauer, 1996).

Occasionally a group is found to be dysfunctional. For example, one student may be dominating the group or have poor attendance. In such a case, it is best to have students try to work out the problems on their own as an exercise in team-building. If the efforts of the group fail, a group may need to be restructured. Some students also do not immediately see the value of cooperative learning groups, complaining that they "were required to attend class," "had to do all the work in class, even though the instructor was being paid to do it," and even "had to think in class; none of my other classes required me to think." However, other students have claimed that, "I felt a part of a community in this class," "working in our group encouraged us to form a study group outside class," and "the group work helped me to understand and to pass the course."

The Rocky Mountain Teacher Education Collaborative (RMTEC) provided funds for a number of studies of the use of cooperative learning. In a 1995 RMTEC evaluation of cooperative learning in a class of 215 students, 69.8% agreed or strongly agreed with the statement, "Cooperative learning activities helped me to understand chemistry concepts better," 65.1% agreed that, "Working problems in groups, during lecture, helped me develop my own problem-solving strategies," and 70.7% agreed that, "If I had a choice between two similar lecture sections, I would pick the one that uses cooperative learning groups." Fewer than 19% of the students disagreed with any of these statements. These results are consistent with those of Fasching and Erickson (1985), who found that students' problem-solving skills improved when group discussions were introduced.

Preliminary studies conducted as part of the RMTEC project also indicate that cooperative learning encourages equal participation of both male and female students in classroom discussions (Geiger, Pentecost, and Straushein, 1996). Not only was the involvement of female students higher in a lecture hall using cooperative learning groups (Fig. 4), but the female students asked more higher order questions. This is in contrast to the results found in a lecture-only classroom, where the male students dominated most of the classroom discussion, a situation that has been observed by others (Kahle, Parker, Rennie, & Riley, 1993). These observations are in agreement with the observations of instructors in other fields who have observed that group learning encourages the participation of female and minority students in classroom discussion (Kirk & Zander, 2002; Rosser, 1995).

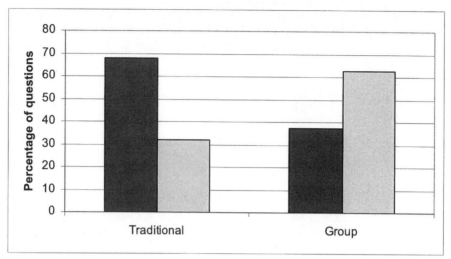

Figure 4. Percentages of male (dark bars) and female (light bars) students who asked questions during general chemistry lectures taught by traditional means and with group work. The traditional class was 56.9% female out of 51 total students and the class with cooperative group work was 63.0% female out of 35 total students.

Preliminary RMTEC evaluation data have also found that use of cooperative learning in the classroom results in a change in learning in the classroom. In the preliminary study the same final exam was given to a class that used cooperative learning as was give a previous semester where no cooperative learning was used in the classroom. Both classes were taught by the same instructor. While the averages and standard deviation were not significantly different, the shapes of the distributions were. In the cooperative learning classroom there was an increase in the number of scores in the middle range and a decrease in scores at either end of the distribution, primarily in the lower region. Consequently, the distribution was flatter than that of the lecture-only classroom across C's and B's (Fig. 5).

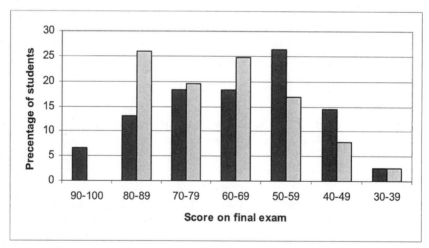

Figure 5. Scores on the final exam for general chemistry classes taught with group work (light bars) and by traditional means (dark bars). Although the mean scores were not significantly different (traditional, 65.0%; group, 68.0%), the distribution of scores was flatter for the class taught with group work.

In a study of the effect of the lecture hall environment on cooperative learning groups, it was found that, although the lecture hall environment posed certain problems, students were able to participate in effective learning groups in both environments (Reamer and Jones, 1995). In this study the same instructor taught two sections of a general chemistry course and assigned the same in-class group activities on Tuesdays.

Both classes met four days a week in a lecture hall with armrests and a steep rise, but on Tuesdays one section met in a classroom with movable tables and chairs that could be arranged for group work. Observations of the two sections conducted on Tuesdays showed that students in the classroom with tables had more frequent interactions with the instructor, as it was easier for them to contact her; in the lecture hall only groups on the aisles had frequent contact with the instructor. The instructor spent more time organizing the group activities in the lecture hall, because some students in the lecture hall did not sit with their groups except during group work. The groups that worked in the classroom with tables always sat together on Tuesdays. They were also more likely to share materials such as calculators and books with their group members. At the end of the semester, no difference in achievement between the two classes was seen.

Although cooperative learning groups function well in a steep lecture hall, the new science lecture halls at the University of Northern Colorado were designed to facilitate cooperative learning. Both rooms have two long tables on each tier that span the room so that students at the front table of each tier can turn their chairs to work with group members at the table behind them. The rise is shallow and the tables are far enough apart to allow the instructor to walk along the rows and reach all the groups (Fig. 6). These lecture halls have become two of the most popular rooms on campus.

Figure 6. A student cooperative learning group solving a general chemistry problem. The role of the instructor, as Lynn Geiger demonstrates, is to facilitate the group's work.

Acknowledgements

Some of the development described in this chapter was supported by grants from the National Science Foundation Division of Undergraduate Education Collaboratives for Excellence in Teacher Preparation Program (DUE-9354033) and the Division of Research, Evaluation, and Communication (REC-0440103). Ideas that influenced our work came from conversations with our colleagues and from the members of the Rocky Mountain Teacher Education Collaborative Chemistry Team. We were also influenced in helpful ways by colleagues John Cooney, M. Lynn James, and Clark Fields (University of Northern Colorado) and Tom Pentecost (Aims Community College), and our strategies were refined with the help of our perceptive and cooperative students. We would particularly like to thank former University of Northern Colorado Teacher in Residence Belia Straushein, Northglenn High School, Northglenn, Colorado, for her helpful contributions and for making classroom observations that gave us important feedback on the effectiveness of cooperative learning activities for the lecture hall.

Suggested Readings and Resources

Active learning: Cooperation in the college classroom, by Johnson, Johnson, and Smith, is the classic work on cooperative learning and active learning in higher education. It offers many practical suggestions for improving instruction through group work (Johson, Johnson, & Smith, 1998).

Chemistry Conceptest Website, part of the *JCE Digital Library* maintained by the *Journal of Chemical Education,* contains a large number of thought-provoking questions for most areas of college chemistry. These tests may be used with no charge and are suitable for use with a Personal Response System and informal groups as well as with intact groups. See http://www.jce.divched.org/JCEDLib/QBank/collection/ConcepTests/

Experiences in Cooperative Learning: A Collection for Chemistry Teachers edited by Susan Nurrenbern and published by the Institute for Chemical Education (ICE) at the University of Wisconsin-Madison, contains many examples of cooperative learning activities and a good discussion of how the instructor's role is changed when using cooperative learning teams (Nurrenbern, 1995).

Small Group Learning Page, maintained by the National Institute for Science Education at the University of Wisconsin-Madison, contains a variety of group learning techniques that can easily be applied to chemistry classrooms (NISE, 2005). See http://www.wcer.wisc.edu/archive/cl1/CL/ as well as the related book by Landis et al. (2001).

Student Companion for Chemistry: Molecules, Matter and Change, Second Edition, published by W. H. Freeman, contains a set of cooperative classroom activities for general chemistry. The accompanying instructor manual contains many suggestions for implementing the activities as well as solutions (Geiger, Straushein, and Jones, 2000).

Related chapters in this volume:
POGIL, Process-Oriented Guided-Inquiry Learning, by R. S. Moog, F. J. Creegan, D. M. Hanson, J. N. Spencer, A. Straumanis, D. M. Bunce, and Troy Wolfskill. POGIL has stimulated the development of a national network of instructors who are developing inquiry-based activities for general and organic chemistry courses. POGIL uses a structured approach that students can easily learn and apply to new learning situations. Guidelines and some sample activities are also available at http://www.pogil.org.

Peer-Led Team Learning in General Chemistry: Scientific Discovery and Learning, by D. K. Gosser. The PLTL project has produced a substantial body of classroom activities for learning chemistry in groups led by peer leaders. The materials support intensive investigation of concepts and problem-solving, are tested, and can be used in the lecture hall as well as in peer-led teams.

Peer-Led Team Learning: Organic Chemistry, by J. A Kampmeier and P. Varma-Nelson. The PLTL project has also produced complete sets of materials to support peer-led group learning in organic chemistry. Team learning has been found to be an effective means of helping students develop improved learning strategies for organic chemistry.

Using Visualization Technology and Group Activities in Large Chemistry Courses, by J. P. Birk, R. C. Bauer, and D. E. Leedy. This chapter describes a comprehensive general chemistry course reform that incorporates frequent group activities. The impact of the reforms on the course structure and student learning are discussed.

References

ACS (1996). Cooperative learning and teamwork. *CPT Newsletter, II*(1), 5; American Chemical Society.

Bauer, C. F. (1996). Making the Large Lecture Chemistry Classroom Seem Small, *American Chemical Society National Meeting,* New Orleans.

Cooper, M. M. (2004). An Introduction to Small-Group Learning. In Pienta, N. J., Cooper, M. M., & Greenbowe, T. J., *Chemists' Guide to Effective Teaching.* NJ: Prentice-Hall.

Cooper, M. M. (1995). Cooperative Learning: An Approach for Large Enrollment Courses. *Journal of Chemical Education.* 72, 162.

Falvo, D. A., and Pastore, R. (2005). Exploring the Relationship between Learning Styles and Technological Collaborations. *Proceedings of the National Educational Computing Conference of the International Society for Technology in Education,* Philadelphia, June, 2005.

Fasching, J. L., and Erickson, B. L. (1985). Group discussions in the chemistry classroom and the problem-solving skills of students. *Journal of Chemical Education, 62,* 842-846.

Geiger, L., Pentecost, T., and Straushein, B. (1996). in *Annual Report of the Rocky Mountain Teacher Education Collaborative, NSF Project #DUE-9354033.*

Geiger, L., Straushein, B., and Jones, L. L. (2000). *Student Companion for Chemistry: Molecules, Matter and Change,* Second Edition. New York: W. H. Freeman.

Johnson, D. W., and Johnson, F. (2003). *Joining Together: Group Theory and Group Skills* (7th edition). Boston: Allyn & Bacon.

Johnson, D. W., Johnson, R.W. (2004). Cooperation and the use of technology, 785-811, in *Handbook of Research on Educational Communications and Technology* (ed. D. H. Jonassen). Mahwah, NJ: Lawrence Erlbaum Associates.

Johnson, D. W., Johnson, R.W., and Smith, K. A.. (1998). *Active learning: Cooperation in the College Classroom* (2nd edition). Edina, MN: Interaction Book Company.

Jones, L. L., Stillings, N. A., and Jordan, K. D. (2005). Molecular visualization in chemistry education: The role of multidisciplinary collaboration. *Chemical Education Research and Practice,* **6**(3), 136-149.

Judson, E., and Saawada, D. (2002). Learning from past and present: Electronic response systems in college lecture halls. *Jounral of Computers in Mathematics and Science Teaching, 21*(2), 167-181.

Judy, R. W., and D'Amico, C. (1997). *Workforce 2000: Work and Workers for the 21st Century,* Indianapolis: Hudson Institute.

Kahle, J. B., Parker, L. H., Rennie, L. J., & Riley, D. (1993). Gender differences in science education: Building a model. *Educational Psychologist*, 28, 379-404.

Karre, I. (1994). *Busy, Noisy, and Powerfully Effective: Cooperative Learning in the College Classroom.*

Kirk, M., and Zander, C. (2002). Bridging the digital divide by co-creating a collaborative computer science classroom. *Journal of Computing Sciences in Colleges, 18*(2), 117-125.

Landis, C. R.., Ellis, A. B., Lisensky, G. C., Lorenz, J. K., Meeker, K., and Wamser, C. C. (2001). *Chemistry ConcepTests: A pathway to interactive classrooms,* Prentice-Hall: Saddle River, NJ.

National Institute for Science Education (NISE), *Collaborative Learning: Small Group Learning Page,* at http://www.wcer.wisc.edu/nise/CL1/CL/default.asp. Accessed October 2005.

Nurrenbern, S. C., ed. (1995). *Experiences in Cooperative Learning: A Collection for Chemistry Teachers,* Institute for Chemical Education, University of Wisconsin-Madison.

Orzechowski, R. F. (1995). Factors to consider before introducing active learning into a large, lecture-based course. *Journal of College Science Teaching, March/April,* 347-349.

Reamer, S., and Jones, L. L. (1995). in *Annual Report of the Rocky Mountain Teacher Education Collaborative, NSF Project #DUE-9354033.*

Regis, A., Albertazzi, P., and Roletto, E. (1996). Concept maps in chemistry education. *Journal of Chemical Education, 73*(11), 1084-1088.

Rickey, D., and Stacy, A. (2000). The role of metacognition in learning chemistry. *Journal of Chemical Education, 77*(7), 915-920.

Rosser, S. (1995). *Teaching the Majority: Breaking the Gender Barrier in Science, Mathematics, and Engineering,* New York: Teacher's College Press.

Secretary's Commission on Achieving Necessary Skills (1991). *What Work Requires of Schools: A SCANS Report for America 2000,* Washington, DC: US Department of Labor.

Summerlin, L. R., and Ealy, Jr., J. L. (1985). *Chemical Demonstrations: A Sourcebook for Teachers,* Washington, DC: American Chemical Society.

Thompson, C., Koon, E., Woodwell, W. H., & Beauvais, J. (2002). Training for the Next Economy: An ASTD State of the Industry Report on Trends in Employer-Provided Training in the United States, Alexandria, VA: ASTD.

Using Visualization Techniques in Chemistry Teaching

Vickie M. Williamson
Department of Chemistry
Texas A & M University

Thomas J. José
Department of Chemistry
Blinn College

Abstract

Visualization techniques in the chemistry classroom are used to promote more expert-like mental models in students. A chemist can visualize a chemical reaction on the macroscopic level, what the reaction will look like to the human eye in the laboratory, and on the particulate level, what changes are taking place in the atoms and molecules. Techniques to help students create these mental images include laboratory simulations and demonstrations on the macroscopic level. Techniques that promote mental images on the particulate level include physical models, role-playing, fixed computer models, dynamic computer animations, student-generated drawings/animations, and interactive computer models. Implementation strategies for each technique will be discussed.

Biography

Vickie M. Williamson received her B.S. in natural science/chemistry from Central Oklahoma University and her M.S. in chemistry/chemical education from the University of Oklahoma. Her career has included teaching at the secondary and junior college levels. Her Ph.D. in science education was awarded in 1992 from the University of Oklahoma. After graduation, she worked on the Integrated Mathematics, Science, and Technology Project at Illinois State University and was a member of the chemistry department at ISU. Since 1997 she has been a faculty member at Texas A & M University, where she teaches freshman chemistry and graduate level courses in chemical education. She directs the research for chemical education masters students. She serves as a feature editor for the Chemical Education Research Feature of the Journal of Chemical Education. Her research and teaching articles have appeared in the *Journal of Research in Science Teaching*, *The Journal of Chemical Education*, *The Journal of Science Education and Technology*, and *Monographs of the Society for College Science Teachers*. She has written inquiry-based curriculum materials for middle school through university. Her research interests include visualization to aide student understanding of the particulate nature of matter and inquiry-based teaching in lecture and laboratory.

Thom José received his B. S. in Biochemistry from Indiana University in 1994. After a six-year career as a biochemist he turned his focus to education entering Texas A&M University's Department of Chemistry Master's Program in Chemical Education. After completing his degree in 2002, he joined the faculty of Blinn College, Bryan, Texas. His experience ranges from using visualizations in the large university classroom to integrating interactive activities into small junior college classes. His publications have appeared in both chemical education and biochemistry journals. Thom's current research interests are in the areas of molecular visualization and assessment of group learning.

Introduction

Visualization can be defined a number of ways: "1. the creation of a clear picture of something in the mind, 2. a clear picture of something created in the mind, or 3. a technique whereby somebody creates a vivid positive mental picture of something such as a desired outcome to a problem" (Microsoft Soft Corporation, 1999). Visualization can be classified into two types. The first is macroscopic, which reproduces what would be seen in everyday life or in the laboratory. This type can be an actual demonstration performed by an instructor or filmed and shown as a video. The second type is at the particulate nature of matter (PNM) level, for example, molecular animations. These two types of visualizations represent two of Johnstone's three basic components of chemistry: the macroscopic, the symbolic and the submicroscopic (particulate) (Johnstone, 1993). In chemistry, the mental images at the particulate level are as important as those at the macroscopic level, since chemists most often explain phenomena in terms of particle behavior.

A number of misconception studies cite students' inability to visualize abstract models as a reason for their difficulties in understanding chemistry (e.g., Abraham, Williamson, & Westbrooke, 1994; Haidar & Abraham, 1991). Taber (2002a) describes the importance of visual depictions of chemical processes to student understanding in order to deter misconceptions. Other studies have shown that visualizations can help create more expert-like mental models and increase conceptual understanding (e.g., Williamson & Abraham, 1995; Sanger, Phelps, & Fienhold, 2000). The way in which visualization is used with a class must also be considered. Active learning strategies have been found to be superior to traditional strategies (Silberman, 1996). These same strategies are thought to be beneficial with visualization techniques.

This chapter will explore various visualization techniques that have been proven to be effective in the chemistry classroom. Selected references for each type of visualization are described which give evidence that the visualization technique is useful in the chemistry classroom. Instructors should consider the points given at the conclusion of each section. The chapter is arranged to describe techniques that promote the formation of macroscopic mental models first (macroscopic visualizations), followed by techniques that promote the formation of particulate mental models (particulate visualizations).

Macroscopic Visualizations

The following techniques can promote the formation of mental models of the macroscopic world. These are the mental images of chemical phenomena similar to the scenes that your eyes perceive in the laboratory or in the natural world. The use of a wet laboratory, macroscopic laboratory simulations, and demonstrations (both live and electronic) will be discussed.

Wet Laboratory

While students may form macroscopic mental images of substances used in their experiments during the laboratory portion of the course, this chapter focuses on macroscopic images formed in situations where the students are not physically in contact with the materials. As a result, other chapters in this series should be consulted for wet laboratory ideas. Some of the techniques that are covered in the chapter can be incorporated into the laboratory portion of the course, but are not part of the usual traditional or inquiry-based wet laboratories.

Laboratory Simulations

The word simulation is defined as "1. the reproduction of the essential features of something, for example, as an aid to study or training" and "2. the construction of a mathematical model to reproduce the characteristics of a phenomenon, system, or process, often using a computer, in order to infer information or solve problems "(Microsoft Soft Corporation, 1999). In the context of a chemistry course, simulations represent a means for students to interact with materials and equipment traditionally encountered in laboratory. Laboratory simulations visualize experiments at the macroscopic level and are most often delivered via computer.

The authors have reviewed no conclusive studies that have found that macroscopic laboratory simulations are any better than a real lab experience. For example, two early studies report opposite results; Bourque & Carlson (1987) show that students learned more when performing hands-on experiments than with simulations alone, while Jackman, Moellenberg & Brabson (1987) demonstrate that computer simulations are more effective than other instructional methods. Proponents of laboratory simulations point out that time is saved when using simulations versus wet lab experiments. They also include limiting the use of hazardous chemicals or expensive equipment/glassware, safety concerns, and waste issues as reasons to use these simulations. Instructors who use laboratory simulations cite the ability for the student to redo an experiment or to try the experiment multiple times with different variables as a plus.

The literature is also conflicting about how to use a computer simulation in concert with hands-on lab experiences. Bourque & Carlson (1987) in a second study reported that simulations might be best used as post laboratory exercises to optimize student comprehension *after* the wet laboratory is completed rather than using the simulation before the hand-on experience. On the other hand, Martinez-Jimenez et al. (2003) found that using a virtual laboratory *prior* to the wet lab experience led to a higher level of performance. It may be that the best consistent use of computer laboratory simulations is with a wet laboratory, but the exact use of the simulation may depend on the laboratory in question. The timing of whether to use the simulation before or after the wet laboratory depends on the function the instructor desires in the curriculum. Another issue is whether the instructor decides to use the laboratory simulation in a student active versus traditional manner.

A website that contains many laboratory simulations is housed at Iowa State University: http://www.chem.iastate.edu/group/Greenbowe/sections/projectfolder/animationsindex.htm. One simulation, allows the students to control the variables of a titration experiment (http://www.chem.iastate.edu/group/Greenbowe/sections/projectfolder/flashfiles/stoichiometry/acid_base.html) is shown in Figure 1. Step-by-step, students are directed to select the type of titration to perform, the material to use to fill the buret and flask, and the exact acid, base, and indicator to use. Students may even overshoot the endpoint in this particular simulation. Alternatively, an instructor may decide to display the simulation in front of the class to help prepare them to encounter the equipment and situations that might be encountered in lab.

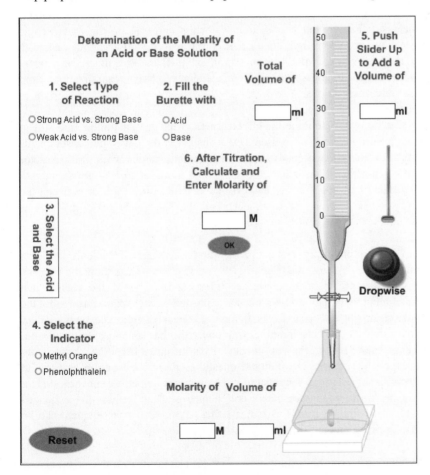

Figure 1. Titration Laboratory Simulation
(http://www.chem.iastate.edu/group/Greenbowe/sections/projectfolder/flashfiles/stoichiometry/acid_base.html)

Other laboratory simulations are commercially available from many sources. Instructors can also investigate ancillary textbook materials for laboratory simulations.

Points to consider when implementing laboratory simulations:
- A laboratory simulation *alone* may not have any better affect than a hands-on lab experience (Bourque & Carlson, 1987; Jackman, Moellenberg & Brabson, 1987).
- Physical constraints such as materials, safety, and equipment may be the driving force for an instructor's decision to use a laboratory simulation.
- When used *with* a hands-on laboratory, simulations may enhance comprehension and performance in the lab (Bourque & Carlson, 1987; Martinez-Jimenez, Pontes-Pedrajas, Polo & Climent-Bellido, 2003).

Demonstrations

Demonstrations are experiments that are preformed for the students to view. These can be as complicated as clock reactions or as simple as observations of ice melting. Demonstrations are viewed by the student and can be done live before a student audience or can be taped for playing during a class. Demonstrations leave students with macroscopic views of chemical phenomena.

Demonstrations tend to improve student attitudes (Ophardt, Applebee, & Losey, 2005), but can be used for more than just to enhance attitude (the gee-whiz factor). Allowing students to generalize observations and to hypothesize the underlying reasons or driving forces for the observed phenomena can also be used to promote learning. Student explanations can be gathered by means of a demonstration assessment. These activities usually involve the students watching the demonstration done by the instructor without explanation, the class agreeing on the macroscopic observations, then students answering questions or making hypothesis concerning why the observations occurred. The demonstration assessment can be used as a quiz, part of an exam, or just an assessment of student understanding. These activities take a more constructivist approach, allowing students to draw generalizations from their observations and propose reasons for those observations.

For example, Deese et al. (2000) conducted a study to determine the effectiveness of the demonstration assessment. Two classes of chemistry for freshman engineering majors were used. One was given demonstration assessments about every two weeks during the course; the other class simply observed the demonstrations while the instructor explained the content. Both classes were given a final conceptual assessment and a pre- and post-attitude survey. There were no significant differences in attitude between the pre- and post-survey for either class or between the classes on the pre-survey or the post-survey. However, the treatment class did show a significantly greater conceptual understanding at the end of the course than the control group.

A similar study highlighted the benefits of cooperative groups with demonstration assessments. Students can learn by discussing and debating with one or more partners. Bowen & Phelps (1997) also attempted to show the efficacy of the demonstration assessment. Two classes of freshman chemistry were used. One of the classes had demonstration assessments, which were attempted by collaborative groups as a portion of each exam throughout the semester. At the end of the course, both the treatment and control classes received the same eight questions on their finals. Four questions were based on the demonstrations, and the other four covered other content. On these latter four questions, there was no significant difference between the two classes. This indicated that both classes were basically equal in achievement. However, on the demonstration-based questions, the demonstration assessment group scored significantly higher. The conclusion was that demonstration assessments helped to enhance student learning on the material covered by the demonstration assessments and helped students retain this enhanced understanding, at least until the final exam. This finding seems to indicate that demonstration assessment can be successful at improving retention of student understanding.

Demonstrations can be done in both the laboratory and the lecture portion of the class. For example, the burning book demonstration can be used on the first day of class in lecture to launch a discussion about the use of evidence and scientific thinking. The same demonstration can also be used to illustrate combustion, activation energy, balancing equations, etc. The burning book demonstration can be seen in Figure 2. In this demonstration a prepared book bursts into flames as a start button is depressed (Battino & Fortman, 1996). As with the other visualization techniques, demonstrations can be use in a traditional or verification style or in an inquiry-based approach.

Figure 2. Dr. L. Peck, Texas A & M, demonstrating his burning book

Sources for demonstrations include the instructor's manual for your textbook and other demonstration books. Among the best-known demonstration books are Shakhashiri (1983-1994) and Bilash, Gross & Koob (1995)

Points to consider when implementing the use of demonstrations:
- Demonstrations can be used to enhance attitudes. (Ophardt, Applebee, & Losey, 2005)
- Demonstration assessments can enhance student understanding by soliciting students' understanding of the underlying rationale for the phenomena observed during the demonstration. Deese et al. (2000)
- There is a benefit of students working together on demonstration assessments. Bowen & Phelps (1997)

Particulate Visualizations

The following techniques can promote the formation of mental models of the particulate world. These are the mental images of the particle behavior during chemical phenomena, which are abstract mental models. The use of physical models, role playing, fixed computer models, dynamic computer models or animations, student generated drawings or animations, and interactive computer models will be discussed.

Physical Models

Physical models are concrete, tangible objects that illustrate the chemical structures/processes at the particulate level. The physical models can take the form of commercial model kits, magnets, Play-Doh, or food items (gumdrops, raisins, marshmallows).

There are a number of studies that show increased visualization ability results from building and using physical models. Talley (1973) found that ball and stick models used by freshman students throughout the semester aided in visualization of chemical concepts, which in turn resulted in greater achievement in college level general chemistry. He concluded that students who increased their ability to visualize were able to perform at higher cognitive levels on problems about the phenomena, shifting from rote recall to critical thinking. Further, he found that students were able to transfer from the specific models they used to other concepts due to the increase in the ability to visualize. It is important to note that in this study students observed a model built by the instructor, then built their own model, and finally, that they used the models to show the chemical interactions as these were described in the lecture.

Students need to personally manipulate physical models into order to gain improved problem solving. To help students develop the ability to visualize, they need experience observing and manipulating the model from different angles. Gabel and Sherwood (1980) found that students who manipulated models performed significantly better on solving general chemistry problems that those who only saw demonstrations with the models. Friedel, Gable, & Samuel (1990) found that viewing and manipulating physical models helped students construct more understanding between the models and underlying chemistry concepts.

The lack of availability of model kits does not preclude the use of physical models. Others have reported similar success using Play-Doh, clay, gumdrops, raisins, and marshmallows (e.g., Nicoll, 2003). These items allow students to decide on the angles and other attributes of the molecule, which may give the instructor more information on what the students actually understand. Benefits have also been seen with use of small magnets to represent particles on pizza pie pans as the working surface.

A simple application, well suited for use in front of a classroom, is to use balloons to illustrate multiple geometries/hybridizations encountered in chemistry. Inflated latex balloons, are often used to mimic the characteristic lobes of hybridized orbitals. When held in the hands of an instructor, the balloons will naturally assume the proper three-dimensional arrangement (Figure 3). Another example would be to take combinations of balloons of one color and balloons of another color to illustrate cis-/trans- & fac-/mer- isomerism seen in coordination compounds (Figure 4). Used in an inquiry mode, the shapes and patterns can be determined by the students whether the balloons are in the hands of the instructor or the students.

Figure 3. Balloons portray a tetrahedral structure   **Figure 4.** Balloons portray cis and trans isomerism

Points to consider when implementing the use of physical models:

- Models should be used throughout the semester to show structure AND interactions (Talley, 1973).

- Students need to build the models (Nicoll, 2003).

- Instructors should encourage students to rotate the model (to view it from different angles; Gabel and Sherwood, 1980; Friedel, Gable, & Samuel, 1990).

- Instructors should encourage students to make connections between the model and chemistry concepts (why is the model build in a certain way and how will the model change in chemical interactions; Talley, 1973).

Role-Playing

Role-playing to aide visualization can be defined as a non-conventional method of teaching in which students participate in acting, drama, skits, or dance to portray particles in a reaction or process. These presentations can be done in lecture or laboratory and throughout the course with volunteers or assigned as a specific project.

Role-playing during lecture may help increase student understanding and retention of concepts by helping students to better understand abstract concepts through participation. Role-playing may also be helpful in developing interest towards the subject. It is important to have an area of open floor space for these activities. Also, the manner in which the initial group of volunteers or recruited students is treated will determine the number of future volunteers. At the college level, Battino (1979) referred to particulate role-playing as participatory lecture demonstrations. He described a number of concepts that students could act out during the lecture. These included chromatography, chemical kinetics, balancing equations, gas laws, kinetic molecular theory, gas solubility, electronic energy levels, isomers, etc. Battino suggested that the benefit of role-playing was that these activities appeal to students, help with understanding of abstract concepts, and appear to aide in retention of ideas over time. Battino also stated that these participatory demonstrations actually saved lecture time, since the concept could be more quickly grasped after such a demonstration. For example, six students, three of which were given straw hats, illustrated chemical kinetics. The collisions occur to form molecules between the hat and non-hat atoms. The effects of increased concentration, increased temperature, and addition of a catalyst were also be illustrated by adding more students, having students move faster, and adding a matchmaker to speed reactions.

Projects that allow students to portray common applications of chemistry increase student interest. Lerman (1986) describes the benefits of linking chemistry to students' interests by the use of projects, which portray chemical phenomena through dance, photography, song, journalism, etc. These projects included reports or lectures on the applications of chemistry in the field, plus a presentation using the tools of the student's major. For example, a dance to illustrate the chemical reactions that occur in muscles during dancing would accompany a lecture on the topic. Lerman asserts that students develop a more meaningful understanding of chemistry through these activities.

Points to consider when implementing the use of particulate role-playing:

- Space is needed for the role-playing activity.

- Students must receive positive reinforcement for their participation.

- Topics to be used for role-playing in lecture must be generated by the instructor and incorporated into lecture at multiple times during the semester.

- Topics for projects should be generated by the students, but approved by the instructor before students proceed. (Lerman, 1986)

- Student interest and retention may be increased. (Battino, 1979; Lerman, 1986)

Fixed Computer Models

Fixed computer models are images of atoms or molecules whose coordinates are static. These coordinates may be produced in a variety of ways, but are most often derived from existing crystallographic determinations. By means of a program or browser plug-in, these models may be rotated, translated across and toward the screen or have different attributes highlighted.

The benefits from using fixed computer models may be achieved with fair short contact time. Ealy (1999) conducted a study where students were asked to use the Spartan molecular modeling program to complete exercises that had been prepared for use with the software. In a series of four, two-hour computer sessions, students completed exercises on the topics of: 1. periodic trends, 2. molecular structure, 3. electronic structure, and 4. organic molecules. By the end of the semester, students who had used the software has performed better on final exam question that dealt with resonance, dipole moments and atomic/molecular stoichiometry than students who had not used Spartan.

There is some evidence that fixed computer models may have greater benefits that physical models, especially since merely building the physical model does not lead to the maximum learning as was discussed earlier. Another study used Desktop Molecular Modeler as its software, but compared students who had used ball-and-stick models v. fixed computer models (Barnea & Dori, 1999). Again, those who used the fixed computer models did not spend much time at the computer (three, two-hour sessions) but did work through material designed specifically for the study. The study compared students' achievement on structure and bonding tests as well as spatial ability. Students who used the computer program displayed greater improvement in structure and bonding and spatial ability than did students that used ball-and-stick models. The same best practices may be required for fixed computer models as were required for physical models- to direct students to rotate the models and to use the models to show relationships.

Fixed computer models also seem to give students a better impression of the structure of the molecule. Another study by Dori & Barak (2001) compared two groups: one group used plastic ball-and-stick models as teacher demonstrations while the other group used a computer modeling program for an organic chemistry unit. It was found that students who used the computer program gave better explanations of phenomena and were better able to transform or transfer types of information (e.g. 1 or 2 dimensional representation to 3 dimensional model) than the ball-and-stick model group.

Sanger (2000) cautioned that instructors, who use particulate drawings to evaluate student understanding, must give the students adequate exposure and practice with interpreting drawings. He called for instructors to use particulate drawings in their instruction. This use would allow students to build a visual literacy concerning particulate drawings. Sanger (2005) reported similar findings.

An application of using fixed computer models in the classroom may involve showing students models of representative electronic and/or molecular geometries of covalent compounds. One website which demonstrates this application well is based at Purdue University (http://www.chem.purdue.edu/gchelp/vsepr/cmp2.html). The site allows users to display two fixed models at once. The utility in this function is that while one frame is used to display the basic electronic geometry, the other frame can show the suitable molecular geometry when one or more bonded atoms have been replaced with electron pairs (Figure 5). Rather than displaying images such as Figure 5 to student in a lecture setting, students can be instructed to download the coordinate files and view the models for themselves on their home computers.

Trigonal bipyramidal	Seesaw
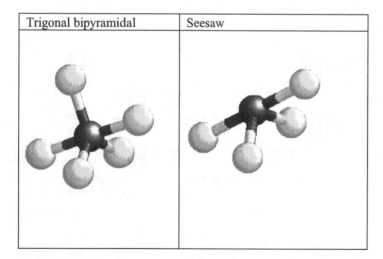	

Figure 5. Chime Structures

Rasmol and *Chime* are molecular viewers that are freely available for download (*Rasmol*: http://www.umass.edu/microbio/rasmol/getras.htm; *Chime*: http://www.mdl.com/downloads/downloadable). The most common type of file to designate coordinates for a molecule is .pdb files, which are also available online (*Protein Data Bank*: http://www.rcsb.org/pdb/home/home.do). *Jmol* is a free program, which can utilize a wide variety of file types, including pdb files (see http://jmol.sourceforge.net/download). *Jmol* is the next generation of molecular viewers. Other computer programs may also be used in a fixed model mode, like *Spartan* in the Ealy (1999) study. Computer programs that allow the students to draw or build molecules are discussed under the "student-generated models" section.

Points to consider when implementing fixed computer models:

- Lengthy sessions at a computer are not required, especially if students work through well-prepared materials (Ealy, 1999; Barnea & Dori, 1999; Dori & Barak, 2001).

- There may be an advantage to using a fixed computer models rather than physical models (Barnea & Dori, 1999; Dori & Barak, 2001).

- Students who use fixed computer models give better explanations of structure (Dori & Barak, 2001).

- Students need exposure and practice in order to correctly interpret particulate drawings. (Sanger, 2000; Sanger, 2005)

Dynamic Computer Models – Animations

Animations, in this context, are a series of images shown in rapid sequence that mimic movement and show a model of the molecular world. These are ready-for-viewing movies that are shown to students via computers, videotape, DVD, or other media. Animations show dynamic processes, rather than the fixed computer models described above. Others have defined animations in a similar manner, e.g., see Burke, Greenbowe, & Windschitl (1998).

It is important that animations are consistently used in instruction. These animations need not be lengthy or take up too much lecture time. Williamson and Abraham (1995) in their study of the effects of computer animations found that animations of less than 2 minutes shown daily for two weeks to general chemistry students increased the students' conceptual understanding. The authors proposed that animations helped students create dynamic mental models of particulate phenomena. Further, students treated with static diagrams created mental models that included misconceptions of the phenomena and failed to visualize adequate particulate behavior.

Conceptual understanding is enhanced when animations are with coupled with demonstrations. Russell, et al. (1997) found that students' conceptual understanding and ability to create dynamic mental models improve when both types of visualizations are used. Additionally, students better correlate the symbolic, macroscopic, and microscopic levels of representation. Velazquez-Marcano, et al. (2005) found that order of animation/ demonstration does not matter when predicting the correct outcome of fluid experiments at the macroscopic scale. Either combination created the same predictive ability. They also found that only one type of visualizations was not enough and that both were needed for maximum effect. The linking of the macroscopic(video) and particulate (animations) can be powerful. Burke, Greenbowe, & Windschitl (1998) in their summary of the literature on the development and use of animations also noted that animations of short duration and the use of demonstrations with animations could be effective.

For example, after discussing a vacuum and the properties of a gas, it is very powerful to show a particulate animation. Figure 6 is a screen shot of an animation that removes the barrier when the stopcock is opened to allow the gas particles to randomly fill both areas. Students can begin to visualize the action of gas particles. This animation was used in the Velazquez-Marcano et al. (2005) study.

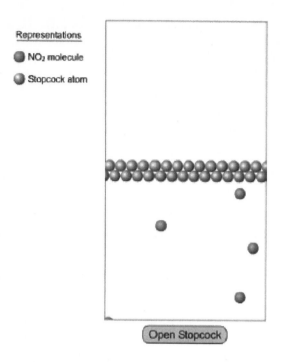

Figure 6. Animation to show the mixing of a flask of gas and an evacuated flask. Created by Roy Tasker for the Velazquez-Marcano et al. (2005) study.

One source for animations is the instructor's materials for the textbook you are using; many of these include particulate animations. Instructors can also purchase commercial animation CD-ROMs or videotapes of particulate animations (for example, the Chemistry Animation Project tapes from Caltech). Many web-based animations can be found; for example, there are those from Iowa State University,
http://www.chem.iastate.edu/group/Greenbowe/sections/projectfolder/animationsindex.htm
Other sources include websites that contain links to a number of animations for general chemistry and to the programs/ plug-ins needed to use them.   An   example   of   this   type   of   web   page   is
http://chemed.tamu.edu/vis_collective or http://www.merlot.org/merlot/index.htm .

Points to consider when implementing the use of animations:

- Animations can be short in duration. (Williamson & Abraham, 1995, Burke, Greenbowe, & Windschitl, 1998)

- Animations must be used consistently during the course of instruction. (Williamson & Abraham, 1995)

- Animations should be coupled with demonstrations or macroscopic representations. (Russell, et al., 1997, Burke, Greenbowe, & Windschitl, 1998)

- The benefit of animations is that students seem to create dynamic mental models that are more representative of nature. (Russell, et al., 1997, Williamson & Abraham, 1995)

- Instructors could consult the chapter on animations in this volume.

Student-Generated Drawings/Animations

One way to determine students understanding is to require students to create their own particulate drawing or animation. These tasks can be as simple as asking students to draw a particle view of a reaction or as complex as having students storyboard a reaction showing the transition from reactants to products. Even more complex versions include computer programs that allow students to construct molecules, rather than access predetermined coordinates, or to construct animations. These activities are done to assess student understanding. It should be noted that instructor-constructed animations are outside the scope of this section, a good reference for building effective instructional animation sequences is Burke, Greenbowe, & Windschitl (1998).

It is often hard to determine what mental model a student holds of a chemical reaction. One way to elicit these models is to ask students to draw their ideas. Harrison & Treagust (1998) used student drawings to evaluate student understanding. They proposed that instructors should select visualization techniques appropriate to the cognitive ability of their students and should gradually challenge students to use more abstract models. One of their key positions was that more than one model or representation should be used in instruction.

Some computer programs allow students to construct molecules. Most of these will optimize the student drawing to correct angles and other aspects of the drawing. Further, the programs often allow multiple representations to be viewed simultaneously. Wu, Krajcik, & Soloway (2001) reported that high school students who used *eChem*, a computer program that allows students to build molecules, had significantly improved learning. They concluded that building computer models can aide students in generating mental images. The program allowed students to make connections between 2-D and 3-D models.

Construction of student-generated animations can help the instructor more deeply evaluate student understanding. The animation can be assigned as part of lab report or quiz. With only note cards and pencils, an 'animation' can be constructed using individual drawings that are assembled so to provide a dynamic chemical reaction as seen through a flipbook (Milne, 1999). With the use of multimedia tools Schank & Kozma (2002) found that using *Chemsense,* a molecular drawing and animation tool, students were significantly better at representing chemical phenomena at the particulate level. Additionally, they found that students were more focused on the dynamic nature of chemical reactions. For example: Students can be asked to make an animation of the neutralization of HCl by NaOH. Figure 7 shows the construction of an animation with *Chemsense* that currently has three frames.

Some computer programs that allow molecule construction are available for download; however, the availability is not reliable, nor are updates consistently preformed. Currently, an older version of *echem* is available at http://hi-ce.org/echem/index.html , but is not being updated. Other free drawing programs include *Chem Sketch Freeware* and *Isis Draw*, both available at http://www.acdlabs.com/download/.

There is currently only one animation program that is developed for assessing student understanding. *Chemsense* may be downloaded at http://chemsense.org/. Commercial programs may be a good option, if you want presentation quality drawings and animations, but these are costly and have a large learning curve.

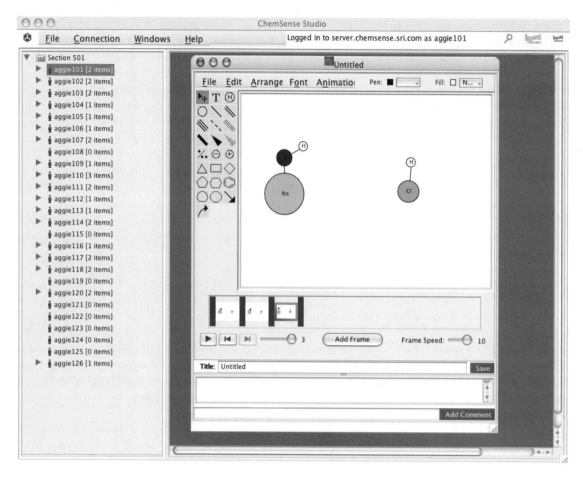

Figure 7. Chemsense animation tool

Points to consider when implementing the use of student-generated drawings/animations:

- Student-generated drawings/animations can be used to evaluate student understanding. (Harrison & Treagust, 1998)

- It may be hard to interpret and grade student drawings. (Harrison & Treagust, 1998)

- Instructors should select models appropriate to the level of the students involved. (Harrison & Treagust, 1998)

- Students should be asked to create drawings or animations (Schank & Kozma, 2002)

Interactive Computer Models

Of the types of visualizations discussed, interactive computer models are the newest addition to the instructor's repertoire. These computer models, in a sense, are a combination of fixed computer models and student-generated animations. Students/instructors not only view the particulate animation, but also are in control of the particle motion/behavior and therefore become directors of the actions on the screen.

Experts in the field of molecular visualization have called for the use of more interactive computer models in science education. Expert participants at an NSF workshop on molecular visualization recognized simplicity and interactivity as important characteristics that any molecular visualization should possess prior to the workshop (José & Williamson, 2005). The importance of the interaction of students with visualization software and of students having control over what is displayed are ideas that originated before the workshop activities began, but were adopted by the group as a whole during the workshop. The idea of student control of variables was a new idea to many who where not actively engaged in chemistry instruction. In the workshop report, participants encouraged educators to not only *use* molecular visualization in a demonstrative mode but also provide students the option to *modify* its presentation.

Some interactive animations have already been developed which allow the student to control variables and to view multiple representations (particulate, graphical, numeric). One example is from the Molecular Laboratory Experiments created by Abraham, Gelder & Haines, which can be found at http://genchem1.chem.okstate.edu/CCLI/Startup.html (Figure 8). When students change variables in these models, they control the movement of the particles in the animation field that is linked to the other representations. Therefore, instructors can direct students to collect data from the simulation in an inquiry or learning cycle mode (see Chapter 4 in Vol. 1 of this series for information on inquiry and the learning cycle approach; for information about interactive animations, see Chapter 12 in this volume by Gelder & Abraham).

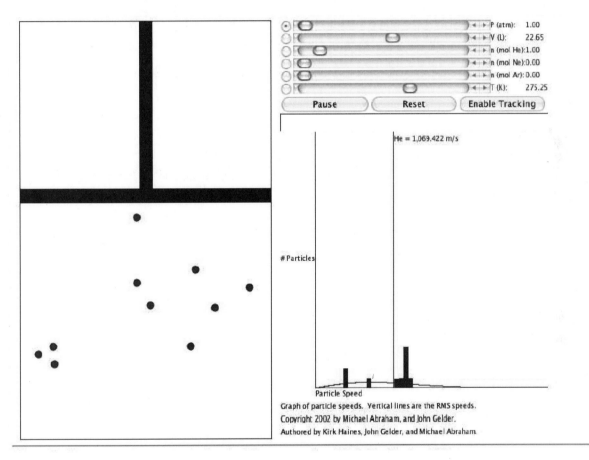

Figure 8. Interactive computer visualization (Abraham, Gelder & Haines, 2001)

Some textbook ancillaries contain interactive modules that allow students to control variables. Some interactive models may be found online (http://www.merlot.org).

Points to consider when implementing interactive computer models:

- Some experts suggest that this type of visualization is beneficial to students (José & Williamson, 2005).

- Interactive models fit well with the philosophy of inquiry instruction (Abraham, Gelder & Haines, 2001; http://intro.chem.okstate.edu/2001ACS/Talk.html).

- Many interactive computer models are not yet readily available.

- Research on the benefits of these models is not yet available. Instructors should watch the chemical education literature for subsequent findings.

Assessment or Enrichment?

It is up to the instructor to decide whether the technique will be used only to enrich the lecture or be an assessed portion of the course. In either case, the student should be made aware that the instructor values this activity. If a visualization technique is used as enrichment and is not assessed as a separate activity or a question on an exam or quiz, students are more likely to disregard the visualization. Distributing grading rubrics or point values for assessed activities will focus student participation. If an instructor spends the time to incorporate visualizations into his/her classroom, then the assessments used in the course should also include visual items. Instructors can easily incorporated visual techniques into quizzes and exams. For short response items, students can be asked to draw a particulate view of the phenomena or to illustrate the reactants in one space and the products in another. They can also be asked to storyboard a reaction, to create an animation as described earlier, or to predict particle activity. For multiple-choice items, students can be asked to choose the most appropriate drawing or to choose the most appropriate prediction of particle behavior. Table 1 gives examples of these assessment questions and as comparison an example of an algorithmic question, which only requires mathematical manipulation.

Examples of Assessment Items

Example 1 Requiring Visual Thinking	A Here is a closed flask containing air.	B. Here is the closed flask after it has been cooled and liquefied. Draw the particles.
Example 2 Requiring Visual Thinking	Which is the best explanation to explain why raising the temperature increases the rate of a chemical reaction? (Circle all that apply) A. The number of collisions per second increases. B. The number of reactant molecules increases. C. The average force of a collision increases. D. The size of the particles has expanded.	
Example 3 Algorithmic	For the RXN: n-butane <--> isobutane K = 2.5 If 2 moles of n-butane exist in a 1.0 L flask after equilibrium, what is the concentration of isobutane at equilibrium? (a) 4.5 (b) 3.5 (c) 2.5 (d) 5.0 (e) 2.0	

Example 4 Requiring Visual Thinking	The reaction X (aq) <---> Z (aq) has an equilibrium constant of 2.5. Below are drawings of the 1-liter box containing the solution at equilibrium. Circle the box(es) that shows this equilibrium. 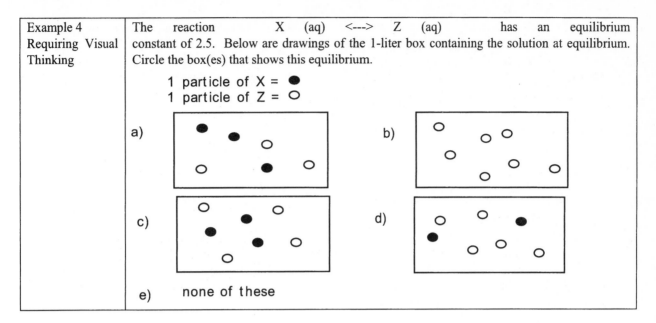

Table 1. Examples of assessment items

Copyright Issues

Instructors who are considering implementing visualizations from the Internet MUST be certain that they are obeying U.S. copyright laws. Free graphics may be copied from the web; however, instructors must obtain permission to use any graphics that are not advertised as free. The same rules apply to animations, simulations, programs, etc, as law protects all these. Instructors must check the permissions granted on the webpage to use, download, copy, or distribute anything on the webpage. Many websites will grant permission to use their visualizations in the classroom, some may ask users to provide e-mail addresses. Instructors should print out the portion of the webpage that grants this permission in case it is needed to justify the use of the material. For further information see http://www.copyright.gov/.

Summary

Some instructors are cautious to implement the use of visualization techniques in their classroom, even though they understand the benefits that students can gain. A summary of the usual objections is included in Table 2, along with the rationale to overcome these objections.

Objections to Using Visualization Techniques

Objection	Rationale to Overcome Objections
I don't know where to find the computer-based visualizations. OR There isn't enough preparation time for me to find the animations	Many textbooks have ancillaries that are CD collections of visualizations. This chapter lists a number of web sites where instructors can find individual visualizations or collections of tested visualizations.
I am not sure when visualizations techniques should be used in the class.	The progression from macroscopic to particulate to symbolic and mathematical helps students link these areas and move from more concrete to more abstract ideas. A visualization technique that builds the mental models of particulate views should be used after the macroscopic feature of the phenomena is addressed.
I don't know what type of visualization techniques that I should use.	An instructor must choose the type of visualization techniques that fit the concept they are teaching, their

OR Role-playing and demonstrations are not my style.	facilities, their class, and their own teaching style.
Animations will take too much time out of the lecture portion.	Most animations are very short clips that can be played in lecture. They can also be used in recitation or assigned as homework.

Table 2. Objections to Using Visualization Techniques

A number of visualization techniques have been discussed. It is important for the instructor to choose visualizations that suit the course they are teaching and align with the instructor's goals and learning objectives for the class. In any case, more than one visualization technique should be used to help students create mental images of chemical phenomena (Singer, Tal, Wu, 2003). With most techniques, recurring usage is required for maximum student benefits. An instructor wanting to implement any of these techniques must plan where the visualization fits in the curriculum. The instructor must prepare the materials, media, and chemicals ahead of time. Further, the instructor must practice all presentations with the equipment at their own institution. Visualizations are important in helping students build mental images and increasing conceptual understanding. It is worth an instructor's time to make use of visualization in their classroom. It is important that instructors use some type of visualization technique to help students build mental models of the particulate and macroscopic views of the world.

Suggested Reading

Glibert, J.K. (Ed.) (2005). *Visualization in science education.* Heidelberg: Springer.

Lerman, Z. M. (2001). Visualizing the chemical bond. *Chemical Education International,* 2 (1), 6-13. (http://old.iupac.org/publications/cei/vol2/0201x0006.html: 2001)

Sanger, M. J. & Badger, S. M. II (2001) Using computer-based visualization strategies to improve students' understanding of molecular polarity and miscibility. *Journal of Chemical Education,* 78(10), 1412-1416.

Taber, K. (2002b). *Chemical Misconceptions-Prevention, Diagnosis and Cure (Volume II: Classroom Resources).* London: Royal Society of Chemistry.

Wu, H., Shah, P. (2004). Exploring visuospatial thinking in chemistry learning. *Science Education,* 88(3), 465-492.

References

Abraham, M.R., Gelder, J. I., & Haines, K. (2001). Managing information flow for flexible assessment of student learning in large lecture classes. *The Chemical Educator.* 6(5), 307-308.

Abraham, M. R., Williamson, V.M., & Westbrook, S.L. (1994). A cross-age study of the understanding of five chemistry concepts. *Journal of Research in Science Teaching,* 31(2), 147-165.

Barnea, N.; & Dori, Y.J. (1999). High-school chemistry students' performance and gender differences in a computerized molecular modeling learning environment. *Journal of Science Education and Technology,* *8*(4), 257-271.

Battino, R. (1979). Participatory Lecture Demonstrations. *Journal of Chemical Education.* 56(1) 39-41.

Battino, R. & Fortman, J.J. (1996). The 'burning' book – a guide to its construction. Chem 13 News, May 18.

Bilash, B., Gross, G.R., & Koob, J.K. (1995) *A Demo a Day.* Batavia, IL: Flinn Scientific.

Bourque, D.R, & Carlson, G.R. (1987). Hands-on versus computer simulation methods in chemistry. *Journal of Chemical Education.* 64(3), 232-234.

Bowen, C. W. & Phelps, Amy J. (1997). Demonstration-based cooperative testing in general chemistry: a broader assessment-of-learning technique. *Journal of Chemical Education.* 74(6), 715-719.

Burke, K. A.; Greenbowe, T. J.; Windschitl, M. A. Developing and using conceptual computer animations for chemistry instruction. (1998). *Journal of Chemical Education.* 75(12), 1658-1661.

Deese, W. C., Ramsey, L. L., Walczyk, J., & Eddy, D. (2000). Using demonstration assessments to improve learning. *Journal of Chemical Education*, 77(11), 1511-1520.

Dori, Y.J.; & Barak, M. (2001, January) Virtual and physical molecular modeling: Fostering model perception and spatial understanding. *Educational Technology & Society,* 4 (1), 61-74. Available at http://www.ifets.info/journals/4_1/dori.html

Ealy, J.B. (1999). A student evaluation of molecular modeling in first year college chemistry. *Journal of Science Education & Technology.* 8(2) 309-321.

Friedel, A.W., Gabel, D.L., & Samuel, J. (1990). Using analogs for chemistry problem solving: Does it increase understanding? *School Science and Mathematics.* 90(8), 674-682.

Gabel, D., & Sherwood, R. (1980). The effect of student manipulation of molecular models on chemistry achievement according to Piagetian level. *Journal of Research in Science Teaching.* 17(1) 75-81.

Haidar, A. H.; Abraham, M. R. (1991). A comparison of applied and theoretical knowledge of concepts based on the particulate nature of matter, *Journal of Research in Science Teaching*, 28(10), 919-938.

Harrison, A.G., & Treagust, D.F. (1998). Modeling in science lessons: Are there better ways to learn with models? *School Science and Mathematics.* 98(8), 420-429.

Jackman, L.E., Mollenberg, W. P., & Brabson G.D. (1987). Evaluation of three instructional methods for teaching general chemistry. *Journal of Chemical Education*, 64 (9), 788-796.

Johnstone, A. H. (1993). Development of chemistry teaching. *Journal of Chemical Education.* 70(9), 701-705

José, T.J. & Williamson, V.M. (2005). Molecular visualization in science education: An evaluation of the NSF – funded workshop. *Journal of Chemical Education.* 82(6), 937-943.

Lerman, Z. (1986). Chemistry for art and communication students. *Journal of Chemical Education.* 63(2), 142-143.

Martinez-Jimenez, P., Pontes-Pedrajas, A., Polo, J., Climent-Bellido, M.S. (2003). Learning in chemistry with virtual laboratories. *Journal of Chemical Education.* 80(3), 346-352.

Microsoft Corporation. (1999). Encarta World English Dictionary [Computer software] within Microsoft Word 10.1.6

Milne, R.W. (1999). A low-cost activity for particle conceptualization at the secondary level. *Journal of Chemical Education.* 76(1), 50-51.

Nicoll, G. (2003). A qualitative investigation of undergraduate chemistry students' macroscopic interpretations of the submicroscopic structure of molecules. *Journal of Chemical Education.* 80(2), 205-213.

Ophardt, C.E., Applebee, M.S., & Losey, E.N. (2005). Chemical demonstrations as the laboratory component in nonscience majors' courses. *Journal of Chemical Education.* 82(8), 1174-1177.

Russell, J.; Kozma, R.; Jones, T.; Wykoff, J.; Marx, N.; Davis, J. Use of simultaneous-synchronized macroscopic, microscopic, and symbolic representations to enhance the teaching and learning of chemical concepts. (1997). *Journal of Chemical Education*, 74 (3), 330-334.

Sanger, M.J. (2000). Using particulate drawings to determine and improve students' conceptions of pure substances and mixtures. *Journal of Chemical Education*, 77 (8), 762-766.

Sanger, M.J. (2005). Evaluation students' conceptual understanding of balanced equations and stoichiometric rations using a particulate drawing. *Journal of Chemical Education*, 82 (1), 131-134.

Sanger, M. J., Phelps, A.J., & Fienhold, J. (2000). Using a computer animation to improve students' conceptual understanding of a can-crushing demonstration. *Journal of Chemical Education*, 77 (11), 1517-1520.

Schank, P., & Kozma, R. (2002). Learning chemistry through the use of a representation-based knowledge building environment. *Journal of Computers in Mathematics and Science Teaching.* 21(2), 253-279.

Silberman, M.L. (1996). *Active learning*. Needham Heights. MA: Allyn and Bacon.

Singer, J.E., Tal, R.T., & Wu, H.K. (2003). Students' understanding of the particulate nature of matter. *School Science and Mathematics*, 103(1), 28-44.

Shakhashiri, B.Z. (1983-1994). Chemical Demonstrations: A Handbook for Teachers of Chemistry, Volumes 1-4. Madison, WI: The University of Wisconsin Press.

Taber, K. (2002a). *Chemical Misconceptions-Prevention, Diagnosis and Cure (Volume I: Theoretical Background).* London: Royal Society of Chemistry.

Talley, L.H. (1973). The use of three-dimensional visualization as a moderator in the higher cognitive learning of concepts in college level chemistry. *Journal of Research in Science Teaching*, 10 (3), 263-269.

Velazquez-Marcano, A; Williamson, V. M.; Ashkenazi, G.; Tasker, R.; Williamson, K. C. (2004) The use of video demonstrations and particulate animation in general chemistry. *Journal of Science Education and Technology.* 13(3), 315-323.

Williamson, V. M.; Abraham, M. R. (1995). The effects of computer animation on the particulate mental models of college chemistry students. *Journal of Research in Science Teaching.* 32(5), 521-534.

Wu, H., Krajcik, J.S., & Soloway, E. (2001). Promoting understanding of chemical representations: Students' use of a visualization tool in the classroom. *Journal of Research in Science Teaching*, 38(7), 821-842.

Part II

Implementing Specific Approaches to Teaching and Learning Chemistry

POGIL: Process-Oriented Guided-Inquiry Learning

Richard S. Moog
Franklin and Marshall College

Frank J. Creegan
Washington College

David M. Hanson
Stony Brook University

James N. Spencer
Franklin and Marshall College

Andrei Straumanis
College of Charleston

Diane M. Bunce
The Catholic University of America

Troy Wolfskill
Stony Brook University.

Abstract

POGIL is an instructional strategy that provides opportunities to teach both content and key process skills simultaneously. POGIL emphasizes that learning is an interactive process of thinking carefully, discussing ideas, refining understanding, practicing skills, reflecting on progress, and assessing performance.

In a POGIL classroom or laboratory, students work on specially designed guided inquiry materials in small self-managed groups. The instructor serves as a facilitator of learning rather than as a source of information. The objective is to develop learning skills as well as mastery of discipline-specific content.

POGIL activities are based on research that reveals how students learn most effectively. The activities guide students in the classroom and laboratory through a learning cycle consisting of three steps: First, there is an exploration of data, a case study, or other evidence that leads to the second step, the invention of the desired concept, the third step is an application of the concept.

POGIL has been tested at a variety of institutions across the nation with consistent results. Compared to traditional lecture sections, in a POGIL section, WDF rates fall dramatically, with the lower half of the class showing the most improvement, performance on standardized exams is higher, and student response is positive.

Biographies

The authors comprise the senior personnel of the NSF–funded POGIL project (DUE 0231120). All have been actively engaged in promoting the use of POGIL as a teaching strategy and philosophy for many years, and all have made numerous presentations and facilitated workshops around the country for instructors interested in learning about this approach to instruction and the evaluation of its effectiveness. Richard Moog is a Professor in the Chemistry Department at Franklin & Marshall College, Diane Bunce is an Associate Professor in the Department of Chemistry at The Catholic University of America, Frank Creegan is the W. Alton Jones Professor of Chemistry at Washngton College, David Hanson is a Professor of Chemistry at Stony Brook University, Andrei Straumanis is an Assistant Professor of Chemistry at the College of Charleston, Troy Wolfskill is a Lecturer and Education Specialist in the Chemistry Department at Stony Brook University, and James Spencer is the William G. and Elizabeth R. Simeral Professor of Chemistry at Franklin & Marshall College.

> *Some few years ago I was looking about the school supply stores in the city...We had a great deal of difficulty finding what we needed, and finally one dealer, more intelligent than the rest, made this remark: "I am afraid we have not what you want. You want something at which the*

children may work; these are all for listening." That tells the story of the traditional education. It is all made for listening.

John Dewey (1959)

Introduction

Recent developments in cognitive learning theory and classroom research results suggest that students generally experience improved learning when they are actively engaged and when they are given the opportunity to construct their own knowledge (Lawson, 1995, 1999). These approaches counter the widespread misapprehensions that effective teaching must be instructor-centered, and that content and understanding can be passed directly from the expert (professor) to the novice (student) (Johnstone, 1997).

Process Oriented Guided-inquiry learning (POGIL) is built around a philosophical approach to teaching that provides the pedagogical basis for structuring the learning environment. POGIL goals are to develop learning and process skills while guiding the student to a conceptual understanding. Classroom and laboratory activities are designed so that students can invent or form the desired concept from an examination of data, a model, or information presented to them. The abilities to reason from evidence to concept and to test the concept form the basis of POGIL.

Rather than focusing solely on the mastery of course content, the POGIL approach also recognizes the need to be concerned with the development of important process skills for acquiring, applying, and generating knowledge. The seven process skill areas that POGIL focuses on are: *information processing, critical and analytical thinking, problem solving, communication, teamwork, management, and assessment.* Surveys of managers and leaders in industry generally show that employees are sought who are knowledgeable and have such skills, i.e. are quick learners, critical and creative thinkers, problem solvers, communicators, team players, and self motivated (Runquist and Kerr, 2005; Apple, 1993; Carnevale, Gainer, and Meltzer, 1988). The general conclusion of one such survey (Maxfield, 1997) was that industrial employers "would like chemistry-trained employees whose education included greater preparation in communication, team skills, relating applications to scientific principles, and problem solving, without sacrificing thorough preparation in basic science concepts and experimental skills.". Process skills, just like skills in laboratory work and athletics, can be developed, strengthened, and enhanced. The development of these skills is therefore explicitly targeted in POGIL courses, not only to help students be successful in these courses but also to prepare them for the workplace and for life in general.

Lecture as a teaching method and the assumptions behind it are at odds with research on how people learn, which is summarized in a recent book with that title, *How People Learn* (Bransford, Brown, and Cocking, 1999). This book was commissioned by the National Academy of Sciences and the U.S. Department of Education specifically to facilitate moving research-based knowledge into practice in the classroom.

There are five key ideas that arise from this research. All of these ideas are incorporated into the design of POGIL, a new philosophical and pedagogical approach to instruction. POGIL adopts the **constructivist model** for learning, uses the **learning cycle** as a paradigm for the construction of classroom and laboratory activities, provides students class time to work with models and draw pictures to help **make connections and visualize the material**, incorporates students teaching students through **cooperative learning** groups, and explicitly teaches **metacognitive** skills .

Constructivism. Educators agree that it is not possible to transmit information intact from the head of the instructor to the head of the student (Bodner, 1986). Knowledge is personal and is constructed in the mind of the learner. This construction depends on the misconceptions, biases, prejudices, beliefs, and likes and dislikes of the learner (Karplus, 1977). This learning model, called constructivism, is one of the leading pedagogical paradigms for enhancing student learning. New approaches to teaching, more aligned with this model, center on the learner as the focus of the learning experience (Caprio, 1999; Herron and Nurrenbern, 1999; Johnstone, 1997; Phye, 1997). An excellent review of constructivist principles, and their relationship to brain physiology can be found in Volume 1 of this series (Cracolice, 2005).

The Learning Cycle. Student-centered learning environments can be particularly effective if the focus of student work is a discovery exercise based on the learning cycle, an inquiry strategy for teaching and learning that is based on constructivist principles. This approach and its effectiveness are discussed in some depth in Volume 1 of this series (Abraham, 2005); a brief summary is given here. As described by Lawson (1995), a learning cycle has three phases (see Figure 1) The first phase is an "Exploration" phase in which a pattern of regularity in the environment or data is sought, A model, data, laboratory experiment, demonstration, or a reading designed to raise questions or complexities that students cannot resolve with their accustomed way of thinking may be used in the "Exploration" phase. Students generate and test hypotheses in an attempt to explain or understand the information that has been presented to them. The second phase is "Concept Invention" (or "Term Introduction"), in which a concept is developed from the pattern and a new term can be introduced to refer to the trends or patterns discovered in the "Exploration" phase. By placing the "Term Introduction" phase after the "Exploration" phase new terms are introduced at a point when the student already has a mental construct in place to which a term may be attached. In the third phase, "Concept Application", the concept is applied in new situations (Abraham and Renner, 1986; Lawson, 1999).   This phase generalizes the concept's meaning to other situations, generally requiring deductive reasoning skills. In this way, a Learning Cycle exercise leads students to develop a concept for themselves, imparting a sense of ownership and participation, and provides valuable epistemological insight into the nature of scientific inquiry.

In some contexts, however, this structure for a learning experience is not the most appropriate. For example, developing an understanding of the postulates of quantum mechanics is unlikely to arise from an examination of experimental data. In this case, an alternative structure to the activity is desired in which the concept to be understood (the postulates) is presented first, followed by a phase in which the concept is explored to help students fully formulate an understanding. This structure is known as a *concept formation* approach, to differentiate it from the *concept invention* structure described in the standard Learning Cycle.

Connecting and Visualizing. Facts and ideas are not remembered in isolation or understood by simple associations but rather must be connected in intellectual schemas built around core concepts and a deep understanding of the big ideas. Such a conceptual network facilitates the identification, retrieval, and application of relevant knowledge in new contexts. Visualizing and understanding chemical phenomena includes representing these phenomena in three ways: by using macroscopic, particulate, and symbolic representations. The facility with which a student moves between these representations can indicate the degree of understanding of a chemical phenomenon. In Volume 1 of this series, Gabel (2005) provides an interesting overview of these ideas.

Discussing and Interacting. At its best, the POGIL approach utilizes small group discussion as the medium for construction and restructuring of knowledge in the minds of the learners. Key cognitive steps in this process include making inferences, identifying misconceptions, resolving contradictions, generalizing, integrating with previous knowledge, and posing and solving problems (Johnson et al., 1991; McKeachie and Gibbs, 1999). All these are natural elements of small group discussion. Active involvement in the classroom, including student-student and student-instructor interactions, has been identified as having the largest positive effect of numerous environmental factors on the academic achievement, personal development, and satisfaction of college students (Astin, 1993; Hewitt and Seymour, 1991; McKeachie and Gibbs, 1999).

Reflecting and Assessing. Metacognition means thinking about thinking and refers to the learner's awareness of his or her own knowledge and learning process. It involves reflecting on what has been learned and assessing the learning process itself. In assessing learning performance, students identify successes, strengths, and improvements that are needed in their performance, and then develop and implement plans to generalize the successes and strengths and produce improvements. Reflection on learning and self-assessment of performance (metacognition and self-regulation) are essential to produce learners who continuously improve their learning process and abilities to apply their knowledge in new contexts. Research has shown that metacognitive strategies can be taught and lead to improved learning and performance.

As detailed in *How People Learn* (Bransford et al., 1999), "there now is a massive amount of evidence from all realms of science that unless individuals take a very active role in what it is that they're studying, unless they learn to ask questions, to do things hands-on, to essentially recreate things in their own minds and transform them as is needed, the ideas just disappear." The remainder of this chapter describes how these research-based ideas are incorporated into the design of POGIL.

Structure and Characteristics of POGIL Materials

There are three key elements that characterize the materials that are used in a POGIL learning environment. POGIL materials:

1. are designed for use with self-managed teams that employ the instructor as a facilitator of learning rather than as a source of information;

2. guide students through an exploration to construct understanding;

3. use discipline content to facilitate the development of important process skills including higher-level thinking and the ability to learn and to apply knowledge in new contexts.

At the heart of the guided inquiry component of POGIL materials is a carefully developed set of critical-thinking questions (CTQs; see Figure 1). These questions build on each other in complexity and sophistication, leading student groups toward discovery of a chemical concept. Typically, the first few questions direct attention to the information provided in the concept model, often incorporating students' prior knowledge. A concept model can consist of a figure, graph, table, set of written relationships, a methodology, an interactive computer simulation, a brief discussion, a demonstration, or a laboratory activity. It is analogous to the data a researcher would collect in a true discovery situation, yet streamlined and focused to facilitate the learning process. The next few questions help promote thought to develop relationships and find patterns in the data toward development of a concept. The final questions, the application phase of the learning cycle, require divergent thought to find relevance or to look for the boundaries in generalizing students' new knowledge and understanding. Students work in teams to answer these questions by thinking about what they see in the model, what they know, and what they have learned by answering previous questions. Activities for full year courses in general, organic, and physical chemistry are available (Hanson, 2006; Moog and Farrell, 2006; Moog, Spencer, and Farrell, 2004; Spencer, Moog, and Farrell, 2004; Straumanis, 2004). and materials for other courses including allied health chemistry, analytical chemistry, and biochemistry are under development. A general chemistry guided inquiry activity is provided at the end of this chapter.

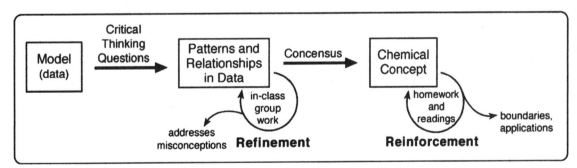

Figure 1. Conceptual Framework of POGIL Activities

Structure of Classroom and Instructor/Student Roles

There are a wide variety of ways that the POGIL approach can be implemented, depending on such factors as the institutional culture, class size, the nature of facilities, and instructor preferences. A few successful models include replacing essentially all lectures with POGIL sessions (Farrell, Moog, and Spencer, 1999), replacing one lecture session each week with a POGIL session (Lewis and Lewis, 2005), and converting standard recitation sessions at a large university to POGIL sessions (Hanson and Wolfskill, 2000). In fact, every implementation of POGIL is different, adapted to the unique institutional, departmental, and individual circumstances and goals inherently present for each instructor and course. Here we give a brief description of the structure of a typical classroom implementation (Farrell et al., 1999).

As mentioned above,

- lectures are not given; the instructor acts as a facilitator;

- students have assigned roles within groups (usually of 4);

- specially-designed activities that follow the learning cycle paradigm are used to develop and learn concepts;

- there is a textbook for the course, and students are expected to reinforce learning by reading the appropriate sections of the text *after* introduction of concepts in class; and,

- students are graded individually on hour exams and a final exam.

Almost all of the class time is spent working in groups. Every day, each member of the group is assigned a new role. Assigning each student a role enhances the engagement of the students by providing them with a specific responsibility (in addition to contributing to the completion of the activity), and also helps students develop the various skills associated with each role. Typical roles include:

- **Manager**. Manages the group, including assuring that other members are fulfilling their roles and all are contributing. The manager also asks questions of the facilitator on behalf of the group.

- **Recorder**. Records the names and roles of the group members for each session, and also records the group answers and explanations, along with any other important observations and insights.

- **Reflector** or **Strategy Analyst**. Observes and comments regularly on group dynamics and behavior with respect to the learning process and the strategies that the group employs to solve problems and answer questions.

- **Presenter**. Presents oral reports on behalf of the group to the class. Presenters may also "rotate" between groups to compare answers and resolve differences.

Instructor's Interaction with Groups

Generally, the instructor spends most of the period moving among the groups, observing and listening to their discussions. The instructor can examine the Recorder's answers to the CTQs to gauge how the group is progressing. If the instructor finds that students are proceeding at an adequate pace and demonstrating appropriate understanding, no intervention is needed; after staying briefly and listening to the group interaction, the instructor moves on. Occasionally a question may be posed to one or more group members to make sure that he or she understands a concept or to elicit a verbal explanation of an answer that may be correct. If one or more of the answers to the CTQs are incorrect, the instructor must make a decision whether to intervene. There is a strong temptation to do so, but this should be avoided if possible. With well-designed activities, students will often encounter a seeming contradiction or conflict at a later point in the activity and thereby uncover their own error.

A written report is submitted by each team at the end of the POGIL session. Several approaches for this report can be used. One approach is to have the report contain the group's answers to the various critical thinking questions that were addressed during that session. Alternatively, the students may be asked to provide a summary of the important concepts that they developed from the activity. Or, the report may be a combination of both, providing the results and summary of their work. In all cases, however, the report gives students the opportunity to assess their performance and reflect on what they have learned.

The POGIL Laboratory

The POGIL laboratory (http://www.pogil.org/materials/labs.php) follows the same philosophical and pedagogical guiding principles as the classroom sessions. Generally, the students, in advance of any classroom work on underlying principles, work in groups of three or four to conduct experiments that lead to the development of a concept, rather than exercises that verify previously taught principles. The POGIL approach to the laboratory component is modeled on the guided-inquiry framework first introduced by Pavelich and Abraham (1977, 1979) and popularized by Ditzler (Ditzler and Ricci, 1991, 1994), (Ricci,

Ditzler, and Nestor, 1994) and the faculty at the College of the Holy Cross as the Discovery Chemistry Approach (Ricci, Ditzler, Jarret, McMaster, and Herrick, 1994).

Indeed, collaboration between chemists from thirteen colleges in the mid-Atlantic region and Mauri Ditzler led to the creation of the Middle Atlantic Discovery Chemistry Project (MADCP), which, with financial support from the U.S. Department of Education's FIPSE Project (Fund for the Improvement of Post-Secondary Education), developed a series of guided-inquiry (discovery-based) experiments. Many of the POGIL practitioners are MADCP members and MADCP continues to promote the POGIL approach to learning. Over time the MADCP consortium developed a set of criteria to assist faculty in the development of guided inquiry experiments. With permission, POGIL has modified this list of criteria, dividing it into required criteria and desirable (but not essential) criteria, as shown in Figure 2.

Required Criteria

- Begins with a question.

- Uses observation or data collection to develop theoretical construction rather than confirming a concept.

- Involves minimal instructor input.

- Prior to experiment, outcome is known to instructor but not to student.

- Designed so that <u>students</u> can get reliable data.

- Guides students to the appropriate conclusion.

- Reinforces the developed concept through application.

- Guides the student in recognizing what has and has not been learned from the experiment through use of appropriate in-lab and post-lab questions.

- Promotes teamwork

Desirable Criteria

- Encourages students to develop questions for further research.

- Promotes active decision making

- Allows student input in design of experiments.

Figure 2. Criteria for POGIL Experiments

Two criteria merit special emphasis. The POGIL approach is one of guided inquiry and not open inquiry. It is vitally important that the instructor, acting as facilitator, knows in advance the outcomes of the experiments. The experiments must be tested so as to produce reliable data, which when pooled allow students to develop chemical concepts. All the POGIL experiments are designed to follow the three-stage learning cycle paradigm desribed previously, involving an exploration phase, concept invention phase, and application phase. The application phase may be an additional set of experiments or additional data in the form of exercises and problems.

The Laboratory Setting and Experience.

In a pre-lab session, which may be real or virtual, the instructor poses a focus question or question of the day (note the first POGIL criterion), and students, working within their groups, propose a set of tentative answers, which the instructor posts on a blackboard or transparency and which remain visible throughout the laboratory period. To test these hypotheses, students run (previously tested and reliable) reactions and/or collect data (the "Exploration" phase), which are pooled and then analyzed with the aid of post-experiment or post-laboratory guided-inquiry questions ("Concept Invention" phase). Figure 3 illustrates the three stages of the POGIL laboratory activity.

Pre-lab Session	Experiment	Post-Experimentation
• Present focus question	• Each team is assigned a variation	• Graphical analysis
• Solicit hypothesis or predictions	• Pool data	• Interpretation of data
• Discuss appropriate experiments	• Discern trends	• Discovery of concept

Figure 3. POGIL Laboratory Structure

Farrell, Moog and Spencer (1999) describe one such experiment in some detail. In that experiment, which works well in general chemistry as well as an introduction to the sophomore-level organic chemistry laboratory, the instructor asks, *How is the structure of a molecule related to its boiling point?* Groups are presented with the boiling points of n-octane and 1-butanol and asked to list all the factors related to molecular structure that might influence the boiling point. This discussion takes place *prior* to the introduction of the concept of intermolecular forces in the course; at this point the students have no reason to suspect that the number and distribution of the electrons has anything to do with how strongly molecules interact with each other. Typically, the students propose that the "larger" the molecule the higher the boiling point, and also that the stronger the intramolecular bonds, the higher the boiling point. On a rare occasion, students may suggest that dipole moment may be relevant. The groups are then given a set of four liquids and asked to measure the boiling points. The data are collected. First, using the group data and then by using the class data, students test their hypotheses. Several of the groups are assigned a set of homologous alkanes, or alcohols, or ketones, or alkyl bromides, but one or more is assigned a set composed of representatives from each of the four classes. In examining the data from a homologous series students quickly find that molecular weight correlates with boiling point. However, it is in the pooling of the class data that students come to see that additional factors need to be considered in order to explain how a ketone and an alkane with nearly identical molecular weights have considerably different boiling points (2-hexanone, MW=100.16; BP=127°C and n-heptane, MW 110.21; BP=98°C). Such examples of discrepant behavior provide for lively discussions that lead to the development of an understanding of the factors that contribute to intermolecular forces. The instructor can facilitate this discussion to guide students to examine the various possible structural features that underlie these factors, including the number and distribution of the electrons.

At Washington College a full year of POGIL experiments for the organic chemistry course has been developed, tested, and implemented. Each follows the learning cycle paradigm that Abraham and Pavelich (2000, 2004) first brought to the undergraduate chemistry laboratory curriculum in 1979 with their pioneering text, *Inquiries into Chemistry*. Illustrative of a POGIL experiment in organic chemistry is one, conducted midway in the first semester, in which students are asked; *Can an alcohol react as a base? What role might substituents play?* To test their hypotheses a set of isomeric C-6 alcohols are treated with 85% phosphoric acid and in turn heated under reflux during which low-boiling material is removed by distillation. Students know that all the alcohols have boiling points that range from 130°-150°C. In a set of pre-lab questions students are encouraged to recall, by returning to data from the first experiment of the semester on boiling points, the factors that might be responsible for these observations. In the "Exploration" phase students note that the boiling points of the distillates are nearly half that of the alcohol substrate, and that tertiary alcohols produce the low-boiling distillate (react) at a much faster rate than do the secondary alcohols, which react much faster than the primary alcohols. Students examine the distillates by GC or GC/MS and discover the products to be mixtures of isomeric, low boiling alkenes. The pooled chromatographic data reveal structural features that are best explained by invoking skeleton rearrangements arising from a mechanism that involves carbocation intermediates. The rate data and product distribution allow students to develop the E_1 mechanism for acid-catalyzed dehydrations.

Using the POGIL approach students are able to develop laboratory techniques *and* develop concepts in advance of any discussion in the classroom component of the course. Often the data that are generated in laboratory are incorporated into the ChemActivities used in a later classroom setting. Numerous experiments for general and organic chemistry are available from the POGIL website: www.pogil.org.

Effectiveness of POGIL

The effectiveness of POGIL has been assessed at a range of institutions and for a variety of courses.(Farrell et al., 1999; Hanson and Wolfskill, 2000; Hinde and Kovac, 2001; Lewis and Lewis, 2005; McKnight, 2004; Straumanis, 2006). Several common, and important, outcomes are observed in all of these studies:

- Student attrition is lower for POGIL than traditional methods.
- Student mastery of content is generally higher for POGIL than traditional methods.
- Most students prefer POGIL over traditional methods.

Below, we provide some details from studies of general chemistry and organic chemistry.

A previously published study compared the performance of general chemistry students taught using a traditional approach during the period 1990-1994 (n = 420) to students taught during the subsequent four years by the same instructors, but using the POGIL approach (n= 485).(Farrell et al., 1999) The attrition rate (D, W, F) decreased from 21.9% (traditional) to 9.6% (POGIL). The percentage of students earning an A or B rose from 52% to 64%. These data are consistent with a study of general chemistry at a different small liberal arts college in which the 1993 ACS General Chemistry Exam was used as a basis for comparison. Over the ten year period 1993-2003, in traditionally taught classes of about 40, the exam average was 56%, the highest average in a single year was 65%. In the first year of POGIL instruction (2004), the average was 68%.(McKnight, 2004)

POGIL has also been used successfully as a component of large lecture classes. The implementation of a POGIL approach in the recitation sessions in general chemistry at a large, public university in the Northeast resulted in examinations showing significant shifts of students from lower scores to higher scores, uniformly for low through high achieving students.(Hanson, 2000) Lewis and Lewis (2005) studied the effect of replacing one of three general chemistry lectures each week with a peer-led team learning session using POGIL materials. They found that the students who attended the group learning sessions achieved a higher average score on the common examinations.

In a multi-institutional study of the effectiveness of POGIL in organic chemistry (Straumanis et al., in submission), complementary methods were used to compare POGIL and lecture courses with class sizes ranging from 20 to 75 across a range of institutions including a large public university and a small, 1st-tier liberal arts college. The similarities of the findings, despite differences in the studies, provide additional evidence for the general effectiveness of POGIL.

One important finding was that, at each institution, the percentage of unsuccessful students (defined as D, F or W) in the traditional sections was about twice that of the POGIL sections. This result was achieved without a drop in student performance as measured by conventional multiple-choice exams, including the ACS Organic Exam. For example, a medium-size regional university with a historical average of 64th percentile on the ACS Organic Exam (n = 517, 1999-2004), and a section-average range of 39th to 82nd percentile over this same period (20 different sections, 4 different professors), employed POGIL in one section of organic chemistry in the spring of 2005. The POGIL section scored in the 81st percentile despite an attrition rate of 8%, as compared to 26% in the traditional sections of organic chemistry taught that same semester.

A common question heard at POGIL faculty development workshops is: With POGIL, can you cover all the topics found in a traditional chemistry course? The cumulative nature of organic chemistry, and the above ACS Organic Exam data suggest that coverage is achieved using POGIL. This issue was also directly studied by taking students from a lecture organic 1 section and students from a POGIL organic 1 section, and putting them all together in the same organic 2 section (taught by a 3rd professor using traditonal lecture). The result was no signficant difference between the lecture and POGIL-trained students, despite higher throughput from the POGIL organic 1 course into organic 2 (POGIL: 93% vs. lecture: 73%). This result also demonstrates that POGIL students can go on to be successful in a subsequent course taught using traditional methods.

While the above results allow valuable comparisons to be made between POGIL and traditional methods, student grades and performance on exams, particularly standardized exams, are a fairly narrow assessment of the effectiveness of POGIL. For example, exams say little about students' growth with respect to POGIL's targeted process skills such as critical thinking, teamwork, and self-assessment. Growth in process skills is hard to measure directly. An alternative is to measure students' perceptions of their own growth with respect to such skills. This was done using the SALG (Student Assessment of Learning Gains) instrument. SALG questions also measure students' perceptions of the value of certain course elements (e.g. the text, review sessions, tests, lectures, working with peers outside of class). The SALG was administered at four institutions using POGIL in some or all of their organic chemistry sections. Of 30 items tested, POGIL students responded more positively than their traditional counterparts on 29 of them, with 27 items showing significant differences between the cohorts ($p < 0.05$)[1]

Another question that often arises is: How do students respond to POGIL? 688 anonymous surveys were collected from organic students at six different institutions. The survey achieved over 98% compliance, with 381 responses from students enrolled in POGIL sections, and 307 responses from students enrolled in traditional lecture sections.[2] The data shown in Figure 4 indicate that 80% of POGIL students would recommend POGIL over other methods of instruction, whereas less than 50% of lecture students are equally well disposed to a traditional approach. Only 6% of POGIL students appear hostile to the method, versus 30% of lecture students. Chi square analysis confirms that the POGIL students are significantly more positive about the method used in their classroom ($\chi^2 = 102.48$, $p < 0.0005$).

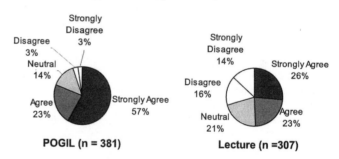

Figure 4. Question from Anonymous Student Survey

Summary

The POGIL approach has been shown to be an effective classroom and laboratory strategy for improved learning. This outcome is not surprising given the hundreds of studies reported on the advantages of cooperative learning pedagogy. In addition to using this proven pedagogy, POGIL students teach students using carefully prepared guided inquiry activities that promote critical thinking and develop higher-order thinking skills. The students seek patterns in an exploration and form hypothesis just as a scientist would in the research laboratory. Traditional instruction assumes that if the method of delivery could be perfected students would understand. Cognitive science, educational psychology, and classroom experimentation have shown that improving delivery is not likely to improve significantly student conceptual understanding.

---

[1] The sole question ranked more positively by the comparison group asked about the value of the textbook.

[2] Some students filled out two surveys: one at the end of Organic I and one at the end of Organic II.

In contrast to traditional instruction, the POGIL pedagogy puts instructors in a position to ascertain what students are thinking and what barriers must be overcome to achieve learning. Thus the instructor is able to construct strategies based on a knowledge of what the students know to provide an environment that is more conducive to thinking and learning.

Suggestions for Further Reading

Abraham, M. R. (2005). Inquiry and the learning cycle approach. In N. J. Pienta, M. M. Cooper and T. J. Greenbowe (Eds.), *Chemists' Guide to Effective Teaching*. Upple Saddle River, NJ: Prentice Hall.

Farrell, J. J., Moog, R. S., and Spencer, J. N. (1999). A guided inquiry general chemistry course. *J. Chem. Educ., 76*, 570-574.

Hanson, D. (2006). *Instructors Guide to Process-Oriented Guided-Inquiry Learning.* Lisle, IL: Pacific Crest.

Hanson, D., and Wolfskill, T. (2000). Process Workshops - A New Model For Instruction. *J. Chem. Educ., 77*, 120-130.

Spencer, J. N. (1999). New Directions in Teaching Chemistry. *J. Chem. Educ., 76*, 566-569.

Much additional information about the background, implementation, and effectiveness of POGIL may be found at the POGIL project website: http://www.pogil.org.

References

Abraham, M. R. (2005). Inquiry and the learning cycle approach. In N. J. Pienta, M. M. Cooper and T. J. Greenbowe (Eds.), *Chemists' Guide to Effective Teaching*. Upple Saddle River, NJ: Prentice Hall.

Abraham, M. R., and Pavelich, M. J. (2000). *Inquiries into Chemistry* (3rd ed.). Prospect Heights, IL: Waveland Press.

Abraham, M. R., and Pavelich, M. J. (2004). *Inquiries into Chemistry* (4th ed.). Prospect Heights, IL: Waveland Press.

Abraham, M. R., and Renner, J. W. (1986). Research on the Learning Cycle. *Journal of Research in Science Teaching., 23*, 121-143.

Apple, D. K. (1993). *Teach for Learning: A Handbook for Process Education.* Corvallis, OR: Pacific Crest.

Astin, A. (1993). What Matters in College: Four Critical Years Revisited. San Francisco: Jossey-Bass.

Bodner, G. M. (1986). A Theory Of Knowledge. *Journal of Chemical Education, 63*, 873.

Bransford, J. D., Brown, A. L., and Cocking, R. R. (Eds.). (1999). *How People Learn*. Washington, DC: National Academy Press.

Carnevale, A. P., Gainer, L. J., and Meltzer, A. S. (1988). *Workplace Basics: The Skills Employers Want.* Washington, DC: U. S. Department of Labor.

Caprio, M. W. (1999). Chaos and Opportunity. *Journal of College Science Teaching*, 387-390.

Cooper, M. M. (2005). An introduction to small-group learning. In N. J. Pienta, M. M. Cooper and T. J. Greenbowe (Eds.), *Chemists' Guide to Effective Teaching*. Upple Saddle River, NJ: Prentice Hall.

Cracolice, M. S. (2005). How students learn: Knowledge construction in the chemistry classroom. In N. J. Pienta, M. M. Cooper and T. J. Greenbowe (Eds.), *Chemists' Guide to Effective Teaching*. Upple Saddle River, NJ: Prentice Hall.

Dewey, J. (1959). In R. B. Winn (Ed.), *Dictionary of Education*. New York: Philosophical Library.

Ditzler, M. A., and Ricci, R. W. (1991). Discovery Chemistry: A laboratory-centered approach to teaching general chemistry. *Journal of Chemical Education, 68*, 228-232.

Ditzler, M. A., and Ricci, R. W. (1994). Discovery chemistry: Balancing creativity and structure. *Journal of Chemical Education, 76*, 685-688.

Farrell, J. J., Moog, R. S., and Spencer, J. N. (1999). A guided inquiry general chemistry course. *Journal of Chemical Education, 76*, 570-574.

Gabel, D. (2005). Enhancing Students' Conceptual Understanding of Chemistry through Integrating the Macroscopic, Particle, and Symbolic Representations of Matter. In N. J. Pienta, M. M. Cooper and T. J. Greenbowe (Eds.) *Chemists' Guide to Effective Teaching*. Upple Saddle River, NJ: Prentice Hall.

Hanson, D. (2006). *Foundations of Chemistry*. Lisle, IL: Pacific Crest.

Hanson, D., and Wolfskill, T. (2000). Process Workshops - A New Model For Instruction. *Journal of Chemical Education, 77*, 120-130.

Herron, J. D., and Nurrenbern, S. C. (1999). Improving Chemistry Learning. *Journal of Chemical Education, 76*, 1354-1361.

Hewitt, N. A., and Seymour, E. (1991). *Factors Contributing to High Attrition Rates Among Science, Mathematics, and Engineering Undergraduate Majors: A Report to the Sloan Foundation*. Denver: University of Colorado.

Hinde, R. J., and Kovac, J. (2001). Student Active Learning in Physical Chemistry. *Journal of Chemical Education, 78*, 93-99.

Johnson, D. W., Johnson, R. T., and Smith, K. A. (1991). *Active Learning: Cooperation in the College Classroom*. Edina: Interaction Book Company.

Johnstone, A. H. (1997). Chemistry Teaching - Science or Alchemy? *Journal of Chemical Education, 74*, 262 - 268.

Karplus, R. (1977). Science Teaching and the Development of Reasoning. *Journal of Research in Science Teaching., 14*, 169-175.

Lawson, A. E. (1995). *Science Teaching and the Development of Thinking*. Belmont: Wadsworth.

Lawson, A. E. (1999). What Should Students Learn About the Nature of Science and How Should We Teach It? *Journal of College Science Teaching*, 401-411.

Lewis, J. E., and Lewis, S. E. (2005). Departing from lectures: An evaluation of a peer-led guided inquiry alternative. *Journal of Chemical Education, 82*(1), 135-139.

Maxfield, M. (1997). The view from industry in *Undergraduate Chemistry Curriculum Reform*. Washington, DC: American Chemical Society.

McKeachie, W., and Gibbs, G. (1999). *Teaching and Learning in the College Classroom: A Review of the Research Literature*. Boston: Houghton Mifflin Co.

McKnight, G. (2004). Unpublished results.

Moog, R. S. and Farrell, J. J (2006). *Chemistry: A Guided Inquiry, 3rd ed.* Hoboken, NJ: John Wiley and Sons.

Moog, R. S., Spencer, J. N., and Farrell, J. J. (2004). *Physical Chemistry: A Guided Inquiry. Atoms, Molecules, and Spectroscopy.* Boston, MA: Houghton Mifflin.

Pavelich, M. J., and Abraham, M. R. (1977). Guided inquiry laboratories for general chemistry students. *Journal of College Science Teaching, 7*(1), 23-26.

Pavelich, M. J., and Abraham, M. R. (1979). An inquiry format laboratory program for general chemistry. *Journal of Chemical Education, 56*, 100-103.

Phye, G. D. (Ed.). (1997). *Handbook of Academic Learning: Construction of Knowledge.* New York: Academic Press.

Ricci, R. W., Ditzler, M. A., Jarret, R., McMaster, P., and Herrick, R. (1994). The Holy Cross discovery chemistry program. *Journal of Chemical Education, 71*, 404-405.

Ricci, R. W., Ditzler, M. A., and Nestor, L. P. (1994). Discovering the Beer-Lambert Law. *Journal of Chemical Education, 71*, 983-985.

Runquist, O and Kerr, S. (2005) *Journal of Chemical Education, 82*, 231-233.

Spencer, J. N., Moog, R. S., and Farrell, J. J. (2004). *Physical Chemistry: A Guided Inquiry. Thermodynamics.* Boston, MA: Houghton Mifflin.

Straumanis, A. (2004). *Organic Chemistry: A Guided Inquiry.* Boston, MA: Houghton Mifflin.

Straumanis, A. (2006). Submitted to *Journal of Research in Science Teaching.*

Sample POGIL Activities for Physical Chemistry, Organic Chemistry and General Chemistry

Spencer, James N., Moog, Richard S., Farrell, John J. PHYSICAL CHEMISTRY: A GUIDED INQUIRY: Thermodynamics. Copyright © 2004 by Houghton Mifflin Company. Used with permission.

<u>ChemActivity</u> **T15**

The Ideal Solution

Model 1:   Benzene and Toluene in the Vapor Phase.

Recall that for a mixture of ideal gases,

$$P_i V = n_i RT \qquad \text{for each component } i \qquad (1)$$

$$P_{tot} V = n_{tot} RT \qquad (2)$$

The partial pressure, P_i, of each component in a mixture of gases is related to the composition of the vapor phase according to the relation

$$P_i = X_{i(\text{vap})} P_{tot} \qquad (3)$$

where $X_{i(vap)}$ is the mole fraction of component i in the vapor phase. Equation (3) is known as Dalton's Law.

Critical Thinking Questions

1. Show how equation (3) can be derived from equations (1) and (2).

2. At a given temperature and volume, does the partial pressure of benzene, P_{bz}, in Figure 1 depend on the *number* of moles of benzene present in the gas phase? Explain.

Figure 2:   Benzene and Toluene in Equilibrium with the Vapor Phase at 300 K

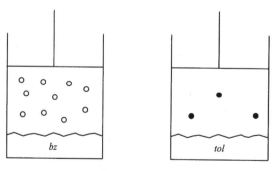

Liquid benzene (*bz*) and liquid toluene (*tol*) at 300 K each in equilibrium with its gas phase.

Information

The vapor pressure of a liquid may be thought of as a measure of the tendency of the molecules to escape into the gas phase. This tendency is directly related to the strength of the interactions in the liquid phase.

Table 1:   Partial Vapor Pressures of Benzene and Toluene for Various Mixtures at 300 K

moles of bz	moles of tol	$X_{bz(sol)}$	P_{bz} (Torr)	P_{tol} (Torr)	P_{tot} (Torr)
1.00	0	1	103.01	0	
0.00	1.00	0	0	32.1	
0.200	1.80		10.3	28.9	
0.400	1.60		20.6	25.7	
0.800	1.20		41.2	19.2	
0.100	0.900		10.3	28.9	
0.800	0.200		82.4	6.4	

$X_{bz(sol)}$ is the mole fraction of benzene present in the liquid solution.

Critical Thinking Questions

3.   Complete Table 1 by calculating the missing values for $X_{bz(sol)}$ and P_{tot}.

4.   What is the vapor pressure of pure benzene, P_{bz}^{*}?

5.   What is the vapor pressure of pure toluene, P_{tol}^{*}?

6.   Are your answers to CTQs 4 and 5 consistent with Figure 2? Explain your reasoning.

7.   Is P_{bz} determined by the *number of moles* of benzene present in liquid solution? Explain your reasoning.

8.   Recall that Dalton's Law describes the relationship between the partial pressure of a component and the composition of the *vapor phase*.

     Use Table 1 to find the relationship between the partial pressure of benzene over the solution and the composition of the *solution*. Provide an answer to this question as both a grammatically correct English sentence *and* as a mathematical relationship.

9.   What is the relationship between the partial pressure of toluene over the solution and the composition of the *solution*? Provide an answer to this question as both a grammatically correct English sentence *and* as a mathematical relationship.

10. Construct a diagram similar to those in Figure 2 (having the same gas phase volume) representing a mixture of 0.8 moles of liquid benzene and 1.2 moles of liquid toluene in equilibrium with its vapor at 300 K.

     Is the composition of the vapor phase the same as the composition of the liquid phase?

ChemActivity 5

Part A: Constitutional Isomers
(Are they the same, or are they isomers?)

Model 1: Representations of Carbon Structures

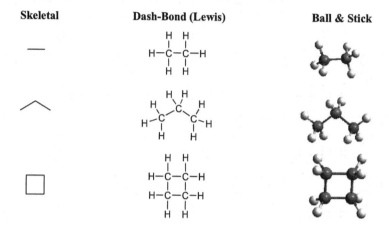

Critical Thinking Questions

1. Draw a dash-bond (Lewis) representation of the molecule shown at right as a skeletal representation.

2. In skeletal representations the hydrogens are not shown. Is it still possible to tell how many hydrogens there are on a particular carbon? Explain how.

Model 2: Constitutional Isomers

Column 1		Column 2	
structure	molecular formula	structure	molecular formula
∿	C_6H_{14}	⬡	C_6H_{12}
	C_6H_{14}		

Critical Thinking Questions

3. Complete the table in Model 2 by writing in missing molecular formulas.

4. What do the molecules in a given column (1 or 2) have in common with the other molecules in that same column?

5. What do the molecules in a given column **NOT** have in common with the other molecules in that column?

6. All the structures in a given column are **constitutional isomers** of one another, but the structures in column 1 are not constitutional isomers of structures in column 2. Based on this information, write a definition for the term **constitutional isomers**.

7. Below each of these structures, draw the structure from Model 2 to which it is identical. Note: For our purposes, two structures are considered identical if they are conformers of

one another. Recall from ChemActivity 4 that **conformers** are structures that can be inter-converted via rotation of single bonds. It will help to make a model of at least one structure.

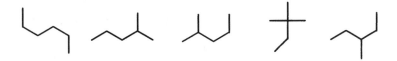

8. Draw the constitutional isomer that is missing from column 1 of Model 2. (Exactly one is missing.)

Exercises For Part A

1. Draw skeletal representations of six constitutional isomers missing from column 2 in Model 2. Are there more than six?

2. Draw the structure of a six carbon hydrocarbon with one ring and one double bond. (hydrocarbon = a molecule containing only carbon and hydrogen.)
    a) Draw a constitutional isomer of the structure you drew above <u>with no rings</u>.

    b) Explain the following statement found in many text books: "In terms of molecular formula, a ring is equivalent to a double bond."

3. Draw as many constitutional isomers as you can with the formula $C_5H_{11}F$.

4. Complete Nomenclature Worksheet I.

5. Read the assigned pages in the text and do the assigned problems.

Moog, R.S., Farrell, J.J. CHEMISTRY: A GUIDED INQUIRY. Copyrighted by John Wiley & Son, Inc. 2006. Used with permission.

ChemActivity 31

Empirical Formula
(Can a Molecule Be Identified by Its Percent Composition?)

Model: Percent Composition.

The **percent composition** (by mass) of an element in a molecule is the mass of the element in the molecule divided by the mass of the entire molecule times 100. Or, because the number of atoms (molecules) is proportional to the number of moles of atoms (molecules),

$$\text{percent composition of element } i = \frac{\text{mass of } i \text{ in one mole of the compound}}{\text{mass of one mole of the compound}} \times 100\%$$

Table 1. Percent composition (by mass) of some common organic molecules.

Name	Structural Formula	Molecular Formula	% Composition (by mass)	
			C	H
ethyne	HC≡CH	C_2H_2	92.26	7.74
benzene				
cyclobutane		C_4H_8		
2-butene			85.63	
1-octene				

Critical Thinking Questions

1. Verify that the % composition given for ethyne in Table 1 is correct.

2. Fill in the missing molecular formulas and % compositions in Table 1.

3. Is it possible, given the original data in Table 1, to determine the % composition by mass of H for 2-butene without using the equation given in the model above? If so, how?

4. Based on the data in Table 1, is it possible to determine the *molecular* formula of a compound solely from its percent composition? Why or why not?

5. What feature related to composition do all compounds with the same % composition have?

Information

The **empirical formula** of a compound describes the relative number of each type of atom in the compound. It is given in terms of the smallest-possible-whole-number ratios (as subscripts). For example, the empirical formula of ethane is CH_3. (Note that the subscript "1" is omitted.)

Critical Thinking Questions

6. What feature related to the composition of a compound can be determined solely by percent composition?

7. Determine the empirical formula of each of the molecules in Table 1.

Exercises

1. The molecule 2-hexene has the molecular formula C_6H_{12}. Refer to Table 1 and determine the percent composition of H in this molecule.

2. Determine the percent composition of each element in acetic acid, CH_3COOH.

3. A molecule containing only nitrogen and oxygen contains (by mass) 36.8% N.

   a) How many grams of N would be found in a 100 g sample of the compound? How many grams of O would be found in the same sample?
   b) How many moles of N would be found in a 100 g sample of the compound? How many moles of O would be found in the same sample?
   c) What is the ratio of the number of moles of O to the number of moles of N?
   d) What is the empirical formula of the compound?

4. A compound used as a dry-cleaning fluid was analyzed and found to contain 18.00% C, 2.27% H, and 79.73% Cl. Determine the empirical formula of the fluid.

5. J. N. Spencer, G. M. Bodner, and L. H. Rickard, *Chemistry: Structure & Dynamics*, Third Edition, John Wiley & Sons, 2006. Chapter 1: Problems: 135, 137, 139, 145, 146, 149, 150, 152, 153, 155, 157, 165, 166, 169, 171.

8

Peer-Led Team Learning: Scientific Learning and Discovery

David K. Gosser Jr.
Chemistry Department
The City College of the City University of New York

Biography

David K. Gosser, Jr. is Professor of Chemistry at The City College of New York (CCNY), the flagship college of the City University of New York system where over 400,000 students attend. He received a B.S. in Chemistry from St. Joseph's University (Philadelphia) in 1981 and a Ph.D. in Physical Inorganic Chemistry from Brown University in 1986. His is the author of a widely used monograph and program on simulation in electrochemistry, and has used electrochemical methods to formulate a now generally accepted theory of electron transfer model of action of the antimalarial drug artemisinin. Dr. Gosser cites as early influences on his thinking about learning science Isaac Asimov, the great explainer of science, and Uri Treisman, proponent of cooperative learning in college mathematics. Dr. Gosser founded the peer-led team learning (PLTL) model, and has worked over a decade with a team of faculty and learning specialists to develop and disseminate the model to general chemistry, to other subdisciplines, and to other scientific disciplines.

Abstract

Peer-led team learning is a model of teaching and learning chemistry that introduces new elements of student participation and leadership. Students who have successfully completed the general chemistry course are recruited to become "peer-leaders": their task is to lead small groups of 6-8 students in problem solving, debate and discussion. Key elements for the success of the PLTL model are faculty involvement in the training of peer-leaders and in the selection and/or preparation of workshop materials. The PLTL model is robust and can be adapted to different approaches to content and merged with other pedagogical models. PLTL emulates many aspects of the process of scientific discovery: the need for debate and discussion, the lack of dependence on authority alone, and use of different modes of thinking. There is a growing body of evidence to demonstrate significant learning gains associated with PLTL, confirming that students are a powerful untapped resource for teaching chemistry.

Introduction: PLTL and Scientific Discovery

The process of scientific discovery requires debate and discussion, builds on prior knowledge – but without slavish adherence to authority: the outcome depends on the evidence, model building, logic, and consensus of a community, not on the source of opinion. However, students often work in isolation, and experience little of the lively interchange that makes scientific work attractive and engaging. Evidence has been presented that there are many capable students in introductory courses, but because they do not become engaged in science, we lose many of these students (Tobias, 1990). A review of the literature suggests some of the reasons for this attrition and points the way towards more effective teaching. Students need to form a sense of belonging to an academic community (Alliance for Undergraduate Education, 1990; Tinto, 1975). Mentoring relationships are powerful influences in students' decisions to stay in science (Tobias, 1992). Students learn in many different ways, including through visual, verbal, kinesthetic, and other means (Gardner, 1985; Bretz, 2005). Furthermore, these factors of community, mentoring, and diversity of modes of thinking are important in the success of the scientific enterprise as a whole. It is not unusual, then, that we may focus on these factors in the context of introductory coursework.

Peer-led Team Learning (PLTL) is a model for teaching undergraduate chemistry that proposes a modest change in course structure which results in an extraordinary change in student enthusiasm, confidence, and learning (Woodward, Gosser, Weiner, 1993; Gosser and Roth, 1998). Essentially, PLTL proposes to replace one hour of lecture or recitation with a two hour peer-led workshop. The peer leaders are students who have done well in the course previously. They lead weekly meetings of six to eight students in problem solving, debate and discussion of course material. Leaders prepare for their role by working together with faculty to examine content of the workshops and becoming acquainted with basic precepts of group leadership.

The PLTL approach is adaptable: it does not require faculty to turn either content or practice upside down. Rather, it provides a new opportunity for faculty to share their expertise and experience with students in an active learning context. It provides a meaningful mentoring and leadership role for large numbers of undergraduates, who bring renewed enthusiasm and insight into the course. And, most importantly, it builds a sense of community among introductory chemistry students, and results in increased student learning.

Assessing PLTL

An important part of assessment is that what we evaluate is clearly defined, in an operational sense. Thus, assessments discussed here are largely of implementations that adhere to "six critical components" (vide infra), a set of guidelines for PLTL.

The Students' View of Peer-led Workshops

In our initial attempts at peer-led workshops, the increase in student participation and enthusiasm was palpable (Woodward, Gosser, Weiner, 1993). Focus groups (Gafney, 1994) of students and student leaders revealed some of the underlying reasons for this change. Students enthusiastically endorsed peer-led workshops. In contrast to lecture, anxiety was reduced, and leaders were accessible and supportive. Students no longer felt isolated in the learning enterprise. The workshop was contrasted to other courses "where they might not say anything the whole semester." It was frequently said that leaders explained things differently. They supplied more background information, broke down the subject material into smaller, more understandable chunks, and used examples to further illustrate their point. The workshops gave students the chance "to make a lot of little mistakes." Students described how leaders made mistakes. The students were not afraid to challenge the leaders, and to argue their point. They said if a professor made a mistake, they would think he was right! Students claimed that the workshops gave them the opportunity to express their own views, and also to hear those of others.

Evidence for increased learning

The PLTL project has been engaged since 1999 in a program of national dissemination. The goal has been to expand the use of PLTL through activities that stimulate interest (e.g., presentations, publications), deepens understanding (one to three day faculty workshops), assists implementation ("Workshop Project Associates," (WPA) a mini-grant program), and develops leadership (national leadership conferences) (Varma-Nelson and Gosser, 2005). Over 40 WPA grants have been awarded by the project for development of PLTL in General Chemistry. Each of these projects' implementers has pursued their own vision of PLTL, for instance in leader training and development and/or adaptation of workshop materials. So, there is a wealth of accumulated experience in implementing and assessing PLTL in general chemistry in a wide variety of settings, including community colleges, technical colleges, small liberal arts colleges, large city or state universities, and private universities.

In order to achieve a practical project wide assessment of the effectiveness of PLTL as a model of instruction, grades were selected as the basic method for comparison because they are generally accepted as a measure of student achievement. Additionally, course grade and GPA comparisons are the standards for assessing the success of academic support programs such as supplemental instruction, and group and individual tutoring (Goodlad, 1998). Faculty have been asked in these studies to report the percentage of A,B and C final grades (%ABC), as a fraction of the incoming class. A series of 20 such reports (9 in General Chemistry) were reported from the original PLTL team and early adapters (Gafney, 2005, 2001). This data shows improved performance by statistically significant and meaningful margins (an average of a 15% increase in %ABC, comparing students in PLTL versus non-PLTL).

Individual reports regarding PLTL, in addition to containing student performance data, also provide valuable insight into how faculty can adapt the PLTL model to local circumstances, the impact on the culture of learning, and how institutional acceptance and support for PLTL is secured (recent examples: Eberlien, T., 2005; Becvar, J.E., 2004; Malik, D.J., 2004; Stewart. B.N., Amar, F.G., Bruce, M.R; 2004; Berkey, A., 2004; The West Georgian, 2004).

At the Miami University of Ohio, a PLTL section was established for "at risk" students (Sarqius, Detchon, 2004). Despite significant differences in preparation (less high school chemistry and lower SAT math scores), the at risk group showed no significant difference in their achievement in general chemistry (as measured by the ACS General Chemistry Exam,) with the other sections of general chemistry. A project at the Finger Lakes Community College (Hewlett, 2005) merged the Case Study Methnd (CSM) with PLTL. PLTL participating students earned 87% %ABC versus 78% ABC for non-participants.

The Chem-2-Chem project, established independently of the PLTL project, at the University of Puerto Rico-Cayey, has utilized an undergraduate mentor/tutor model for general chemistry that "shares the six critical components of the PLTL model" (Baez et. al. 2005). Chem-2-Chem was studied over a four year period, and participants in the program outperformed non-participants 69.0 % to 53.5% (% obtaining ABC), while the two groups were found to be comparable according to admission tests.

In an innovative development at the University of Florida, PLTL was merged with Guided Inquiry – "Peer-led Guided Inquiry" (PL-GI) (Lewis and Lewis, 2005). For one group of students, a PL-GI session was combined with two lectures per week. This group was compared to a control group that had three lectures per week. Comparisons were based on identical course exams and on a final exam from the ACS Examinations Institute. The experimental group outperformed the control group in spite of one fewer weekly lecture.

Impact on peer-leaders

The peer-leaders growth in poise and confidence as they take on their new responsibility of facilitating discussion and mentoring is often cited by faculty as one of the benefits of PLTL. Evidence suggests, perhaps not surprisingly, that peer-leaders of chemistry courses develop a better understanding of chemistry than their non-leader counterparts (Blake, W.; Eberlein, T, 2005), Student leaders report increases in scientific knowledge, communication, teaching, and leadership skills (Tenney, A and Houck, B., 2004). With over a decade of implementations, it has been possible to study the impact of PLTL on former leaders as they took subsequent steps into graduate work and careers. Respondents reported that participation in PLTL deepened their own learning, helped them develop confidence and perseverance, and fostered communication and team-related skills. (Gafney, L and Varma-Nelson, P, 2007).

Getting started with PLTL

The PLTL model proposes that either the traditional weekly recitation, or a modest amount of lecture, be replaced by a new curricular structure: a two-hour peer-led workshop (Gosser and Roth, 1998; Sarquis et al., 2001). The peer leader has done well in the course previously (e.g., the previous semester), has good communication skills and a desire to assist other students. In preparing to implement a PLTL course, one of the first tasks is to find undergraduate leaders (one for each group of six to eight students in the course). The first time around, one is likely to look for advanced students (majors) and for students who have done well in a recent class. However, once the PLTL course is up and running, many students can be recruited directly from the course to serve as peer-leaders for the next semester. It is helpful to have a formalized application and acceptance process, which will serve to clarify the respective roles of faculty and leader. Leaders are typically compensated for their efforts, commensurate with local standards (e.g., tutoring). The weekly time commitment is for the actual workshop and for participation in leader training.

As we hope to convince the reader, the role of the peer leader is different, and more far-reaching, than, for instance out-of-class tutoring. The PLTL model does share significant similarities with other models, such as Emerging Scholars Program (ESP) and Supplemental Instruction (SI). Perhaps the fundamental difference is that PLTL seeks curricular change for all students in course, rather than for a subset of the course students, which is common for ESP (Treisman, 1986, 1992) and SI (Arendale, 2002). This increases the scope of the program, the number of students impacted, and faculty engagement. The programs have closely related goals, and many of those implementing PLTL have found common cause with ESP programs, SI staff or learning centers.

As part of the evaluation of PLTL, a set of six critical components was developed through observation and study of successful implementations. These serve as a useful "checklist" for implementation.

The Six Critical Components

1. The PLTL workshop is a regular course component which all students are expected to attend.

2. The faculty teaching the course are closely involved with the workshops and the workshop leaders

3. The peer-leaders are well trained and closely supervised, with attention to content knowledge and teaching and learning techniques.

4. The workshop materials are appropriately challenging and encourage collaborative problem solving.

5. Organizational arrangements are optimized to promote learning.

6. There is appropriate institutional support for innovative teaching.

A full examination of these important components of a PLTL course are outside the scope of this discussion, but can be found in a guidebook for PLTL (Gosser et. al., 2001). We will focus here on issues we consider to be of immediate practical interest with regard to implementing a program of PLTL within a course.

Leader Training

The new peer-leaders are talented students and enthusiastic about their new role. They meet each week with faculty during the semester to prepare for the workshop, by reviewing the content and problems. While the peer-leaders role is to be a guide, not be a lecturer or an answer giver, a natural inclination is to revert to such roles without training that goes beyond content review. It is very helpful for students to continue to learn about collaborative learning methods such as pair problem-solving, brainstorming, learning styles, and also gain exposure to theories of learning and the value of teamwork. During the weekly "prep" sessions, the faculty can model the desired collaborative learning and listening skills. The meeting with the faculty is also important to establish good communication that helps integrate the workshop with the lecture. Training in leadership skills and pedagogy can be part of the "prep" sessions, led by the faculty, sometimes with the aid of a learning specialist. This specialized training can also be a separate course.

Leader training can usefully begin with a one or two day pre-semester orientation meeting, led by a team of faculty, experienced leaders, and a learning specialist. New peer leaders learn to use a simple ice-breaker to start their group, as well as various tools for collaborative learning such as structured discussions as applied to the introductory content of their first workshop. They also have a chance in this meeting to voice their concerns and apprehensions, often such as, "What if I don't know an answer," or "What do I do with an uncooperative student?"

Following this meeting, a good practice is for students to maintain a reflective journal in which they explore the actual practice of their workshop; this may also include reflections related to pedagogical topics of the leader training course. The Handbook for Team Leaders (Roth, Goldstein, Marcus, 2001), and the PLTL Project newsletter, *Progressions*, are two sources of such pedagogical material, especially the Spring 2001 and Spring 2004 issues (see also the PLTL website, under Leader Training, for further information (Dreyfuss, 2005). A typical curriculum for peer leaders may therefore include articles written by learning specialists, faculty, and peer leaders that are a suitable basis for leader training discussions; sample readings on various topics are suggested below.

Two-Day Pre-semester Orientation Meeting (based on the model used at CCNY)

First Day

1) Ice-breaker – working in pairs, partners interview each other, finding commonalities, and introduce their partner to the whole group;

2) Brainstorming – Definition of words (peer, leader, team, learning) and debriefing;

3) First workshop preparation - Dalton's postulates (with models).

4) Differences in problem-solving styles - (Whimbey & Lochead, 1986);

5) Reflective writing

6) Flow-charts and concept maps (Yusufova, 2001; Romance, 2000)

Second Day

7) What we know and don't know about a problem (D'Adamo, 2004)

8) Working through solving a problem with questions

9) Using levels of questions – Bloom's Taxonomy (Cognitive Domain)

10) Concerns and discussion of being a leader – led by experienced leaders

Session topics – Peer Leader Training (Education 31507 at CCNY) Eight one-hour class sessions

1) Pair Problem-Solving (Narode, 2000; Burg, 1999)

2) Mattering and marginality (Roth, Goldstein, Marcus, 2001)

3) Assumptions and beliefs – Action Science theory of Chris Argyris and Donald Schon

4) Formation of teams (Dixon, 2000)

5) Stages of Development – theory of William Perry

6) Scaffolding and the Zone of Proximal Development – theory of Lev Vygotsky (Cracolice, 2000a)

7) Motivation – theory of Edward Deci and Richard Ryan (Richard, 2001)

8) Learning styles –Richard Felder, David Kolb, Mary Nakleh (McFarlane, 1999; Morrison, 2001)

Each week the leaders write a journal, reflecting on their practice as leaders in workshop, and the lessons of the class and readings. The journal entries demonstrate consistent growth as leaders of learning teams, becoming reflective practitioners in their unique roles (Dreyfuss and Gosser, 2005). An end of course project explores issues raised in relation to actual workshop experience. Leaders often use observation of student responses to practices that they introduce into the workshop, such as specific models of cooperative learning methods. Examples of course posters can be viewed at http://www.pltl-ccny.org.

Materials Development: Scientific Discovery and Learning

Our initial efforts to develop materials for peer-led workshops were intended to assist the leader in promoting more balanced discussion and in developing materials that addressed multiple approaches and learning styles. Each kind of problem or concept in chemistry might follow one or two approaches more suitably than others. For instance, stoichiometry problems were translated to a problem-solving flowchart format similar to that described by Bunce (2005). Looking at overall relationships lends itself to concept-mapping, for instance the concept of chemical bonds. "Penny Simulations" were developed to explore the concept of the particulate nature of matter and its many consequences.

We believe that the utility of these approaches lies in the development of a richer and more conceptual understanding of chemistry. The history of chemistry reveals that multiple modes of thinking are essential, and that many scientific breakthroughs have depended on their creative use. The use of physical model building was critical to the development of the concept of tetrahedral carbon (Rouhi, 1999), the helical protein, and DNA structure of Watson and Crick. Particulate models, so much a part of chemistry, lead to the development of "games" that deepen understanding of equilibrium, dynamics, RNA folding, genetic behavior, and economics (Eigen and Winkler, 1993).

The workshop provides the time, space and guidance necessary to explore these alternate approaches to problem solving, discussion, and introduction of scientific modes of discovery and learning. Examples here are taken from PLTL: General Chemistry (Gosser, Strozak, Cracolice, 2005). These examples should in no way be viewed as prescriptive. They merely suggest ways to shape materials that will engage students. PLTL does not require adherence to a single approach for materials, and allows the faculty to shape the curricular content according to local circumstances and needs.

Example One: Constructing Lewis Diagrams

Using the "Round Robin" technique, the peer leader coordinates discussion so that each person will read and discuss one step. The group member questions and leader prompts ensure each step is thoroughly understood. With each new structure a new person starts the discussion.

1. How many valence electrons are available for bonding?

2. Determine the atom to atom connectivity. For every atom-to-atom connection, make a single bond (a shared electron pair).

3. Distribute the remaining electrons to lone-pair positions on atoms that need an octet.

4. Identify atoms that need an octet, but do not yet have one.

5. Rearrange electrons from lone pairs of adjacent atoms, forming multiple bonds, so that the atoms identified in step 4 have an octet. Count the electrons to make sure you have the number you started with.

6. Calculate the formal charge on each atom.

7. Are the bonds non-polar covalent or polar covalent. Can you draw resonance structures? Can ionic bonds participate in the resonance?

Comments: With facilitation, this algorithm for drawing Lewis structures can be the basis for discussing the nature of chemical bonding. The round robin discussion is a very good model for creating a balanced discussion that can be introduced early. Students report that this allows them a chance to voice their understanding, and listen to others.

Example Two: Creating a Problem Solving Flowchart (Stoichiometry)

Problem-solving is presented in lecture as a general concept that can be applied to stoichiometry. Students are asked in pairs, in the group, to solve different stoichiometry problems. They are asked to reflect on the path that they took, formalizing their reasoning by using a problem solving flowchart template, and present it to their group.

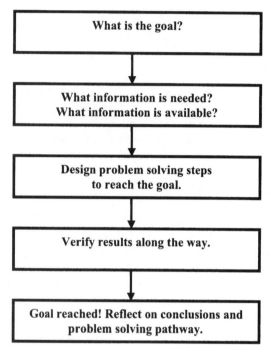

Comments: Students often have trouble knowing how to get started in problem-solving. This exercise develops the ability to approach problems in a systematic manner, and promotes reflective, rather than rote, problem solving. The approach here is very similar to that presented by Bunce (2005). Students report that this enhances problem-solving in other contexts (i.e., other courses).

Example Three: Modeling and Simulation: The Ozone Layer

Physical modeling such as the use of molecular models, or the use of pennies to represent stoichiometric relations, utilize the haptic dimension of learning. This example is taken from a discussion of gases, and illustrates how a complex stoichiometric example, a chain reaction, can be simulated with a handful of coins.

The earth's protective ozone layer is suffering destruction as a consequence of the release of human made chlorofluorocarbons (CFC's) into the atmosphere. The US and a number of nations have banned or agreed to phase out the use of CFC's. Light energy (symbolized by hν) promotes the chain reaction decomposition of $CFCl_3$, a common CFC). The steps of the reaction are:

$$CFCl_3 \text{ (g)} + h\nu \Rightarrow CFCl2 \text{ } ^{.} \text{ (g)} + Cl \text{ }^{.} \text{(g)}$$

$$Cl \text{ }^{.} \text{(g)} + O_3 \text{ (g)} \Rightarrow ClO \text{ }^{.} \text{(g)} + O_2 \text{ (g)}$$

$$ClO \cdot (g) \ + \ O \ (g) \ => \ O_2 \ (g) \ + Cl \cdot (g)$$

Using pennies to represent oxygen, and nickels to represent chlorine, build a small "model" atmosphere and simulate the destruction of the ozone layer. To simulate the reaction, start with five ozone molecules (e.g., three pennies each), five oxygen molecules, and one chlorine atom. Show how a single chlorine atom leads to the decomposition of all five ozone molecules. (Hint: Oxygen atoms can be formed by the light induced dissociation of oxygen molecules.)

Comments: Modeling and simulation similar to this can be used throughout the course, beginning with Dalton's atomic theory and simple stoichiometry, and continuing through acid base dissociation concepts, the relation of kinetics and equilibrium, and the concept of steady state (Gosser, Strozak and Cracolice, 2005). Students appreciate having access to a concrete representation of what can otherwise be presented in a very mathematical and abstract manner.

Interdisciplinary Workshops

Recently, we have encouraged, in our conferences and workshops, that faculty from different disciplines work together to create workshop materials (e.g., Bauer, 2003). Due to differing jargon and terminology of the disciplines (what does "order" mean to the chemist, to the mathematician, to the biologist?) confusion easily arises. In view of the increasing interdisciplinary nature of science, the implication is that a greater integration of disciplines may be needed in teaching.

 Workshop Materials and Lecture

Our approach to constructing workshop materials is consistent with Bloom's taxonomy of learning (Bloom, 1956), which classifies the cognitive domain in levels one through six, consisting of 1) Knowledge; 2) Comprehension; 3) Application; 4) Analysis; 5) Synthesis; and 6) Evaluation. These categories are useful reference points in constructing materials which carefully build a "scaffolding" with which students can tackle more sophisticated problems. The units in the Peer-led Team Learning: General Chemistry (Gosser, Strozak, Cracolice, 2005) have brief readings summarizing essential prior knowledge (with a self-test) followed by the group workshop. The workshops themselves take a variety of approaches, as indicated above, and also include, for instance, working data through data interpretation to discover periodicity deriving carbon stereochemistry from optical properties and model building, based on Van't Hoff's original work. The particular method or approach has been developed often from our own re-examination of our understanding of the content, (see for instance concept analysis in Herron, 1996), and breaking down the workshop into analytic steps to stimulate discussion and activity of the group. Whichever approach is taken, it is essential that the lecture complements the workshop, and is well thought-out in relation to the workshop. It is also important that materials for the actual workshop should not contain extensive reading. Lecture and reading assignments help establish prior knowledge and provide context. Those intending to create workshop materials might well consider consulting the paper by biologists Lemons and Griswold regarding their "Benchmarks Curriculum" (1998), which provides a useful framework to create instructional activities in a process that starts with defining overall educational goals, narrows down to operational statements of understanding, and then to the decision as to the best activities to develop understanding. This process ensures that the curricular materials flow from the necessities of well defined learning objectives.

We have dwelt on the approach we have taken in PLTL for General Chemistry. It is still a work in progress. Some of the materials described have been adapted, for example, by *SparkyIntroChem* (Butcher et al., 2003). Other approaches include using learning cycles (Cracolice, 2000b) and case studies (Hewlett, 2001). Hoffmann (2001) has developed a workshop materials for honors students, while Sarquis has emphasized PLTL for at-risk students (Sarquis and Detchon, 2005), Blake (2005) has developed materials appropriate for introductory chemistry. Lewis has utilized a peer-led approach in conjunction with guided inquiry materials (Lewis and Lewis, 2005); at Coastal Carolina University PLTL is used together with computer activities (Goodiwn, 2001).

Should We Be Preparing Answer Keys?

It is tempting when designing problem sets for peer-led team learning workshops to construct a set of worked-out answers, similar to the traditional answer key. Lack of an answer key creates some discomfort for both faculty and students. Faculty are concerned that without the availability of answer keys students are in danger of obtaining false information. Students and peer leaders may feel more comfortable with a handy set of answers to which they can refer. However, if we define the development of the skills and attitudes of *critical thinking* as a key objective in our courses, then we can understand the need to conduct workshops without readily available pre-prepared answers.

John Dewey has been credited with putting forth the idea of "critical thinking, (which he termed "reflective thinking") by defining it as "active, persistent, and careful consideration of any belief or supposed form of knowledge in light of grounds that support it and further conclusions to which it tends" (Dewey, 1997/1910, p. 6).

Implicit in the statement is the ability to reach conclusions through a process such as described by John Dewey, *independent of appeal to an external authority.* How can we relate this elementary statement of critical thinking to the preparation of materials, and, in particular, the question of answer keys? We can examine the PLTL process and discern, without the existence of an answer key, how the development of critical thinking attitudes is encouraged.

1. In the PLTL process, students are imbued with the feeling of embarking on a venture of self-discovery, in collaboration with their peers. The existence of an answer in black and white has the effect of undermining the spontaneity of the workshop. Answer keys short-circuit the PLTL workshop.

2. In a PLTL workshop it is likely that several different and equally valid approaches to solving a problem will be explored. Answer keys typically present one view of solving the problem, which then becomes the "standard." Yet the problem-solving path and even the answer are not always unique.

3. In PLTL workshop students build self confidence by the authentic experience of problem-solving. This is quite different from a process of verifying an answer prepared by an external authority.

4. Similar to a research group meeting, the focus of a PLTL workshop is to engage in a spirited discussion and debate of scientific principles and their application, arriving at conclusions by the process described by John Dewey. Clearly, in research there are no "prepared" answers.

Finally, we can examine the alternative forms of building constructive supports for students as they engage in solving the more difficult problems. This can be achieved in a multitude of ways, which is at the heart of preparing workshop problems and the training of workshop leaders.

Problems can be graduated in complexity, carefully building the "scaffolding" which students require to move up in problem-solving difficulty.

By working through the problems in workshop style, with faculty as guides, both faculty and student leaders appreciate the actual complexity of the problem-solving process, and can work with more natural and "home grown" answers that exist in their understanding and confidence in leading a PLTL workshop. Without the meeting between the faculty teaching the course and the peer-leaders, a disconnect will emerge between the lecture approach and the workshop approach, and this can easily lead to frustration amongst students.

Connections to teaching

PLTL is a flexible and rich environment that invites connections in many dimensions. The model itself was developed as a collaborative effort between faculty of different chemistry disciplines, learning specialists, and with substantial contributions from the peer leaders. The experience of a teaching role by the undergraduates increases their interest in teaching (Narode, 2001; Gafney, 2002), and a worthwhile connection of a PLTL implementation is with a school of education, so that peer leaders who are science majors are encouraged to teach in middle school, high school, or at the college level (Tien and Kampmeier, 2002-2003). Our experience is that peer-leaders who go on to become high school teachers or college faculty often incorporate the model into their own teaching.

Concluding Note

The peer leader is at the heart of the PLTL model. The support, training of the leader and the connection with the faculty are critical to success. Peer leaders, each semester, experience the joys and frustrations leading a small group of students in the debate, discussion, and consensus leading to deeper understanding of chemistry. The role can begin as early as the second half of the first year, making this a significant experience to a large cohort of students early in their college career. Peer leaders offer invaluable feedback to the instructor, and contribute significantly to our knowledge of the PLTL process, through their journals and comments. Through the leaders' intermediary role, students understand better the professor learning goals, and the professor is drawn closer to the students' view. The peer leaders, an interdisciplinary group with diverse majors, become a part of the departmental community, and add to its vitality.

In view of this, the dichotomy between professor and student begins to blur. With some humility, we, as professors, may admit to misconceptions. As Pauling pointed out in his remarks to university students who participated in a torch lit procession honoring Nobel Prize recipients in 1954, "The world progresses, year by year, century by century, as the members of the younger generation find out what was wrong with what their elders said" (1995, p. 64). Misconceptions are thus an inherent part of the scientific process, not only the province of student thought. Just as in the edges of our own understanding misconceptions arise, it is true for students as well. If we extend our trust in the intellectual abilities of our students, remarkably, we find a great untapped resource to help us solve the problem of teaching.

Acknowledgments

Acknowledgements are due to Victor Strozak and Mark Cracolice for their contributions to the early development of PLTL General Chemistry, and to Leo Gafney, the PLTL project evaluator, for his contribution to our understanding of the dynamics of PLTL. My thanks also go to the student leaders who have made this work possible: their enthusiasm, insight, and seriousness of purpose are a constant source of inspiration. Many thanks go to Jack Kampmeier for helpful discussions, and to A.E. Dreyfuss for her contriubtions to the the leader training program at CCNY: the description of the leader training is based on her course. I also want to acknowledge the many faculty who have embraced PLTL and contributed to its growth and acceptance.

Support from the National Science Foundation, Division of Undergraduate Education, Course and Curriculum Development Program is gratefully acknowledged.

Suggested Reading:

Gosser, D., Cracolice, M., Kampmeier, J.A., Roth, V., Strozak, V.S., Varma-Nelson, P. (2001). **Peer-Led Team Learning: A Guidebook**. Upper Saddle River, NJ: Prentice Hall
A definitive discussion on all the aspects of implementing PLTL; an extensive "how to" for PLTL, which includes information on practical issues of implementation, leader training, materials development, assessement, institutional issues (the "critical components").

Progressions

The Peer-Led Team Learning Project quarterly newsletter was inaugurated in 1999 and includes information of many different implementations of PLTL, including an issue as a short guide to implementation (Winter 2001), and many articles suitable for reading in connection with leader training. Available online at http://www.pltl.org.

Norman, D. (1993). **Things that make us smart: Defending human attributes in the age of the machine**. Cambridge, MA: Perseus Publishing.
A very readable introduction, for the layman, to some new trends in cognitive science that relate very well to the practice of PLTL and to teaching in general. Norman discusses "cognitive artifacts" which are representations of knowledge that can extend our understanding (useful in the context constructing materials for PLTL). Also presented is "distributed cognition", a descendent of Vygotskyian theory, which offers useful insights regarding collaborative learning systems.

References:

Alliance for Undergraduate Education. (1990). The Freshman Year in Science and Engineering: Old Problems, New Perspective for Research Universities. Report of Conference, Ann Arbor, MI.

Arendale, D.R. (2002). History of Supplemental Instruction: Mainstreaming of developmental education. In D.B. Lundell and J.L. Higbee (Eds.), Histories of developmental education (pp. 15-27). Minneapolis, MN: Center for Research on Developmental Education and Urban Literacy, General College, University of Minnesota. Retrieved January 15, 2004 from http://www.gen.umn.edu/research/crdeul.

Baez-Galib, R., Colon-Cruz, H., Resto, W., and Rubin, M. (2005). Chem-2-Chem: A one-to-one Supportive Learning Environment for Chemistry. Journal of Chemical Education 82,12, 1859.

Bauer, C., (2003). A Sample Interdisciplinary Workshop. Progressions, 5, 1, (Fall) p. 9. [Online]. Retrieved August 31, 2005 from http://www.pltl.org.

Becvar, J.E. (2004) Two plus two equals more: Making room for Peer-led Learning. Abstracts of Conferences Papers for the 227th American Chemical Society National Meeting. p. CHED-20. Washington DC American Chemical Society.

Blake, R.E., Jr. (2005). Introductory Chemistry: A Workbook. Upper Saddle River, NJ: Prentice Hall.

Bretz, S. L. (2005). All students are not created equal: Learning styles in the chemistry classroom. In Pienta, N., Greenbowe, T., Cooper, M. (Eds.). Chemists' Guide to Effective Teaching. Upper Saddle River, NJ: Prentice Hall.

Bunce, D. (2005). Solving Word Problems in Chemistry: Why do students have difficulty and what can be done to help (Ch. 9). In Pienta, N., Greenbowe, T., Cooper, M. (Eds.) Chemists' Guide to Effective Teaching. Upper Saddle River, NJ: Prentice Hall.

Burg, N. (2000). Reflections on Leader Training. Progressions, 1, 1 (Fall), p. 10. [Online]. Retrieved August 31, 2005 from http://www.pltl.org.

Butcher, D.J., Brandt, P.F., Norgaard, N.J., Atterholt, C.A., Salido, A.L. (2003). Sparky IntroChem: A Student-Oriented Introductory Chemistry Course. Journal of Chemistry Education, 80, 2 (February), p. 137.

Bloom B. S. (1956). Taxonomy of Educational Objectives, Handbook I: The Cognitive Domain. New York: David McKay Co Inc.

Cracolice, M.S. (2000a). Vygotsky's zone of proximal development: A theory base for peer-led team learning. Progressions, 1, 2 (Winter), p. 3. [Online]. Retrieved August 31, 2005 from http://www.pltl.org.

Cracolice, M.S. (2000b). Learning cycles and Peer-Led Team Learning. Progressions, 2, 1 (Fall), p. 9. [Online]. Retrieved August 31, 2005 from http://www.pltl.org.

D'Adamo, H. (2004). How can the peer leader and the student use questions as action? Progressions, 5, 3 (Spring). [Online]. Retrieved August 31, 2005 from http://www.pltl.org.

Dewey, J. (1997). How We Think. Mineola, NY: Dover Publications, Inc. Originally published 1910. Boston, MA: D.C. Heath & Co.

Dixon, L. (2000) Stages of Group Dynamics: Implications for PLTL. Progressions, 1, 4 (Summer), p. 3. [Online]. Retrieved August 31, 2005 from http://www.pltl.org.

Dreyfuss, A.E. (Ed.). (2005). Internet homepage of the Peer-Led Team Learning Project [Online]. Retrieved August 31, 2005 from http://www.pltl.org.

Dreyfuss, A.E. and Gosser, D.K. (in press-2005). In Their Own Words: Learning to Be a Peer Leader. In Duranczyk, I.M., Higbee, J.L., Lundell, D.B. (Eds.). (2005). Student Standpoints About Access Programs in Higher Education. Minneapolis, MN: Center for Research on Developmental Education and Urban Literacy, General College, University of Minnesota.

Eberlien, T. (2005) Beneficial Effects of PLTL Persist to Later Courses at Penn State Schuykill Progressions, 6, 4 (Summer), p. 3. [Online]. Retrieved January 10, 2006 from http://www.pltl.org.

Eigen, M., Winkler, R. (1993). Laws of the Game: How the Principles of Nature Govern Chance. Princeton, NJ: Princeton University Press.

Gafney, L. (2001). Evaluating Student Performance. Progressions, 2, 2 (Winter). [Online]. Retrieved August 31, 2005 from http://www.pltl.org.

Gafney, L. (2002). PLTL and secondary school teaching. Progressions, 3, 2 (Winter), p. 10. [Online]. Retrieved August 31, 2005 from http://www.pltl.org.

Gafney, L. (2005). Comparing the Performance of Groups of Students With and Without PLTL Workshops (Table 1). [Online]. Retrieved August 31, 2005 from http://www.pltl.org. Comparing student performance (Research and Evaluation).

Gafney, L. and Varma-Nelson, P. (2007). Evaluating Peer-Led Team Learning: A study of Long-term effects on former workshop peer leaders. Journal of Chemical Education, 84, 3, March, 535-539.

Gardner, H. (1985). Frames of Mind: The Theory of Multiple Intelligences. New York, NY: Basic Books.

Goodlad, S., (1998). The effectiveness of peer tutoring in higher education: A typology and review of the literature, in mentoring and tutoring by students (Sinclair Goodlad, Ed.), p. 49-69. London: Kogan Page.

Goodwin, J.A., Gilbert, B.D. (2001) Cafeteria-Style Grading in General Chemistry. J. Chem. Educ. 78 p. 490.

Gosser, D., Cracolice, M., Kampmeier, J.A., Roth, V., Strozak, V.S., Varma-Nelson, P. (2001). Peer-Led Team Learning: A Guidebook. Upper Saddle River, NJ: Prentice Hall

Gosser, D. K., and Roth, V. (1998) The Workshop Chemistry Project: Peer-Led Team-Learning. Journal of Chemical Education, 75, 185.

Gosser, D.K., Strozak, V.S., and Cracolice, M.S. (2005). Peer-Led Team Learning: General Chemistry (Second Edition). Upper Saddle River, NJ: Prentice Hall.

Herron, J.D. (1996). The Chemistry Classroom: Formulas for Successful Teaching.   (Chapter 10). Washington, D.C.: American Chemical Society

Hewlett, J. (2001). Combining PLTL with the case study method of instruction. Progressions, 3, 1 (Fall), p. 7. [Online]. Retrieved August 31, 2005 from http://www.pltl.org.

Hoffman, M.Z. (2001). From Boston University: Yes to workshops! Progressions, 3, 1 (Fall), p. 9. [Online]. Retrieved August 31, 2005 from http://www.pltl.org.

Lemons, D., Griswold, J.G. (1998). Defining the boundaries of physiological understanding: The benchmarks curricular model. Advances in Physiological Education. 275, p. 35.

Lewis, S.E. and Lewis, J.E. (2005). Departing from Lectures: An Evaluation of a Peer-Led Guided Inquiry Alternative. Journal of Chemical Education, 82, 135-139.

Malik, D.J. (2004) Creating a culture for PLTL: Selling the faculty and administration. Abstracts of Conference Papers for the 227th American Chemical Society Meeting. p CHEM-42. Washington, DC. American Chemical Society.

McFarlane, N. (2000). An Application of Learning Theories: Problem-Solving Through Learning Styles. Progressions, 1, 2, (Winter), pp. 10-11[Online]. Retrieved August 31, 2005 from http://www.pltl.org.

Morrison, O. (2001). Algorithmic Problem solvers or conceptual thinkers: Which is more favored in CCNY's chemistry courses? Progressions, 2, 3 (Spring), p. 11. [Online]. Retrieved August 31, 2005 from http://www.pltl.org.

Narode, R. (2000). Pair Problem-Solving: An Effective model for learning. Progressions, 1, 3, p. 8. [Online]. Retrieved August 31, 2005 from http://www.pltl.org.

Narode, R. (2001). PLTL and the future of science teacher education. Progressions, 2, 2 (Winter), p. 10. [Online]. Retrieved August 31, 2005 from http://www.pltl.org.

Norman, D. (1993). Things that make us smart: Defending human attributes in the age of the machine. Cambridge, MA: Perseus Publishing.

Pauling, L. (1995). Linus Pauling in his own words. New York, NY: Simon Schuster.

Pienta, N., Greenbowe, T., Cooper, M. (Eds.) (2005). Chemists' Guide to Effective Teaching. Upper Saddle River, NJ: Prentice Hall.

Richard, C. (2001). Motivation in the workshop: How can leaders use this knowledge? Progressions, 2, 3 (Spring), p. 8. [Online]. Retrieved August 31, 2005 from http://www.pltl.org.

Romance, N. (2000). Concept mapping as a knowledge-based strategy for enhancing student understanding. Progressions, 2, 1 (Fall), p. 5. [Online]. Retrieved August 31, 2005 from http://www.pltl.org.

Roth, V., Goldstein, E., Marcus, G. (2001). Peer-Led Team Learning: A Handbook for Team Leaders. Upper Saddle River, NJ: Prentice Hall.

Rouhi, A.M. (1999). Tetrahedral Carbon Redux. Chemical and Engineering News, 77 (36), September 6.

Sarquis, J.L., Dixon, L.J., Gosser, D.K., Kampmeier, J.A., Roth, V., Strozak, V.S., Varma-Nelson, P. (2001). The workshop project: peer-led team learning in chemistry (Chapter 26). In Miller, J.E., Groccia, J.E., and Miller, M.S. (Eds.). Student-Assisted Teaching: A Guide to Faculty Student Teamwork. Bolton, MA: Anker Publishing Company.

Sarquis, J.L., and Detchon, J.C. (2005). The PLTL experience at Miami University. Project Kaleidoscope, Volume IV: What works, what matters, what lasts. Retrieved from http://www.pkal.org on August 30, 2005.

Stewart, B.N, Amar, F.G., Bruce, M.R. (2004) Measuring the effect of PLTL in a large general chemistry course. Abstracts of Conference Papers for the 227th American Chemical Society Meeting. p CHED-16. Washington, DC. American Chemical Society.

Tenney, A and Houck, B. (2004) Learning about leadership. Journal of College Science Teaching 33 (6) p. 25.

Tien, L. and Kampmeier, J.A. (2002-2003). Promoting the scholarship of teaching. Progressions, 4, 1 & 2 (Fall and Winter), p. 9. [Online]. Retrieved August 31, 2005 from http://www.pltl.org.

Tinto, V. (1975). Dropout from Higher Education: A Theoretical Synthesis of Recent Research. Review of Educational Research, 45 89-125.

Tobias, S. (1990). They're Not Dumb, They're Different: Stalking the Second Tier. Tucson, AZ: Research Corporation.

Tobias, S. (1992). Revitalizing Undergraduate Science. Tucson, AZ: Research Corporation.

Treisman, P.U. (1986). A study of the mathematics performance of Black students at the University of California, Berkeley [Dissertation, University of California, Berkeley, 1985]. Dissertation Abstracts International, 47(05), 1641.

Treisman, U. (1992). Studying students studying calculus: A look at the lives of minority mathematics students in college. The College Mathematics Journal, 23, 362-372.

Varma-Nelson, P. and Gosser, D. (2005). Dissemination of Peer-Led Team Learning and Formation of a National Network: Embracing a Common Pedagogy. In Ouellett, M. (Ed.) Teaching Inclusively: Diversity and Faculty Development. Stillwater, OK: New Forums Press.

The West Georgian (2004). Chemistry Scores improve at UWG. [online] retrieved January 20, 2005 from http://www.thewestgeorgian.com/home/archives. Issue: January 21.

Whimbey, A. and Lochead, J. (1986). Problem Solving and Comprehension. Hillsdale, NJ: Lawrence Erlbaum Associates, Inc.

Peer-Led Team Learning: Organic Chemistry

Jack A Kampmeier
Department of Chemistry
University of Rochester

Pratibha Varma-Nelson
Department of Chemistry
Northeastern Illinois University

Abstract

The traditional sophomore organic course is a challenge to students and instructors alike. In spite of the organizing power of the structure-reactivity paradigm and the rationalization of the subject provided by our mechanistic understanding, many students continue to try to learn organic chemistry by brute force memorization, as if it were a collection of unrelated facts. This approach is a recipe for disappointment and disaffection. Organic chemistry teachers need to find new ways to help their students build enthusiasm for the subject and find success in the course. The Peer-led Team Learning (PLTL) Workshop is a proven pedagogy that "provides an active learning experience for undergraduates, creates a leadership role for undergraduates and engages faculty in a creative new dimension in teaching," (Gosser, 1996). The PLTL Workshop has been adopted by more than 100 different colleges and universities to help more than 20,000 students/year learn chemistry. Approximately one quarter of these implementations are in organic chemistry; statistically significant data show improvement in both the performance and the satisfaction of the Workshop students.

Biographies

Jack A. Kampmeier is Professor of Chemistry Emeritus at the University of Rochester. Having received his A.B. from Amherst College in 1957, followed by his Ph.D. from the University of Illinois, Jack accepted a faculty appointment in Chemistry at the University of Rochester in 1960 to establish a program of teaching and research in organic chemistry with an emphasis on reaction mechanisms and free radical chemistry. His leadership in undergraduate teaching was first recognized in 1974 when he received the University's Edward Peck Curtis Award for Excellence in Undergraduate Teaching for his role in revising the undergraduate curriculum in the Department. From 1975-79, he chaired the Chemistry Department and subsequently served as Associate Dean for Graduate Studies from 1982 to 1985, and Dean of the College of Arts and Science from 1988 to 1991. In 1999, he received the College's Goergen Award for Distinguished Achievement and Artistry in Undergraduate Teaching, as he entered his fortieth year as an instructor. In 1999, he was also the recipient of the Chemical Manufacturers' Association Catalyst Award for Excellence in College Chemistry Teaching. Except for two sabbaticals, as NSF Faculty Fellow at the University of California, Berkeley (1971-1972) and as Fulbright Senior Research Scholar at the Albert Ludwigs Universität, Freiburg, Germany (1979-80), he has been actively involved in teaching organic chemistry from freshman to postdoctoral fellows. In 1995, Jack and Vicki Roth introduced the Peer-led Team Learning Workshop in his course in organic chemistry. Jack strongly supported the implementation of this model in other courses, institutions and disciplines as a superior way to help students learn. The PLTL Workshop has since been adopted by several other departments in the College and is now a signature for a Rochester education in SEM disciplines. Since 1995, Jack has been involved in all phases of the research, development and dissemination work of the Peer-Led Team Learning Project supported by NSF from 1995-2005 and led by David K. Gosser.

Pratibha Varma-Nelson is Professor of Chemistry and Chair of the Department of Chemistry, Earth Science and Physics at Northeastern Illinois University, Chicago. She received her B.Sc. in Chemistry with first class from the University of Poona, India, in 1970 and a Ph.D. in 1978 from the University of Illinois in Chicago in Organic Chemistry. The title of her thesis was "Protein Ancestors: Heteropolypeptides from Hydrogen Cyanide and Water". From 1977-1979 she studied the effect of essential catalytic residue modifications on conformation and binding affinity in anhydro-chymotrypsin while she completed a postdoctoral fellowship in enzymology at the Stritch School of Medicine, Loyola University, Maywood, Illinois before joining the faculty of Saint Xavier University, Chicago in 1979. At SXU she taught courses in Organic Chemistry and Biochemistry and Environmental Science. In 2002 she was awarded the SXU Teacher-Scholar Award. She moved to NEIU in July of 2002. At NEIU she teaches a capstone seminar to chemistry majors and a course on the chemistry of biological compounds. Since 1995 her professional activities have revolved around the development, implementation and dissemination of the Peer-Led Team Learning (PLTL) model of teaching. She has been an active partner of the Workshop Chemistry Project one of the five NSF Systemic Reform Projects in Chemistry. She has been a Co-PI on two NSF National Dissemination Grants awarded to PLTL and Co-PI on the "Multi Initiative Dissemination" (MID) project. She has co-authored several publications and manuals about the PLTL model. Pratibha is the director of the Workshop Project Associate (WPA) Program, which provided small grants to facilitate implementation of PLTL and is currently director of the annual Chautauqua course on PLTL. In addition, she is a Co-PI of the NSF funded Undergraduate Research Center, Center for Authentic Science Practice in Education, (CASPiE).

The Peer-Led Team Learning Model For Teaching Organic Chemistry

The PLTL Workshop is an innovative pedagogical structure that is designed to help students learn science. The Workshop model is based on research results from cognitive psychology, learning theory, cooperative learning, constructivism and student development. In brief, the Peer-Led Team Learning (PLTL) model preserves the lecture, but replaces the recitation with a weekly two-hour Workshop where a group of 6-8 students work as a team to solve carefully structured problems under the guidance of a peer leader. The peer leader is the distinguishing, central characteristic of the PLTL model. The leader is a student who has done well in the course, has good organizational and communication skills and is specifically trained to clarify goals, encourage debate and ensure that team members engage with the Workshop material and with each other. Because the Workshop structure, the role of peer leader and the Workshop problems are designed to help students build conceptual understanding, problem solving skills and intellectual self-reliance, they are especially well suited to help students succeed in organic chemistry. The results of the PLTL Workshop are quite clear: students achieve better grades; retention improves; students like the PLTL Workshop and the majority of the participants would recommend Workshop courses to their peers (Leo Gafney, 2001; Tien, Roth & Kampmeier, 2002; Wamser, 2005). Peer leaders also realize significant growth in their intellectual, personal and pre-professional skills (Tenney & Houck, 2004; Micari, Streitwieser & Light, 2006; Gafney & Varma-Nelson, 2006). Several descriptions of the PLTL Workshop model are available in extended (Gosser, *et al.,* 2001) and abbreviated form (Sarquis, et al., 2001; Varma-Nelson, Cracolice & Gosser, (2004). Rather than repeat what we have written for faculty colleagues, we offer here our *Introduction to the PLTL Workshop*, written for students of organic chemistry (Kampmeier, Varma-Nelson, Wamser & Wedegaertner, 2006).

To The Student. "The peer-led Workshop is a unique curricular structure that provides a weekly opportunity for you to engage with your fellow students in the process of constructing your understanding of organic chemistry and developing new problem solving skills. As part of the process, you will talk, debate, discuss, argue, evaluate, ask questions, answer questions, explain your ideas, listen to the ideas of your colleagues and, ultimately, negotiate your understanding of organic chemistry with them. This active, personal engagement with experimental observations and with the ideas of colleagues is the way that scientists construct meaning and understanding. Practicing scientists do this in a structure called research group meeting. The peer-led Workshop is a group meeting for undergraduates.

Each week's Workshop is built around a set of problems that are designed to help you probe and build your conceptual understanding of a BIG IDEA in organic chemistry. Simultaneously, the problems require you to learn and practice new problem solving skills. The problems are challenging so that you will need the resources and imagination of the group to come to good solutions. We do not provide answers to the problems because the point of the Workshop (indeed, the point of higher education) is to help you learn to construct, evaluate and develop confidence in your own answers and conclusions. Ultimately, your understanding is personal and belongs to you. However, the process of testing and refining your understanding is dramatically facilitated by interaction with your peers.

Because the interaction with your peers is the key to successful learning, each Workshop is guided by a Workshop leader. This leader is not a tutor, or a teaching assistant, or an expert authoritarian answer giver about organic chemistry. Rather, the leader is a fellow student, a peer, who has successfully completed the organic course and is chosen and trained by your organic teacher to lead your Workshop. The job of the leader is to guide the interactions among the disparate participants so that the group becomes a team in which the members work together to ensure that everyone learns organic chemistry. Your leader will be a role model, mentor, cheerleader and friend.

*Workshop problems are not homework; they are designed for cooperative teamwork during the Workshop. That does not mean that there is no homework in the organic course. You need to prepare for the Workshop in order to be a participating, contributing member of the Workshop team. That means you have to study the text, attend and study the lectures, and do the assigned homework problems from the text before you come to Workshop. Each Workshop begins with a statement of **Expectations**. These key words and ideas should guide your preparation for the Workshop.*

*You may be familiar with workbooks that drill you on the empirical knowledge that is associated with a particular subject. This is not that kind of workbook. We assume that you are already skilled at acquiring knowledge. This book is focused on the organization and application of knowledge and ideas in organic chemistry. This book is a workbook in the sense that it provides space for you to make notes, record the results of the team work and reflect on the point of the problem and the big ideas. Each Workshop ends with a **Reflection** section that invites you to identify gains in your understanding and skill. If you use your workbook well, it should become an effective tool for review for exams.*

There are many rewards from the study of organic chemistry. You will discover it is a powerful and wonderful way to understand many aspects of our natural world. The interplay of molecular structure and chemical and physical properties is one of the foundational ideas of modern science. In contrast to the prevailing student mythology, organic chemistry is a coherent, rational subject with an accessible theory to make sense of the wealth of observations. It is also a subject of enormous practical consequence for our health and well being. Organic chemistry is also exceptionally well suited to the development of powerful cognitive skills that are general and transferable to other areas of study and decision-making. In 1964 Benjamin Bloom compiled a taxonomy of cognitive skills, organized in a hierarchy from the simplest to the most complex: knowledge, comprehension, application, analysis, synthesis and evaluation. Successful work in organic chemistry requires you to function at all of these levels. The Workshop problems are designed to help you learn the requisite thought processes.

Finally, it is important for you to understand the central position of students, you and others, in the Workshops. We cannot teach you organic chemistry; at best, we can help you learn the subject. In the end, you will not acquire our understanding. Instead, there is the exhilarating prospect that you will build your own view of organic chemistry and make your own contributions to our understanding."

The Workshop in Practice. Examples of specific Workshop problems will help clarify the roles of the students, the leaders, and the Workshop problems. The first problem in the first Workshop starts right off to explore the connections among molecular structure and chemical and physical properties. It is a real problem that might have been studied in the lab by a practicing organic chemist. Most importantly, the problem is anchored in experimental observations and engages students in the reasoning that is central to doing organic chemistry. Finally, it is a problem that can be analyzed at many different levels of understanding, depending on the goals of the course.

Structure: Functional Groups

Purpose: "Function follows form" is a fundamental principle that helps us make sense of the physical and chemical properties (function) of molecules. There is little room for ambiguity about the structure (form) of a diatomic molecule, AB; the two atoms must be connected to each other. With three atoms, A_2B, there are two different connectivities. Since carbon bonds to itself and other atoms, there are many ways to connect larger sets of atoms. This Workshop provides opportunities to explore the structures of constitutional isomers and logical ways to find those structures. Remarkably, the structures of different isomers can be deduced from experimental observations of their properties. The logic also works the other way around; properties can be predicted from the molecular structure. This Workshop begins to explore these fundamental patterns of reasoning. We will use them throughout the course.

Expectations: To prepare for this Workshop, you should review and understand the following terms and ideas: molecular formula; constitutional isomer; equivalent atoms and molecules; functional group structure and nomenclature; Kekulé structures, primary, secondary, tertiary and quaternary nomenclature; simple roles for naming organic compounds.

1. The following isomers of molecular formula C_5H_{12} were treated under appropriate conditions to give all possible monochloro products, $C_5H_{11}Cl$, in which Cl replaces H. These $C_5H_{11}Cl$ constitutional isomers, derived from each C_5H_{12} compound, could be separated either by careful fractional distillation or by gas chromatography (GC). Work together to find the structures of the following C_5H_{12} compounds and the corresponding $C_5H_{11}Cl$ derivatives.

    a. A C_5H_{12} compound that gives three $C_5H_{11}Cl$ derivatives

    b. A C_5H_{12} compound that gives four $C_5H_{11}Cl$ derivatives

    c. A C_5H_{12} compound that gives only one $C_5H_{11}Cl$ derivative

    d. Are there any other isomers of C_5H_{12}? Explain to each other how to find the answer to this question.

The leader will get the group started by asking: "What is the question? What are we supposed to do?" Part of this step is understanding the language of organic chemistry. This can lead to questions about specific words in the problem such as *constitutional isomer, derivative and separated*. The students will explain these terms to each other, in their own words. The discussion will probably lead to the insight that it is not necessary to understand *fractional distillation* and *gas chromatography*, but that *separation* and *isomer* imply difference. The leader will then ask the group, "Where (How) shall we start?" Some students will try to write a C_5H_{12} structure. The leader might ask whether the molecular formula contains structural information. Undoubtedly, students will get into debates about whether different representations of C_5H_{12} correspond to different isomers. Molecular models are helpful at this stage. For a given C_5H_{12} structure, the leader may then ask, "How many $C_5H_{11}Cl$ isomers can be obtained?" For some students, this question may reveal the important unstated simplification that the carbon skeleton is unchanged when a hydrogen atom is replaced by a chlorine atom. All students will have to recognize that only certain $C_5H_{11}Cl$ isomers can be derived from a given C_5H_{12} and that the experimental observations (how many $C_5H_{11}Cl$ products) ultimately tell which C_5H_{12} is which. The power and rigor of using observations to exclude structures should come out in the discussion. Since most students will arrive at different C_5H_{12} structures by trial and error, someone will probably ask whether there are other C_5H_{12} isomers that might fit the observations, i.e., is the evidence necessary *and* sufficient? The leader might ask for the simplest C_5H_{12}, the next simplest, etc., to lead to the idea of a logical procedure for finding all of the possible isomers.

While the fundamental operating principle is that the leader *and* the students do the asking, the students do the answering. The students discuss and negotiate until they are satisfied with their answers. A good leader will reflect the inevitable demand for **"The Answer"** back to the students, to their discussion and their logic. Two more problems like this one make up the complete Workshop. Finally, the Workshop ends with reflections and discussion of the take-home points from the problems. This first Workshop makes the key point that structural information can be deduced from experimental observations. The mode of thinking (if, then or if not, then not) is new to many students. In the second Workshop, it is presented as a heuristic for solving structure proof problems. The structure of the problem asks students to find all of the experimental OBSERVATIONS and then to make appropriate DEDUCTIONS about structure from each OBSERVATION. The leader helps the students learn to be alert to ambiguities, make multiple hypotheses, gang deductions and, ultimately, use the deductions to eliminate structures and come to reliable conclusions, suitably qualified for incomplete information. In the case of ambiguity, the leader may ask the students to suggest new experiments. The heuristic makes the problem-solving process visible and provides the trail of logic that is the answer to "How do you know?" Workshop 3 works the logical principles in both directions; from experimental observation to structure and from observed structure to predicted properties. Ultimately, we will use the same OBSERVATION/DEDUCTION technique to establish reaction mechanisms in Workshops 7, 8, and 11-13. On reflection, the take-home point from these examples is that the structure of the Workshop problem, the practice of the leader and the active engagement of the students in discussion work synergistically to help the students build their understanding and develop new thinking skills.

Structure and Properties: Acids and Bases

Two examples from Workshop 4 on acids and bases show how the structure of the problems and the Workshop can help students bridge from general chemistry to organic chemistry. A sequence of questions can lead students from the familiar to the unfamiliar and, ultimately, to a unified understanding of a variety of reactions. In addition, the instructions in the problem reveal the steps in the logic that an expert would follow to analyze the reactions. As in the first example, there are many words, ideas and questions that will require discussion among the students.

Purpose: "What reacts with what" is a big question. One fundamental answer to this question is that acids react with bases. In this Workshop you will explore a variety of acid-base reactions and the curved arrow representation of the reactions that follows from Lewis acid-base theory. By the end of the Workshop, you will be able to predict the reactants or the products of acid-base reactions. Making those predictions requires that you understand the idea of acid-base reactions and not simply memorize A+B → C+D.

Expectations: You should come to the Workshop with a good understanding of: Lewis structures; non-bonding electron pairs; molecules with empty orbitals (unfilled octets); antibonding molecular orbitals; polar bonds; K_a, pK_a; and Lewis acid-base theory.

1. Draw complete Kekule/Lewis structures of reactants and products using lines for bonds and showing non-bonding electron pairs. Identify the Lewis acid and the Lewis base for each reaction. Use curved arrows to show bond making and bond breaking processes for the forward and reverse reactions. Explain the origins of the formal charges in the products.

$$CH_3SCH_3 + BF_3 \rightleftharpoons (CH_3)_2\overset{+}{S} - \overset{-}{B}F_3$$

$$(CH_3)_3\overset{+}{C} + H_2O \rightleftharpoons (CH_3)_3C - \overset{+}{O}H_2$$

$$CH_3\underset{OH}{\overset{O}{\overset{\|}{C}}} + NH_3 \rightleftharpoons CH_3\underset{O^-}{\overset{O}{\overset{\|}{C}}} + NH_4{}^+$$

$$CH_3SH + CH_3O^- \rightleftharpoons CH_3S^- + CH_3OH$$

$$CH_3\overset{O}{\overset{\|}{C}}CH_3 + H_3O^+ \rightleftharpoons H_2O + CH_3\overset{\overset{+}{O}H}{\overset{\|}{C}}CH_3$$

$$H_3N + CH_3-Br \rightleftharpoons H_3\overset{+}{N}- CH_3 + Br^-$$

2. The curved arrow formalism tracks the movement of electrons and the bond making and bond breaking changes in an elementary step in a reaction mechanism. A more detailed view identifies the molecular orbitals that are involved. In general, the highest occupied molecular orbital (HOMO) of a Lewis base donates the electrons for the new bond and the lowest unoccupied molecular orbital (LUMO) of a Lewis acid accepts the electrons. In most, but not all, cases the process of accepting electrons leads to bond breaking. For each of the reactions shown below, use curved arrows to track the electrons and show the bond making and bond breaking processes. Identify the HOMO and LUMO involved in the bond making and bond breaking processes. Finally, use the bond making and bond breaking processes to predict the products of each reaction.

$$H_3N + BF_3 \longrightarrow$$

$$H_3O^+ + NH_3 \longrightarrow$$

$$I^- + CH_3Br \longrightarrow$$

$$HCl + (CH_3)_2 C = CH_2 \longrightarrow$$

$$HO^- + (CH_3)_2C=O \longrightarrow$$

The Workshop ends with a *post-mortem* (Schoenfeld, 1985*)*.

Reflection:

a. Explain to your Workshop Colleagues how the following types of reactions are subcategories of the prototypical Lewis acid-base reaction:

Lewis Prototype: $H_3N: + BF_3 \rightarrow H_3N\overset{+}{-}\overset{-}{B}F_3$

Bronsted Acid-Base Reaction: $H_3N: + HA \rightarrow H_3\overset{+}{N}\text{-}H + A:^-$

Organic Reaction: $H_3N: + CH_3\check{S}Br \rightarrow H_3\overset{+}{N}\check{S}CH_3 + Br^-$

b. Write a short coherent paragraph that explains how the curved-arrow formalism is a graphical representation of the Lewis acid-base theory of chemical reactions.

Organic Synthesis

After some practice with functional group interchanges and carbon-carbon bond formation using hydrocarbon starting materials, the challenge of multi-step synthesis is introduced in the following problem from Workshop 10. The scope of the "starburst" invites students to work together and emphasizes the need to master the tools (the reactions) of synthetic chemistry. It quickly becomes apparent that the reactions need to be organized in appropriate sequence. Finally, the idea of retro-synthesis emerges naturally from the insight that all of the C_4 targets come from a common precursor, 1-butyne. The job of the leader is not to show students how to proceed, but to organize a reflective discussion that brings out these key ideas. For example, the leader might ask the group: "What did you need to know to solve this problem?" What steps did you follow to solve the problem?" "Can you identify common precursors to groups of products?"

1. Work together with your colleagues to propose methods for synthesizing the target molecules from acetylene.

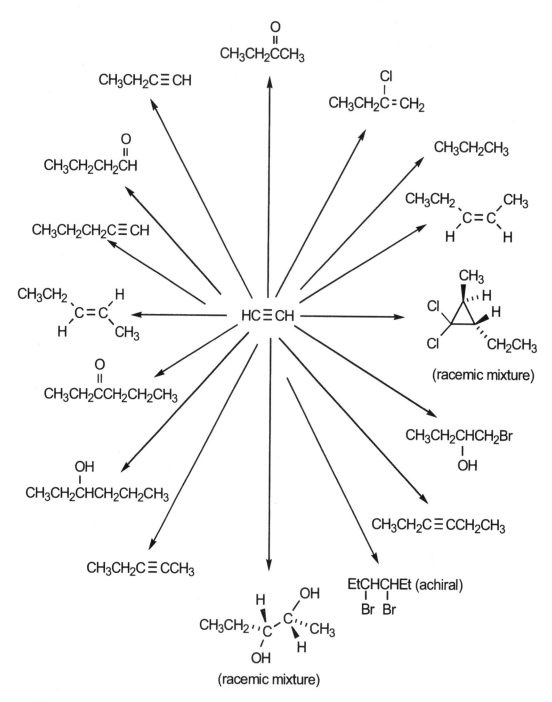

The structure of the Workshop problems is very important. As illustrated in the examples, the problems can help students internalize new modes of analysis and problem solving. They can also help students make connections among ideas and observations and lead them from the specific to the general. In cooperation with the leaders and the Workshop environment, the problems can encourage interaction and debate. In practice, the Workshops are fun, enlivened by social interaction and energized by the power of the students' own minds and voices, liberated by the absence of external authority. Students learn by doing (Woods, 1987) and, in the end, the purpose of the Workshop problems is to provide the structure for the students to do organic chemistry by *themselves*, for *themselves*.

Why Peer-led Team Learning is Useful to Students of Organic Chemistry

In our experience, students in the sophomore organic course are interested in many things, including biology, psychology, engineering, physics and even organic chemistry. Some have crystallized their career plans, but many are still exploring their interests and abilities. It is very hard to be certain about what they want or need to know in a narrow, disciplinary sense. We can be certain, however, about the needs of all students to learn, practice and internalize the habits of thought that will prepare them to solve new problems, sort out complex observations and come to defensible conclusions; in brief, to learn to make up their own minds. These skills are reliable, transferable and transcend the details of any particular discipline. They are the rewards from a good course that endure long after the disciplinary specifics have been lost. In principle, the organic chemistry teacher has a special opportunity to teach the thinking skills that students come to college to learn. High order thinking is required to do what organic chemists do: determine molecular structure; discover reaction mechanisms; design synthetic pathways. There are no algorithmic solutions to such questions; students must confront the experimental observations and find ways to organize them into reliable and useful patterns of structure and reactivity. To do this with confidence requires students to apply their knowledge and understanding to develop new modes of analysis, evaluation and synthesis. The PLTL Workshop is designed to facilitate just these activities.

There are many other reasons why organic chemistry might be considered to be "the most interesting or the most rewarding course I ever took." The insight that molecules have specific structures and that the properties of the molecules are consequences of the structures is as influential as the ideas of the genetic code, quantum mechanics, evolution, plate tectonics, and supply and demand. Since molecules are the basic building blocks of matter, understanding molecules is one of the best ways to understand the matter of life. But, there is even more than that. As Breslow observed, organic chemists also create a world of synthetic materials with new and interesting properties (Breslow, 1997). What more could one want in a course?

Yet, organic chemistry is perceived by many to be a "killer course". Although there is no comprehensive national survey, anecdotal reports suggest that as many as 25-50% of the students in the first organic course are unsuccessful (fail to earn at least a C grade), depending on the school and the course. As shown in Table 1, some data have been reported in the context of attempts to decrease the attrition rate. Levels of attrition like those in the Table are costly to the teacher, to the department and the college, to the discipline, and above all, to the disappointed students.

Success Rates in First Semester Organic Chemistry

Type of School	% Successful[a] (# of terms)	Reference
Community College	52(2)	Vikin (1971)
Comprehensive University	52(2)	Emerson (1975)
4-year College	41	Sevenair (1989)
Research University	46 (5)	Dougherty (1997)
Comprehensive University	71(10)	Paulson (1999)
Research University	53(5)	Huddle (2000)
Research University	66(3)	Tien (2002)
Comprehensive University	69 [b,c] (2)	Carpenter (2003)
Comprehensive University	69 [d] (7)	Wamser (2006)

a. % successful is the number of students who earned C⁻ or better divided by the total enrollment.
b. cumulative after two semesters.
c. % who earned D⁻ or better.
d. % successful in any one quarter of a three-quarter sequence.

Table 1. Success Rates in First Semester Organic Chemistry

Student attitudes about the organic course are also alarming. Generations of students have approached organic chemistry with anxiety and dread. The word on the street is that the subject is all memorization and that the course's major purpose is to weed out students. Bhattacharya (2005) said it well: "They typically regard the course as a bitter pill that must be swallowed *en route* to their future career goals." The difference between the potential to be "most interesting and rewarding" and Katz's (1996) observation of "a bad reputation of mythic proportions" is striking and must have its origins in the difficulties students encounter in the organic course. But, these difficulties are probably not inherent in the subject matter. Successful students report that they had to work hard, but that the material was "not that hard." Although the logic is tight, most of the reasoning is qualitative and sophisticated math skills are not required. To be sure, students have to organize a large volume of material and disciplined effort on a regular schedule is essential. These challenges alone cannot account for the difficulties that many students have with the course. Rather, students have trouble with organic because there are genuine issues of intellectual development. Most fundamentally, organic chemistry is an epistemological challenge. Many students come to organic chemistry with the idea that knowledge (and science) is definitional, factual or algorithmic. Answers are right or wrong. The right answers are received from authoritarian experts such as parents and teachers and the job of the students is to learn (memorize) them (Perry, 1970; Belenky, 1986). A corollary to this reliance on external authority is a failure to understand that personal engagement and responsibility are prerequisite to genuine learning. In contrast, processing experimental observations to arrive with confidence at a structure or a reaction mechanism requires students to confront how *they* know what *they* think *they* know. These are intensely personal activities. As we will see, they do not have to be private activities, but they do have to be personal. In Perry's scheme of intellectual development, making up one's own mind is many steps removed from the dualistic position of many beginning students. The challenge for the organic student is to develop new modes of thinking and learning. This is not an easy task; students are required to change their minds about answers and their role in creating and evaluating answers. The peer-led Workshop in organic chemistry is specifically designed to support, encourage and guide students in this process of epistemological change.

There is another dimension of learning to be considered. Although knowledge is personal, the process of constructing knowledge is social; it is mediated and facilitated by interpersonal interaction. As students work together to solve a problem, they negotiate meaning and develop their conceptual understanding through a process of discussion, debate and question and answer (King, 1990; Brown, Collins, & Duguid, 1991). Students of science need to learn this method of intellectual exchange because practicing scientists use the very same process to construct their understanding of experimental observations. Unfortunately, students are isolated from one another in the traditional lecture setting and even in many recitation sections. The *how* and *why* of the power of student-student interaction are explained in Chapters 10 (Cooper, 2005) and 13 (Varma-Nelson & Coppola, 2005) of the Chemist's Guide to Effective Teaching; that power is mobilized in the peer-led Workshop.

Finally, students respond to opportunities to do what the experts in the discipline do. Organic chemists do not spend their time memorizing reactions or rules for aromatic substitution. They do find connections among experimental observations and patterns of organization that have explanatory and predictive power. These opportunities to put knowledge to work and to demonstrate competence in the discipline are exciting and central to the goals of the peer-led Workshop. In contrast, a course that fails to engage students in the language and the authentic activities of organic chemists will also fail to provide the motivation or the structure that are prerequisite to development (Brown, Collins & Duguid, 1989). The result will, indeed, be a "bitter pill" and a killer course.

The challenge for the organic chemistry teacher is to adopt pedagogical methods that make the intellectual goals explicit, help students over the barriers to epistemological change (Hofer 2004) and make new friends for the discipline by providing opportunities for students to discover first-hand the beauty and power of the structure-reactivity paradigm, the intellectual coherence of modern mechanistic organic chemistry, and the creative excitement of putting it all together to propose ways to construct bigger molecules from smaller pieces. Simultaneously, these methods must be consistent with what we know about how students learn.

Several pioneers responded to these challenges and opportunities. In an insightful paper, Katz (1996) reported success with "student directed learning, technique that promotes independence and responsibility in the student." Ege, Coppola and Lawton (1997) laid out the philosophical basis for change and provided specifics about the Structure and Reactivity course at Michigan. Dinan (1995) and Paulson (1999) improved student performance and attitude with collaborative group work. Libby (1995) used a learning cycle approach to help students progress from the concrete operational stage to abstract formal reasoning. Spencer (1999) summarized the basis for student-focused active learning. Peer-led team learning was first implemented in general chemistry in the early '90's (Woodard, Gosser & Weiner, 1993) and adapted to the organic chemistry course by Kampmeier, Varma-Nelson and Wedegaertner in 1995.

PLTL works in organic chemistry because the structure and practice of the Workshop speak directly to the needs of the students. By design, the Workshop and the behavior of the leader provide a supportive environment that encourages students to be active participants in the reciprocal questioning and answering that is central to conceptual learning and doing science. In the process, they learn that "because the book (or the teacher) says so" is not an acceptable defense of an answer. In the interaction with peers, they learn new ways to think about a problem. In the company of friends, they learn to change their minds. Since the Workshop problems demand conclusions and explanations, students learn to rely on experimental observation, knowledge and reasoning to build and defend their answers. They practice constructing, negotiating, evaluating, and defending their understanding; *i.e.*, they practice making up their own minds.

Implementing the Peer-Led Workshop

A decade of experience with the development, implementation, evaluation and dissemination of the PLTL model has been assessed by Gafney in questionnaires, surveys, focus groups, interviews, project reports and on-site observations. In order to ensure gains for their students and leaders, PLTL faculty and staff must pay close attention to several factors (critical components) that are key to success and acceptance of the PLTL Workshop by the department and the institution (Gafney, 2001; Gafney & Varma-Nelson, 2007). In the following sections, we will summarize best practices, some workable modifications and, for contrast, some approaches that have not been successful.

Faculty. Effective implementation of a PLTL Workshop requires knowledge and commitment from the faculty and staff. Successful adopters are deeply involved in the philosophical and practical integration of the Workshop with the lecture course, training the peer leaders and preparing suitable Workshop materials. To provide leadership in these areas, faculty and staff must learn the PLTL model. There is substantial literature summarizing the research and development work of the NSF project team (Gosser, et. al., 2001; Roth, Goldstein & Marcus, 2001; Tien, Roth & Kampmeier, 2002, 2004; Sarquis et al., 2001, Varma-Nelson, Cracolice & Gosser, 2004; Varma-Nelson & Gosser, 2005). Chautauqua faculty development courses on PLTL and local and national workshops provide specific information and useful contacts (www.pltl.org). Experienced practitioners can be valuable mentors and can often suggest several potential solutions to local problems. The project newsletter, *Progressions*, is an on-line resource that publishes reports from PLTL implementers, tips from leaders, evaluations from Gafney, and stimulating essays by the project Director. Most successful adopters made use of several of these sources of PLTL know-how. A recent study noted "simply including a PLTL component in a course without understanding, supporting and reinforcing the conceptual model does not guarantee that students will realize the benefits" (Quitadamo, Brahler & Crouch, 2006). Gafney's studies of less-than-successful implementations led to the same conclusion (Gafney 2004).

Integrating Course and Workshop. The PLTL Workshop is an integral part of the organic chemistry course, constructed by faculty and staff for the benefit of the students and complementary to the text, lectures, homework problems and exams. Although the course instructor may have substantial help from others, the substance and practice of the Workshops cannot be delegated and the Workshop program cannot stand apart from the course. The Workshop needs to be a key component of "the way I teach this course."

Do Workshops replace lecture? The PLTL model preserves the lecture. The lecture sets the pace, provides an expert's view of the subject, models ways of thinking and analyzing, conveys the professor's enthusiasm and authority for the subject and provides an efficient way to communicate course expectations. The purposes of the Workshop are to help students develop and apply conceptual understanding of observations and ideas introduced in the text and lecture. Conversely, the Workshop is not the place or time to introduce new material. The best results are obtained when the students can see direct connections among the Workshop problems, the lectures and the overall goals of the course and when they are assessed on the understanding and problem-solving skills that are developed in the Workshops. In general, we think of Workshops as productive, organized study time; our preference is to replace a recitation session or to add a

Workshop meeting to the lecture course. In some circumstances, faculty have surrendered lecture time to create a space for a Workshop in an unyielding course schedule, without sacrificing the learning gains associated with PLTL (Quitadamo, Brahler & Crouch, 2006; Lewis & Lewis, 2005).

How do the Workshops connect to the course? There is a rhythm to a Workshop course. In week one, the students read text, attend lectures, and work end-of-chapter problems. The Workshop meets in week two to process and apply the ideas from week one. This rhythm helps the organic student keep up with the course. The Workshop is not a comprehensive review of all that happened in the previous week and is not a collection of problems. Instead, the problems typically build on one another to develop a deeper understanding of a core concept; the students fill in the secondary details from the text and the homework problems. There is a story line to a good course in organic chemistry; Workshops help students connect ideas from week to week to build the narrative structure.

Are Workshops mandatory? The maximum integration of the lecture and the Workshop is achieved when all of the students in the course are also in Workshops. On the other hand, resource allocations may limit the number of Workshop places. Faculty have had success by making the Workshop a one-credit addendum for those who are interested, first come-first served (Wamser, 2006). In this case it is essential to make the Workshop problems available to everyone in the lecture course. In either case, it is important that those who are in Workshop attend as assigned. PLTL Workshops are not casual, drop-in and drop-out study groups or tutoring options. Rather, they are regularly scheduled weekly sessions to which students commit for the duration of the course. In general, the Workshop is designed for learning and not for assessment. That said, some faculty members start the Workshop with a short quiz to encourage students to prepare for Workshop. Others may assign some modest credit for participation. When the Workshop is an extra one-credit course, the course grade (pass-fail) may be based on participation.

How are Workshops formed? We recommend that Workshops be formed randomly so that the group of students has a better chance to evolve into a team "from the ground up." (Michaelsen, et al., 2003). In general, students are grouped according to their availability. The isolated female in a male group or *vice versa* is avoided. Teams stay together for the entire term because it takes time for students to build trust in each other. Because the assignments are intellectually challenging, the team should be large enough to ensure diversity of ideas. On the other hand, groups larger than 6-8 are hard to manage and tend to take on the characteristics of recitations (Michaelsen, 2003; Sarquis et.al, 2001). Because of resource restrictions, some faculty have tried Workshops of 15-20 students led by a leader circulating among smaller groups. Gafney observed less interaction among the students in these groups and the learning gains usually seen in PLTL programs were not realized. While two hours is the optimum length for a Workshop, ninety minutes is also adequate if the number and the scope of the problems are sized to the available time. Workshops that are too short or problems that are too long promote answer-giving sessions. The process of setting up a peer-led Workshop is discussed in detail by Roth, Goldstein, and Snyder (2001).

Selecting, Training and Supporting Peer Leaders. A Workshop leader wrote "the PLTL model is a power tool to engage undergraduates by learning actively in a group setting." (Pampena 2005) Following the metaphor, the peer leader is the power source that drives the PLTL motor. An effective leader is competent in pedagogy and content, is aware of the needs of each individual in the group and can guide the transformation from a random group to a productive team. In addition, the peer leader gives practical structure and meaning to an active participatory model of learning. This is a daunting job for an undergraduate student. Even though leaders were once Workshop students, they need a structure that helps them learn how to provide peer leadership. Without leader training, leaders default to the "show and tell" model of teaching and the PLTL motor stalls (Gafney, 2001).

What does a leader do? The leaders meet their Workshop each week. By example, the leaders set the idea of honoring and respecting active participation by all group members. As recently successful learners in the subject matter, in this course and at this institution, leaders are insider guides to success; they are intellectual and social role models. One of their important jobs in the organic chemistry Workshop is to debunk the myths that the subject is straight memorization, impossible to understand, uninteresting and a barrier to professional goals. Leaders facilitate discussion and group problem solving. As described in the discussion of specific problems, the leaders provide direction, advice, and information without giving answers. Surveys of past leaders revealed difficulties with: uninterested students; unprepared students;

dominant students; students who think they learn best in isolation. Peer leaders develop a variety of tactics to keep the group on task, motivate reluctant students and channel the energy of the students into roles that help others. Ultimately, the leader's job is to catalyze the transformation of a group into a team, capable of functioning without a leader. Typically, a leader spends 1.5 - 2 hours per week facilitating a Workshop. Leader training sessions, other preparation for the Workshop and a modest amount of administrative bookkeeping adds up to about 6-8 hours of total commitment each week, comparable to many other on-campus jobs. Some students facilitate two Workshops per week, but that is probably enough for an undergraduate leader.

How are the leaders selected? Undergraduate students who have successfully completed the course and demonstrate good communication and interpersonal skills are recruited to serve as peer leaders. To be successful in this role requires more than content knowledge, so not all successful leaders are "A" students, nor are they necessarily chemistry majors. Leaders must be successful college students, but they are not expected to be experts about organic chemistry. Enthusiasm for the subject, motivation to be a leader, a sense of ownership and a desire to give back to the course are useful predictors of success. Current leaders are well positioned to identify and encourage the next generation of leaders. Some schools invite a selected group of students to an interest meeting and use a formal application and interview process where faculty, staff and experienced leaders review qualifications and suitability. Students can be interviewed in groups in sessions that simulate a Workshop environment.

Can graduate students be peer leaders? Leading a Workshop builds confidence, leadership, communication and teamwork skills and a new appreciation of the diversity of human thought, valuable lessons for any career path. For those students with a developing interest in teaching, the leader training and the Workshop are unparalleled opportunities to study how students learn and to practice a new pedagogy. Our experience with graduate leaders has been very positive when the student recognizes the potential rewards and seeks out the opportunity to be a Workshop leader. Several graduate students have subsequently used their Workshop experiences as a significant component of their applications for faculty positions.

How are leaders compensated? We recommend paying the leaders because it professionalizes the relationship of the leader to the Workshop responsibilities. And, in fact, most leaders are paid. The amount of compensation is scaled to other work on campus (tutors, laboratory assistants). In some cases, leaders are given credit *in lieu* of pay. One interesting variation is to give leaders credit for the first Workshop course because they are learning the PLTL model and pay for subsequent Workshop courses. The question of compensation is ultimately resolved at the local level, according to the campus culture, competing opportunities, and supply and demand (Gafney, 2004).

How are leaders trained and mentored? Most leaders are trained in regular weekly meetings lasting 1-1.5 hours. These meetings take place during the term in which the students are leading their Workshops. Sometimes, leader training is a regular credit-bearing course. In other cases, participating in the leader training is simply one part of the responsibilities of the leaders. In either case, the leader training sessions are not optional for leaders or faculty. When this crucial component is omitted, many of the gains of PLTL Workshops are not realized by the students or the peer leaders. In the absence of explicit models for a new pedagogy, the peer leaders resort to dispensing answers because it is easier than facilitating debate and discussion. Training usually starts with an orientation session before the term begins. This is a time to do an overview of the PLTL Workshop model, to set the tone of faculty, staff and leader teamwork, to address anxieties and concerns of the new leaders, to begin a discussion about the leaders' response to students' needs and differences and to be explicit about the responsibilities of the leaders. While the orientation is necessary, it is not sufficient. There is much to be learned and accomplished in subsequent leader training sessions. Detailed curricula for one-semester training courses have been provided in *A Handbook for Team Leaders* (Roth, Goldstein & Marcus, 2001) and in a recent publication (Tien, Roth & Kampmeier, 2004). The student response to the leader training class is reported by Dreyfuss & Gosser (2006).

Why is a weekly class important? There are usually three parts to each weekly session: debriefing; pedagogy; and chemistry. In turn, these three elements provide opportunities for encouragement, support and feedback, time to learn more about how students learn and how novices and experts approach problems, and time to brush up on content and practice group work in the context of the next Workshop.

The best sessions are very interactive as leaders reflect on their experiences, revisiting pedagogical ideas and discussing how new ideas can be applied to the next Workshop. For example, the kind of leader prompts that were suggested for Workshop 1 would get worked out when the team of leaders practiced the problem. As the semester progresses, the leaders, the students and the Workshops evolve and "issues of the week" change. Interpersonal dynamics are usually important at the beginning. Ways to help students who are struggling with the course are most pertinent after one or two exams. And, the chemistry gets more complex with time, requiring weekly discussion about connections to previous ideas and Workshop problems. The latter is especially important because the students must find the patterns and relationships that organize an otherwise bewildering array of observations.

Who trains the leaders? Ideally, leaders should learn with two different experts whose perspectives are complementary and mutually respected: the course instructor who can clarify content issues and articulate goals for the course and the Workshops; an educational specialist who can help the leaders learn how to build a productive team and teach the content. Both work together to situate the pedagogical ideas in the context of the upcoming Workshop. This being said, there are successful programs in which the faculty member plays both roles. Most of our leaders are new each year in order to make the opportunity available to as many students as possible. However, it is extremely useful to have a few experienced leaders; we have dubbed them Super Leaders. They continue to lead Workshops, but take on new responsibilities as mentors for novice leaders. They can also arrange and monitor Workshops, respond to journals and organize feedback about Workshop problems. Above all, their experience provides a special credibility in the leader training class.

We recommend that the leaders keep a weekly journal reflecting on their experience in the Workshops. Journal entries should be a page or two and take no more than 15-30 minutes to complete. A few simple prompts can direct the leaders to analyze the dynamics of the group, evaluate the Workshop problems, reflect on the progress and needs of individual students or identify concerns about their leadership. The primary value of the journal is to the leaders as they pause to formulate and articulate their thoughts about various aspects of their Workshop. The journals also give faculty and staff unprecedented feedback about the course and the Workshop materials.

Workshop Materials. Because the PLTL Workshop environment is unique, it invites faculty to rethink traditional problems. The best problems focus on big ideas, misconceptions, difficult concepts, connections among ideas, and new problem solving skills. To support these goals, the best problems invite participation and are structured to lead students to new insights. "Drill" problems are appropriate only as warm-up events. Good problems are challenging for most individuals, but are within the reach of a team of students working together. Workshop problems that are too hard, too easy, too long, out of synch with the lecture or irrelevant (i.e., out of synch with the exams) will undercut student support for the Workshop. The general problem of writing Workshop materials is discussed by Strozak and Wedegaertner (2001), and more recently by Gosser (2006).

The Workshop problems set goals and epistemological standards for students. If the problems ask for definitional knowledge, students will learn to define. However, if the problems ask students to apply knowledge, make deductions, solve problems, make connections and explain their reasoning, then students will learn these skills. As illustrated in the examples, well-structured Workshop problems offer a "cognitive apprenticeship" (Collins, Brown & Holum, 1991) in the patterns of thought and analysis that are required for success in organic chemistry. Explicit instructions to build models, brainstorm, map connections, exchange questions and answers, and work in collaborative fashion set expectations for active participation by the team members and remind the leader to move away from center stage. A requirement to "explain your reasoning" provides an excellent opportunity for students to observe and respond to the rich diversity of individual thought patterns and learning styles. Time for reflection after the problem is solved builds metacognitive skills.

Where will I get appropriate problems? Course instructors, in collaboration with experienced leaders, are the best sources of instructional materials because they have insider knowledge about the course. The instructor's favorite problems from old exams are also good starting points. They will need to be revised for Workshop use, but have the advantage of being perfectly relevant. Peer leaders are superb critics and can suggest modifications based on their real-time Workshop experiences. Creating problems for Workshop is a significant challenge, but in the words of a colleague, "it is interesting because it makes me think about the key issues in the course." Collections of Workshop problems for organic chemistry are available (Kampmeier, Wedegaertner & Varma-Nelson, 2001, and Kampmeier, Wamser, Wedegaertner, & Varma-Nelson, 2006). The first edition was written for faculty; each Workshop in the first edition (2001) is accompanied by a gloss that explains the pedagogical ideas behind the problems and offers tips to the leaders for working with the problems.

And, what about answer keys? In general, the Workshop is not about answers, *per se*. Rather, it is about finding, evaluating and defending answers. This is especially clear in organic synthesis problems. Several routes (answers) are possible, but some are better than others. More generally, the process of generating and testing multiple hypotheses is central to the organic chemistry Workshop, just as it is to scientific investigation. In our view, an answer key would short out the PLTL motor. This question is discussed by David Gosser (2000, 2006). Peer leaders also addressed this issue in a skit (Morrison, et. al, 2001).

Logistics. Workshops need regularly scheduled space and time of their own. The place must be conducive to learning, encourage group interaction and be psychologically comfortable for all of the members of the group. A lounge in a residence hall is neutral territory, but a lounge in a fraternity house is not. A cafeteria might work in off hours, but a 24-7 coffee shop is not a good learning environment. Private space works to minimize distractions and to reinforce a sense of togetherness.

Where and when do Workshops meet? The ideal room has space for up to 10 students to move around easily, a round table that brings students face-to-face, moveable chairs, ample board space and Internet access. Workshops meet in conference and seminar rooms, learning centers, cafeterias, laboratories, and lounges. Residence halls are often eager to encourage academic work in their spaces and libraries usually look for ways to get students to come in. Peer leaders often know of good Workshop places that do not belong to the Registrar. Dedicated space is special because it announces that Workshops are special.

When to meet is a multi-dimensional question that involves the availability of Workshop space, the schedules and preferences of the leaders and students and the rhythm of the course. The most general answer is to pick one or two adjacent days for Workshops, find places, schedule several different times and match leader and student preferences to Workshop times.

Institutional Support. Even the Lone Ranger had help (Millar, 2005). Pedagogical change is full of traps and the PLTL adopter needs allies. The guiding principle is to find others on the campus whose goals overlap with those of the adopter and to make common cause. This principle and a range of other institutional issues are discussed in *PLTL: A Guidebook* (Kampmeier and Varma-Nelson, 2001).

Who are my intramural allies? Obvious allies are colleagues, department chairs and Deans who support innovations in the classroom. There may be useful connections to other campus initiatives such as learning communities and Schools of Education. The head of the campus learning center is an invaluable source of advice and support and, in the ideal case, may co-teach the leader training class and even share budget with the PLTL program. This is an especially good example of the strength of alliances that are based on an exchanging knowledge and combining capabilities and resources to create "competitive advantage" (Dryer & Sing, 1998). PLTL students and peer leaders are important opinion makers on the campus and can be powerful forces for change. In one classic interaction, a potential adopter asked the class to choose Workshops or recitations. The response sent the faculty member scrambling for more rooms and leaders because *all* of the students voted for Workshops.

Who are my extramural allies? There is a national PLTL Workshop project (www.pltl.org) and a network of experienced and enthusiastic PLTL faculty, learning specialists and former peer leaders. This network can provide advice, support and professional opportunity for new adopters. There is an informal network of organic chemists, as well (pltlorg@rochester.edu). Local contacts can provide special opportunities; in one case a four-year college provided Workshop leaders for organic chemistry at the neighboring community college. Peer leaders are especially inspired by meeting other peer leaders and finding that they are part of a larger initiative.

What about the time and energy costs? There are real costs to implement a PLTL Workshop program and they translate into a significant activation energy. Fortunately, many of the costs to faculty and staff are first year, start-up costs for organizing Workshops, recruiting and training leaders and assembling Workshop materials. In the steady state, the commitment of time and energy is greater than just giving three lectures a week, but is comparable to programs that offer recitations, office hours and review sessions. The Workshop directly replaces recitation sections. By providing an effective feedback mechanism and by explicitly making students responsible for their own learning, the PLTL Workshop eliminates most of the demand for tutorial reviews.

What are the financial costs? In practice, the actual cost/student/semester is determined by local decisions and practice. If all the Workshop leaders are paid $500/semester and 8 students are assigned to a Workshop, then the primary cost is $62.50/student/semester. Some schools pay less or substitute credit for pay. Other schools do not offer Workshops for every student in the class, thereby reducing the total cost. Some schools hire or charge for help from educational specialists, adding to the total cost. Other schools already have such individuals on the faculty or the staff so that the costs of leader training are covered by other budgets.

Where does the money come from? In most cases, the expenditures for the PLTL Workshops are new costs to the institution. The theoretical answer to this question is to find the parts of the institution that 1) have agenda that overlap with the PLTL goals and 2) have money. In practice, faculty and institutions have been marvelously creative in finding ways to fund PLTL. Local connections and insider information about institutional priorities are most helpful. For example, Deans, Provosts and Presidents often have funds to support teaching initiatives. Some equally successful approaches involve: pre-existing budgets to support tutorial or supplemental instructional programs; institutional programs to establish learning communities or peer-mentor programs; "lab or course fees"; work-study programs; direct alumni support; scholarship funds to support the development of specific groups of students, e.g. women in science, underrepresented minority students; and learning center budgets. Kampmeier (2003) has offered a cost/benefit analysis.

Outcomes

The peer-led team model of active learning is remarkably adaptable and has been successfully implemented in many different college settings. In 2005 - 2006, the PLTL model is in use in organic chemistry courses in 25-30 institutions for approximately 2500 students; each year, more than 100 leaders are learning to facilitate PLTL Workshops. The adopter schools are distributed in roughly equal proportions among two and four-year colleges and comprehensive and research universities. The range of successful implementations supports the assertion that PLTL is "realistically doable" (Goroff, 1998). While the nature of the stumbling blocks vary from campus to campus, imaginative faculty, students, and administrators have found ways to get over or around the barriers. A few PLTL courses are beyond their 10th anniversary and several are past the 5-year mark. In some cases, new faculty members have joined to take over from the original implementers. The model is both robust and durable. On the other hand, the current PLTL courses in organic chemistry are reaching only about 1% of the student population; we are clearly in the "early adopter" stage of the diffusion of innovation (Rogers, 1962).

Impact on Students. From the start, the PLTL project has been lifted up and carried forward by the enthusiastic support of the students and the leaders. Interviews with leaders and reflective journal responses pinpointed three reasons for the student support: the Workshop is a community of learners; students negotiate meaning and refine their conceptual understanding in the Workshops; students acquire expert thinking skills in the weekly Workshops (Tien, Roth, & Kampmeier, 2002). Students usually reserve their time for activities they consider rewarding. In contrast to most recitation sections, attendance at Workshops is high and the grade in the course increases linearly with the number of Workshops attended. The Student Assessment of Learning Gains (SALG) questionnaire asks students to judge how various course components helped their learning. Workshops and Workshop problems tied for first place (4.4/5), and lectures were twelfth (3.2/5), on a scale where 4=agree and 5=strongly agree. A student survey of organic chemistry students at City College showed related reasons for the student enthusiasm (Gonzalez, 2001).

Although the evidence that cooperative learning works is incontrovertible, it seems to be necessary to re-establish the validity in each new domain. Preliminary studies showed that across institutions, teachers and courses (general chemistry and organic chemistry), PLTL students were more successful than their non-PLTL counterparts (Gafney, 2001; www.pltl.org). In a serial study at Rochester, the performance of PLTL Workshop students (1996-1999) was compared to historical data (1992-1994) for students in a traditional organic course with recitation sections led by graduate students (Tien, Roth & Kampmeier, 2002; Lyle & Robinson, 2003). A concerted effort was made to minimize all other variables: lecturer, text, exams, course goals, content and grading. Table 2 compares the two modes of supporting instruction.

Alternate Modes of Supporting Instruction

Characteristic	Course Structure	
	Lecture plus Recitation (1992-94)	Lecture plus Workshop (1996-99)
class size	20-25	6-10
leader	graduate TA	peer leader
instructional mode	transmission	constructivist
student activity	listening	Talking
leader training	TA meeting	weekly class
choice of problems	TA or student	Faculty
total points earned on exams [a]	475	558
% success [a,b]	66	77

    a.   differences are statistically significant, $p < 0.01$.
    b.   % of the enrolled students who earned C or better

Table 2. Alternate Modes of Supporting Instruction

In a study at Portland State University (Wamser, 2006), students in a large lecture course in organic chemistry were offered an optional 1-credit PLTL Workshop. Enrollment in the Workshop remained constant at about 35% of the lecture class over five years and fifteen quarter-courses. Annual surveys (PLTL Student Survey) showed that the students believed that the Workshops helped them do better and improved their problem-solving abilities. The students credited these gains to interactions with their peer leaders and their fellow students. On a 1-5 scale, students agreed or strongly agreed (average 4.5/5) that they would "recommend Workshop courses to other students." The performance of the PLTL Workshop group was compared to the group of students who chose the "lecture only" option. As shown in Table 3, the performance of the PLTL Workshop group exceeded that of the lecture-only control group.

Student Performance in Organic Chemistry

Criterion	Course Structure	
	Lecture only [a]	Lecture and Workshop [b]
% success [c,d]	69	85
% Persistence [d,e]	28	57
ACS exam percentile [f]	72	80

    a.   students who did not enroll in the Workshop section in any of the three quarters
    b.   students who enrolled in the Workshop section in one (or more) of the quarters
    c.   % of enrolled students earning C or better
    d.   differences are significant, $p < 0.01$
    e.   % of students who successfully completed all three quarters in a given year.
    f.   percentile ranking of the average scores of non-PLTL and PLTL groups in the final quarter of organic chemistry.

Table 3. Student Performance in Organic Chemistry

The Portland State results are strikingly similar to the Rochester observations; Workshop students perform better than non-Workshop students. The data are complementary since the Rochester experiment is a serial comparison across years, while the Portland State experiment runs in parallel with students in the same class at the same time. Both experiments controlled for differences in the PLTL and control groups, as judged by SAT or GPA. The persistence data, over three quarter courses, give striking evidence of the impact of gains in percent success in any one quarter. Some faculty members assume that collaborative learning always comes at the expense of content. The strong ACS exam scores show that this is not true at Portland State. Nor is it true elsewhere. The PLTL students at the University of the Pacific ranked at the 75th percentile on the 1994 organic chemistry ACS exam over a five-year period (Wedegaertner, 2005). PLTL was implemented in the organic chemistry courses at Monroe Community College over a five-year period; ACS exam scores improved from below the national norm to the 83rd percentile in 2005 and 2006 (Cullen & Edelbach, 2006).

PLTL Workshops were implemented and tested for impact on the development of critical thinking skills in math and organic chemistry courses at Washington State University (Quitadamo, Brahler & Crouch, 2006). The California Critical Thinking Skills Test (Facione, 1990) was administered pre- and post-course in PLTL and non-PLTL classes. The test results were represented as changes in percentile rankings, based on a national norming sample of 4- year colleges and universities. The PLTL courses, as a group, showed statistically significant gains when compared to the non-PLTL courses. Unfortunately, there was no direct, intra-course comparison of PLTL and non-PLTL students in organic chemistry. Nevertheless, the PLTL organic courses showed an average increase in critical thinking skills of 7 places in percentile rank (68 to 75). These critical thinking gains in the organic chemistry courses are significant and comparable to those observed in courses specifically designed to teach critical thinking skills (Facione, 1990). The study is promising and points to a more nuanced assessment of the nature and magnitude of learning gains in PLTL organic chemistry courses than is provided by total points and percent success data.

Wamser and Stillings also attempted to be more specific by using a Mental Molecular Rotation Test (Wamser and Stillings, 2005) to assess students' ability to visualize three-dimensional organic molecules, testing before and after the chapters on stereochemistry. Males outscored females before instruction. Both PLTL and non-PLTL groups did better after learning stereochemistry, but the male/female difference persisted in both groups after instruction. Different people used different tactics to analyze the MMRT test questions. Because the PLTL Workshop easily accommodates different learning styles, it may be a superior venue to help female students develop 3-D skills. More research of this kind is needed to understand how students learn organic chemistry and, more pointedly, to gain detailed insight into the power of the PLTL Workshop. Opportunities for good research abound (Cracolice & Dening, 2005). In that spirit, a study of the Rochester organic chemistry course showed that student perceptions of peer leader support were a significant determinant of the students' subjective experience *and* objective performance in the course (Black & Deci, 2000). A second study of PLTL classes demonstrated that perceptions of the classroom environment lead to achievement goals and that achievement goals lead to intrinsic motivation and achievement outcomes (Church, Elliot & Gable, 2001).

Although the PLTL Workshop was originally designed to help students in lecture courses, McCreary, Golde and Koeske (2006) successfully implemented peer-led labs in general chemistry at Pittsburgh. Peer-led Workshops in the organic and general chemistry laboratory are also an integral part of the Undergraduate Research Center CASPiE Consortium supported by the NSF. There are no reports of systematic exploration of the PLTL model in the organic laboratory course. In one promising result at Rochester, a notoriously challenging problem of analysis and data interpretation was resolved with dispatch by suspending lab work for one period and turning the students loose to work cooperatively in small groups. The application of PLTL to the lab course is a fruitful area for further research and development. In particular, the PLTL model would seem to be well matched to the spirit and practice of guided inquiry and open-ended project labs (Mohrig, 2007; Cooper & Kerns, 2006).

Impact on Leaders. The distinctive feature of PLTL links the power of peer leadership and active small group learning to the more traditional parts of the organic chemistry course. The faculty, staff and the peer leaders work together to help the students make connections among text, lecture, homework and Workshop problems. The opportunity to collaborate with the faculty and staff defines new mentoring relationships.

The leader is transformed from a customer to a participating, contributing member of the academic community; the change is similar to the experience of students who join research groups. It is no surprise that students compete for peer leader positions and are deeply disappointed when they are not chosen. In their applications for peer leader positions, students tell us that they see other rewards and opportunities as well: to see the subject matter from a new perspective; to review for the MCAT's; to develop leadership and communication skills; to help others and make new friends; to share their enthusiasm for the subject and for learning; to learn more about learning and to test out a potential interest in teaching.

The impact of peer leadership was explored more systematically by surveying former leaders from nine institutions (Gafney & Varma-Nelson, 2006). The majority of the students had been leaders in organic chemistry. They were presented a menu of different activities and asked to "indicate the degree of impact on your learning when you were in college." The highest value was assigned to acting as a peer leader (4.3/5, where 5 = very strong impact and 4 = strong impact). In general, leaders consider peer leadership to have been a formative, influential part of their college education. Roth & Tien (2000) reported the results of extensive interviews with organic chemistry Workshop leaders. This study pointed to the potential of peer leadership to be a component of pre-professional training for future faculty.

Since the leaders report that they acquired a "more complete knowledge and understanding" of chemistry, we administered the ACS exam to groups of Rochester students as they were finishing the one-year organic course at Rochester (Kampmeier, 2006). The groups were made up from students who were invited to apply for peer leader positions and included those who were chosen, as well as a control group who did not apply or were not chosen as leaders. Both groups of students were retested one year later, as the leaders were finishing a full year of peer leadership. The specific composition of non-leader control group changed, but the control students all continued to meet the criteria of being invited to apply, but not serving as peer leaders. No attempt was made to match the groups in any other way; all of the students did whatever students do after a year of organic chemistry. Some took more chemistry and some did not. The results are presented in Table 4.

Percentile ranking on ACS Exam[a] for non-leaders and leaders.

	April 2004	April 2005	April 2005 (MCAT)	April 2006 (MCAT)
Non-leaders percentile	76 (8) [b, c]	37 (12) [c]	60 (6) [c]	53 (8)
Leaders percentile	80 (20)	77 (14)	86 (7)	72 (6)

    a. ACS Exam 2004
    b. the number of students is given in parentheses
    c. only 4 non-leaders took the exam in both 2004 and 2005

Table 4. Percentile ranking on ACS Exam[a] for non-leaders and leaders.

The scores in April 2004 show that the control and the leader groups were well matched (t-test, $p=0.48$) when they finished the organic course. One year later, the ACS Exam ranking of the control students had dropped from well above average to well below average (76 to 37 percentile, $p<0.01$). In contrast, the peer leaders showed an insignificant decrease (80 to 72 percentile, $p=0.45$). The non-leaders recovered somewhat if they studied for the MCAT exam in Spring 2005. Not surprisingly, leaders performed better than the control students, in both non-MCAT and MCAT groups in Spring 2005. More interestingly, the peer leaders retained their knowledge one year after being peer leaders; the performance of the leaders in April 2006 was statistically indistinguishable ($p=0.24$) from their performance when they completed the course in April 2004 or when they completed one year of peer leadership in April 2005. A similar study at Northeastern Illinois tested leaders in September at the start and again in May at the end of a full year of peer leadership in the organic course. The number of peer leaders was small, but they averaged 19 percentile point gains on the 1998 ACS exam (Fraiman, 2005).

Impact on Faculty and Institution. Six post secondary peer cooperative learning programs were reviewed recently and divided into programs that 1) provide out-of-class adjunct support with little change by the course instructor or 2) provide a transformed classroom-learning environment (Arendale, 2004). While PLTL shares some characteristics with the other five peer learning programs reviewed, it is distinguished from them because the faculty members are deeply involved in peer-leader training, preparation of suitable Workshop materials and the philosophical and practical integration of the PLTL Workshop and the lecture course. These three critical components of the PLTL model must be organized by the faculty into a coherent, persuasive presentation of goals, content and practice. PLTL teachers need classroom knowledge about motivation, student development, interpersonal dynamics, and diverse learning styles; content knowledge; and pedagogical content knowledge. The latter refers to knowing how to teach the subject to a diverse group of students and bridges from knowing fundamental ideas and techniques for learning to the implementation of these ideas to teach students and peer leaders. The challenge to develop pedagogical content knowledge is a major opportunity for faculty growth. In practice, the leader training class provides a syllabus for faculty development (Tien, Roth, & Kampmeier, 2004) and colleagues from the learning center often provide the instruction. There has been no systematic study of the impact of PLTL on faculty development, but various interviews and surveys with PLTL faculty reveal that they think and talk about teaching in ways that differ from their colleagues (Gafney, 2005). Clearly, faculty development is a potential outcome of the PLTL model that is ripe for careful study.

The PLTL Workshop can be a catalyst for institutional change and is on its way to becoming a signature for undergraduate education in SEM disciplines at Rochester. Starting from the organic chemistry course in 1995, the model propagated to courses in biology, general chemistry, biochemistry, physics, computer science, mathematics, economics, electrical engineering and physical chemistry. After eleven years of development, fifteen to twenty faculty members, the College office of Learning Assistance Services and approximately 125 trained peer leaders are now mentoring 1500 students per year. The peer leaders played a major role in the early expansion of the program by lobbying faculty to try the model. More recently, a consortium of Workshop faculty has provided support and counsel to new adopters.

The chemistry department at Ohio University showed considerable imagination in their implementation of PLTL. The university was working to establish learning communities for beginning students. Chemistry argued that the PLTL Workshop is a learning community and won institutional support for general and organic chemistry. When faced with difficulty finding suitable space for Workshops, the department bought picnic tables and installed them in the lobby of the building. The success of PLTL in improving student attitude and performance in both general chemistry and organic chemistry (averaging a 15 point change in % success in organic chemistry over a three-year period) made a significant change in the department culture. Department faculty and peer leaders (aka learning community mentors) are new spokespersons for the propagation of the model to other departments, colleges and universities and student mentors are helping in local high schools. Professor Varma-Nelson brought PLTL with her to Northeastern Illinois University. Following her leadership, the model is now firmly in place in organic chemistry, with four faculty members teaching PLTL courses. PLTL has propagated from chemistry to math where it is implemented in both pre-calculus and calculus courses. The campus culture is changing as the expectation of PLTL students and leaders change.

Conclusion

The Peer-Led Team Learning Workshop is exciting because it franchises the undergraduate students to become active participants in the education of one another; it liberates a powerful force for better learning. This force operates in the Workshop when students discover the power and the beauty of the structure-reactivity paradigm by questioning and explaining to one another. It works when the members of the Workshop become a team that shares ideas and comes to agreement about a reaction mechanism or the best path for a multi-step synthesis. And, it operates when the leaders generously share their understanding and enthusiasm for the subject and for learning. That generosity is dazzling; no institution could afford to purchase the eagerness to help others learn, the tolerance for differences, and the support for individual students that the peer leaders bring to the Workshop. The power of the students and leaders is an elemental force for good for higher education. It has already transformed several organic courses, but there remains challenge and opportunity to spare.

Acknowledgement

It is a pleasure to thank Ashley Bennett Golomb for her role in assembling some of the data reported in this article, Brian Coppola, David Gosser and Leo Gafney for stimulating advice and Marguerite Weston for her infinite patience in preparing this manuscript for publication. This work was supported by NSF/DUE awards 9455920, 9972457, 0004159 and 0231349.

Suggested Reading

Gollub, J.P., Bertenthal, M.W., Labov, J.B., & Curtis, P.C. (2002) *Learning and Understanding*, Washington, D.C., National Academy Press, Ch. 6.

Felder, R.M. & Brent, R. (2004) The Intellectual Development of Science and Engineering Students. Part I: Models and Challenges, Part 2: Teaching to Promote Growth, *Journal of Engineering Education,* 269-291.

Seymour, E. (2001) Tracking the Progress of Change in US Undergraduate Education in Science, Mathematics, Engineering, and Technology. In *Issues and Trends*, Stephen Norris, ed., New York, John Wiley & Sons, Inc.

References

Arendale, D.R. (2004). Pathways of persistence: A review of postsecondary cooperative learning programs. In Duranczyk, I.M., Higbee, J.L., Lundell, D.B., (Eds.), *Best practices for access and retention in higher education.* Minneapolis, MN: Center for Research on Developmental Education and Urban Literacy, General College, University of Minnesota. Retrieved Mar. 23, 2006 from http://www.gen.umn.edu/research/crdeul/monographs.htm.

Belenky, M.F., Clinchy, B.M., Goldberger, N.R., Tarule, J.M., (1986). *Women's ways of knowing: the development of self, voice, and mind*, New York: Basic Books.

Bhattacharya, G. (2004). *A recovering organic chemist's attempts at self-realization: how students learn to solve organic synthesis problems* (Doctoral Dissertation, Purdue University, 2004).

Black, A.E., Deci, E.L., (2000). The effects of instructor's autonomy support and students' autonomous motivation on learning organic chemistry: A self-determination theory perspective. *Science Education*, 84, 740-756.

Breslow, R. (1997). *Chemistry today and tomorrow*. Sudbury, MA: Jones & Bartlett.

Brown, J.S., Collins, A., Duguid, P. (1989). Situated cognition and the culture of learning. *Educational Researcher* 18, 32-42.

Carpenter, S.R., McMillan, T. (2003). Incorporation of a cooperative learning technique in organic chemistry. *Journal of Chemical Education* 80, 330-332.

Church, M.A., Elliot, A.J., Gable, S.L. (2001). Perceptions of classroom environment, achievement goals, and achievement outcomes. *Journal of Educational Psychology* 93, 43-54.

Cullen, J., Edelbach, B.(2006). Private communication.

Collins, A., Brown, J.S., Holum, A., (1991). Cognitive apprenticeship: making thinking visible. *American Education*, Winter, 6-11, 38-46.

Cooper, M.M. (2005). An introduction to small-group learning. In Pienta, N.J., Cooper, M.M., & Greenbowe, T.J., (Eds). *Chemists' guide to effective teaching*, Vol.1. Upper Saddle River, NJ: Pearson Prentice Hall.

Cooper, M.M., Kerns, T.S. (2006). Changing the laboratory: effects of a laboratory course on students' attitudes and perceptions. *Journal of Chemical Education*, 83, 1356-1361.

Cracolice, M.S., Dening, J.C. (2005). Measuring the effects of peer-led team learning. *The Workshop project newsletter, Progressions: peer-led team learning.* 6(2), 3-4. Retrieved June 12, 2006 from http://www.sci.ccny.cuny.edu/~chemwksp/newsletter.html.

Dinan, F.J., Frydrychowski, V.A. (1995). A team learning method for organic chemistry. *Journal of Chemical Education* 72, 429-431.

Dougherty, R.C. (1997). Grade/study contracts, enhanced communication, cooperative learning, and student performance in undergraduate organic chemistry. *Journal of Chemical Education* 74, 722-726.

Dreyfus, A.E., Gosser, D.K. (2006). In their own words: learning to be a peer leader. In Lundell, D.B. Highbee, J.L., Duranczyk, I.M., Goff, E.(Eds). Student standpoints about access programs in higher education. Minneapolis, MN: Center for Research on Developmental Education and Urban Literacy, General College, University of Minnesota, 143-157. Retrieved June 12, 2006, from http://www.gen.umn.edu/research/crdeul/docs/monograph/6.pdf.

Dryer, J.H., Sing, H. (1998). The relational view: cooperative strategy and sources of interorganizational competitive advantage. *Academy of Management Review* 23, 660.

Ege, S.N., Coppola, B.P., Lawton, R.G. (1997). The University of Michigan undergraduate chemistry curriculum 1. Philosophy, curriculum and the nature of change. *Journal of Chemical Education* 74, 74-83.

Emerson, D.W. (1975). Teaching organic chemistry by a modified Keller plan. *Journal of Chemical Education* 52, 228-229.

Facione, P.A. (1990). The California critical thinking skills test-college level. Technical report #1. Experimental validation and content validity. Millbrae, CA: Insight Assessment. Retrieved Feb. 15, 2006, from http://www.insightassessment.com/pdf_files/TECH1.pdf.

Fraiman, A. (2005). Unpublished results.

Gafney, L. (2001). Workshop evaluation. In D.K. Gosser, M.S. Cracolice, J.A. Kampmeier, V. Roth, V.S. Strozak, & P. Varma-Nelson (Eds.), *Peer-led team learning: A guidebook.* Upper Saddle River, NJ: Prentice Hall.

Gafney, L. (2004). Finding support for peer leaders. *The workshop project newsletter. Progressions: peer-led team learning.* 5(2), 1. Retrieved Jan. 30, 2006 from http://www.sci.ccny.cuny.edu/~chemwksp/newsletter.html.

Gafney, L. (2004). What if a citical component is missing? Reviewing the PLTL model. *The Workshop project newsletter. Progressions: peer-led team learning.* 5(4), 1. Retrieved June 12, 2006 from http://www.sci.ccny.cuny.edu/~chemwksp/newsletter.html.

Gafney, L., Varma-Nelson, P. (2006). Peer-led team learning: a study of former workshop leaders. *Journal of Chemical Education*, 84, 535-539. See also: What happens next? A followup study of Workshop leaders at St. Xavier University. *The Workshop project newsletter. Progressions: peer-led team learning.* 3(2), 1. Retrieved Jan. 30, 2006, from http://www.sci.ccny.cuny.edu/~chemwksp/newsletter.html.

Gafney, L., Varma-Nelson, P. (2008). *Peer-led Team Learning: Implementation, Dissemination, and Institutionalization of a College-level Educational Initiative.* Dordrecht Springer. Manuscript in press.

Gonzalez, C. (2001). Positive changes through workshops seen in organic chemistry at CCNY. *The Workshop project newsletter. Progressions: peer-led team learning,* 3(1), 11-12. Retrieved Jan. 30, 2006, from http://www.sci.ccny.cuny.edu/~chemwksp/newsletter.html.

Goroff, N. (1998) *Report on "Workshop Chemistry".* Retrieved Mar. 21, 2006, from The Chemical Educator Web site: http://chemeducator.org/papers/0003001/31nsg897.pdf.

Gosser, D.K. (2000). Where do answers come from? *The Workshop project newsletter. Progressions: peer-led team learning.* 1(3), 2. Retrieved Jan. 30, 2006, from http://www.sci.ccny.cuny.edu/~chemwksp/newsletter.html.

Gosser, D.K. (2006). Peer-led team learning in general chemistry: scientific discovery and learning. In Pienta, N.K., Cooper, M.M., Greenbowe, T.J. *Chemists' guide to effective teaching.* Upper Saddle River, NJ: Pearson Prentice Hall.

Gosser, D. K., Roth, V., Gafney, L., Kampmeier, J.A., Strozac, V., Varma-Nelson, P., Radel, S., & Weiner, M. (1996). *Workshop Chemistry: Overcoming the Barriers to Student Success.* Retrieved Mar. 21, 2006, from The Chemical Educator Web site: http://chemeducator.org/papers/0001001/11gos897.pdf.

Gosser, D.K., (2001). The Peer-led team learning Workshop. In Gosser, D.K., Cracolice, M.S., Kampmeier, J.A., Roth, V., Strozak, V.S., & Varma-Nelson, P. (Eds.), *Peer-led team learning: a guidebook.* Upper Saddle River, NJ: Pearson Prentice Hall.

Gosser, D.K., Cracolice, M.S., Kampmeier, J.A., Roth, V., Strozak, V.S., & Varma-Nelson, P. (Eds.) (2001), *Peer-led team learning: a guidebook.* Upper Saddle River, NJ: Pearson Prentice Hall.

Hofer, B.K. (2004). Exploring the dimensions of personal epistemology in differing classroom contexts: students' interpretation during the first year of college. *Contemporary Education Psychology* 29, 129-163.

Huddle, P.A. (2000). A poster session in organic chemistry that markedly enhanced student learning. *Journal of Chemical Education* 77, 1154-1157.

Kampmeier, J.A., Wedegaertner, D.K., Varma-Nelson, P. (2001). *Peer-led team learning: organic chemistry.* Upper Saddle River, NJ: Pearson Prentice Hall.

Kampmeier, J. A., Varma-Nelson, P. (2001). Institutionalizing the Workshps. In Gosser, D. K., Cracolice, M.S., Kampmeier, J.A., Roth, V., Strozak, V.S., & Varma-Nelson, P. (Eds.), *Peer-led team learning: a guidebook.* Upper Saddle River, NJ: Pearson Prentice Hall.

Kampmeier, J.A. (2003). Compared to what? The cost-benefit analysis of PLTL. *The Workshop project newsletter. Progressions: Peer-led team learning,* 4(3,4), 1. Retrieved Jan. 30, 2006. from http://www.sci.ccny.cuny.edu/~chemwksp/newsletter.html.

Kampmeier, J.A. (2006). Unpublished results.

Kampmeier J. A., Wamser, C.C., Wedegaertner, D.K., Varma-Nelson, P., (2006). *Peer-led team learning: organic chemistry,* 2nd ed. (student edition) Upper Saddle River, NJ: Pearson Prentice Hall.

Katz, M. (1996). Teaching organic chemistry via student-directed learning. *Journal of Chemical Education* 73, 440-445.

King, A. (1990). Enhancing peer interaction and learning in the classroom through reciprocal questioning. *American Educational Research Journal* 27, 664-687.

Lewis, S.E., Lewis, J.E. Departing from lectures: an evaluation of a peer-led guided inquiry alternative. *Journal of Chemical Education* 82, 135-139.

Libby, R.D. (1995). Piaget and organic chemistry. *Journal of Chemical Education* 72, 626-631.

Lyle, K.M., Robinson, W.R. (2003). A statistical evaluation: peer-led team learning in an organic chemistry course. *Journal of Chemical Education* 80, 132-134.

McCreary, C.L., Golde, M.F., Koeske, R. (2006). Peer instruction in the general chemistry laboratory: Assessment of Student Learning. *Journal of Chemical Education* 83, 804-810.

Micari, M. Streitwieser, Light, G. (2006). Undergraduates leading undergraduates: peer facilitation in a science workshop program. *Innovative Higher Education* 30, 269-288.

Michaelsen, L. K, Knight, A.B., & Fink, L. D. (2002). *Team-based learning: a transformative use of small groups.* Westport, CT: Praeger Publishers.

Millar, S., (2005). Personal communication.

Mohrig, J.R., Hammond, C.N., Colby, D.A., (2007). On the successful use of inquiry-driven experiments in the organic chemistry laboratory. *Journal of Chemical Education* 84, 992-998.

Morrison, O., Boehmler, D., Yusufova, E., Hughes, S., Tinney, S., Edwards, C, Hoying, S., (2001). The answer key. *The workshop project newsletter. Progressions: peer-led team learning,* 2(4), 9-11. Retrieved Jan. 30, 2006, from http://www.sci.ccny.cuny.edu/~chemwksp/newsletter.html. Pampena, C., (2005). Personal communication.

Paulson, D.R. (1999). Active learning and cooperative learning in the organic chemistry lecture class. *Journal of Chemical Education* 76, 1136-1140.

Perry, W.G. (1970) *Forms of intellectual development of science and engineering students in the college years: a scheme.* San Francisco, CA: Jossey-Bass.

Pienta, N.J., Cooper, M.M., Greenbowe, T.J. (Eds.) *Chemists' guide to effective teaching*, Vol.1. Upper Saddle River, NJ: Pearson Prentice Hall.

Quitadamo, I.J., Brahler, C.J., Crouch, G.J. (2006). Evaluating the effect of peer-led team learning on critical thinking skills performance in undergraduate science and mathematics. *Journal of Research in Science Teaching*, submitted for publication.

Rogers, E.M., (1962). *The diffusion of innovations.* New York: The Free Press.

Roth, V., Tien, L. (2000). The impact of the PLTL experience on Workshop leaders: An investigation. *The Workshop project newsletter. Progressions: Peer-led team learning,* 1(3), 1. Retrieved Jan. 30, 2006, from
http://www.sci.ccny.cuny.edu/~chemwksp/newsletter.html.

Roth, V., Goldstein, E., & Marcus, G. (2001). *Peer-led team learning: a handbook for team leaders.* Upper Saddle River, NJ: Pearson Prentice Hall.

Roth, V., Cracolice, M.S., Goldstein, E., Snyder, V. (2001). Workshop leader training. In Gosser, D. K., Cracolice, M.S., Kampmeier, J.A., Roth, V., Strozak, V.S., & Varma-Nelson, P. (Eds.), *Peer-led team learning: a guidebook.* Upper Saddle River, NJ: Pearson Prentice Hall.

SALG. Retrieved Feb. 3, 2006, from http://mc2.cchem.berkeley.edu/Evaluation/class_ev.html.

Sarquis, J. L., Dixon, L. J., Gosser, D. K., Kampmeier, J. A., Roth, V., Strozak, V. S., & Varma-Nelson, P. (2001). The Workshop project: Peer-led team learning in chemistry. In J. E. Miller, J. E. Groccia, & M. Miller (Eds.), *Student-assisted teaching: a guide to faculty-student teamwork,* Boston, MA: Anker Publishing Company 150–155.

Schoenfield, A. H. (1985). Mathematical problem solving. New York: Academic Press.

Seveniar, J.P., O'Connor, S.E., Nazery, M. (1989). A nontraditional organic course. *Journal of College Science Teaching,* 236-239.

Spencer, J.N., New directions in teaching chemistry: a philosophical and pedagogical basis. *Journal of Chemical Education* 76, 566-569.

Strozak, V. S.; Wedegaertner, D. K. (2001). Writing Workshop Materials. In Gosser, D.K., Cracolice, M.S., Kampmeier, J.A., Roth, V., Strozak , V.S., & Varma-Nelson, P. (Eds.) *Peer-led team learning: a guidebook.* Upper Saddle River, NJ: Pearson Prentice Hall.

Tenney, A., Houck, B. (2004). Learning about leadership; team learning's effect on peer leaders. *Journal of College Science Teaching,* 25-29.

Tien, L.T., Roth, V., Kampmeier, J.A., (2002). Implementation of a peer-led team learning instructional approach in an undergraduate organic chemistry course. *Journal of Research in Science Teaching* 39, 606-632.

Tien, L.T., Roth, V., Kampmeier, J.A. (2004). A course to prepare peer leaders to implement a student-assisted learning method. *Journal of Chemical Education* 81, 1313-1321.

Treisman, U., Emerging Scholars Program. Retrieved January 9, 2006, from http://cns.utexas.edu/esp/.

Varma-Nelson, P., Coppola, B.P. (2005). Team Learning. In Pienta, N.J., Cooper, M.M., & Greenbowe, T.J., (Eds.), *Chemists' guide to effective teaching.* Vol.1. Upper Saddle River, N.J.: Pearson Prentice Hall.

Varma-Nelson, P., Cracolice, M.S., Gosser, D.K., (2004). Peer-led team learning: a student-faculty partnership for transforming the learning environment. In *Invention and impact: building in undergraduate science, technology, engineering, and mathematics education.* Retrieved Jan. 30, 2006, from http://www.aaas.org/publications/books_reports/CCLI/.

Varma-Nelson, P., Gosser, D.K., (2005). Dissemination of peer-led team learning (PLTL) and formation of a national network: embracing a common pedagogy. In Ouellett, M., (Ed.), *Teaching inclusively: Diversity and Faculty Development.* Stillwater, OK: New Forums Press.

Vikin, J. (1971). A tutorial approach to organic chemistry. *Journal of Chemical Education* 48, 614-615.

Wamser, C.C. (2006). Peer-led team learning (PLTL) in organic chemistry: Effects on student performance, success and persistence in the course, *Journal of Chemical Education* 83, 1562-1566.

Wamser, C.C., Stillings, N.A. (2005). Private communication.

Wedegaertner, D.K. (2005). Private communication.

Woods, D.R. (1987). Developing critical thinking and problem solving abilities. Stice, M.E. (Ed.), *New directions for teaching and learning,* No. 30. San Francisco, CA: Jossey Bass.

Woodward, A.D., Gosser, D.K., Weiner, M. (1993). Problem-solving Workshops in general chemistry. *Journal of Chemical Education* 70, 651.

10

Practical Issues on the Development, Implementation, and Assessment of a Fully Integrated Laboratory-Lecture Teaching Environment

Maria T. Oliver-Hoyo
Department of Chemistry
North Carolina State University

Abstract

This chapter presents the key features of the Student-Centered Activities for Large Enrollment Undergraduate Programs project, SCALE-UP, and a summary of the steps taken in developing, implementing, and assessing SCALE-UP Chemistry. The interlocking assets discussed in this chapter include physical facilities, activity-based curriculum, technological resources, and classroom management techniques. Even though these have been developed specifically for the SCALE-UP project they may be adapted and modified for a variety of settings. The thought process and practical issues are included in hopes that our experience helps others in their educational efforts.

Biography

Dr. Maria T. Oliver-Hoyo graduated in 1981 with a B.S in Chemistry from the University of Puerto Rico, Rio Piedras. She received a NSF Minority Fellowship to pursue graduate studies at Georgetown University (M.S. 1984) and an exciting excursion into the field of Forensic Sciences at George Washington University. As a military wife, moving from place to place was the norm, and it was not until the mid 90's that she contemplated going back to school. She completed a Ph.D. in Chemistry with the dissertation in Chemical Education at Drexel University in 1999. Currently she is an Associate Professor of Chemistry at North Carolina State University. She has developed a unique graduate program in chemical education that targets the design, development, and assessment of resources for chemistry instruction with a major emphasis on accessibility as her 2004 NSF CAREER Award for "Development and Evaluation of Active, Cooperative, Disability-Sensitive Pedagogies for Chemistry" attests. She has been responsible for the development and implementation of the Student-Centered Activities for Large Enrollment Undergraduate Programs chemistry curriculum at NC State University in Raleigh, NC.

Introduction

Have you ever thought your lecture was crystal clear and felt the students understood everything you said only to find out later they couldn't do a simple problem related to that particular topic?

Have you ever speculated what could be missing when students cannot apply concepts discussed in class to new situations even though you worked out multiple examples on a regular bases?

Have you ever been amazed at how your students think the responsibility for their learning is yours and yours alone?

Have you ever wanted to promote active learning, teamwork, communication and writing skills but thought it would not be possible to responsibly "cover" content material at the same time?

If the answer to any of these questions is "yes" I invite you to read further into this chapter. The Student-Centered Activities for Large Enrollment Undergraduate Programs format, SCALE-UP, has provided me with tools to attain some answers.

The mediocre teacher tells.   *Learning is not attained by chance.*
The good teacher explains.   *It must be sought for with ardor.*
The superior teacher demonstrates.   *It must be attended to with diligence.*
The great teacher inspires.
        William A. Ward   *Abigail Adams*

I share these two quotes with my students every semester during the first day of classes. These quotes summarize my teaching philosophy, which the SCALE-UP format has allowed me to live by. Numerous studies have shown the benefits and flaws of lecture (Birk, 1993; Tobias, 1992; MacGregor, 2000) and laboratory environments (Domin, 1999; Lazarowitz and Tamir, 1994; Pickering, 1993) not to mention reports on the state of instruction in our schools and colleges (Education Commission, 1995; Meador, 1994; Fortenberry 2000; Boyer Commission, 1998). SCALE-UP Chemistry embodies the directions suggested by these studies and emphasizes practices proven to work in small educational settings but implements them in large enrollment classes of up to 99 students. These practices include group work, inquiry-guided and activity-based instruction with the tenet that the responsibility of learning must be shifted from the instructor to the student and the role of the instructor is one of facilitator and instigator of learning rather then conveyor of information. In addition, there is a focus on the effective use of technology and the promotion of scientific skills including communication skills. It is not my intention to provide in this chapter the body of research that validates the use of these pedagogical practices but to discuss our practical approach at putting these to work in large enrollment classrooms.

The development and implementation of the SCALE-UP Chemistry project has goals that are probably shared by many chemical educators. These include:

- To improve graphical skills including representation and interpretation of graphs.

- To use technology for information acquisition, data handling, and class management.

- To develop teamwork and communication skills.

- To improve student understanding of chemical phenomena by promoting the use of higher order cognitive skills.

- To increase the interest of students towards chemistry and/or decrease the apprehensions our students have toward the discipline.

Four interlocking elements have played an important role in addressing these goals: physical facilities, curriculum development, technological resources, and classroom management techniques. These elements are guided by the overarching theme of activity-driven, inquiry-based instruction. The important features of each element will be highlighted in hopes that interested readers may adopt and/or modify these to fulfill their needs at their particular institutions.

Physical Facilities

To promote in-class interactions students sit in round tables of nine students per table and work in groups of three. Instructor and assistants constantly monitor group conversations and discussions. Two screens at opposite ends of the room project all materials from the instructor station, which is equipped with both a computer and a document camera. White boards surround the room where students write answers or results that are shared with the class as a whole. The SCALE-UP pilot room was a standard room that originally held 55 desks and was converted to a six table, 54-students setting. Our newest facility holds 11 tables and 99 students. Figure 1 shows snapshots of these facilities at North Carolina State University.

Figure 1. SCALE-UP classrooms at NC State University

A variety of SCALE-UP classroom designs currently used across the country can be found at http://scaleup.ncsu.edu.

Due to the demand of the large enrollment SCALE-UP room, SCALE-UP Chemistry has started using a different setting to promote the SCALE-UP format. Two traditional laboratories separated by an instrument room have been outfitted with projectors and screens, document camera and instructor laptop, and a microphone and speaker system to simulate the SCALE-UP environment but in a traditional laboratory setting. Windows at each side of the instrument room allow the instructor to see what goes on in the laboratories. Students may still work in groups of three with inquiry-guided and activity-based instruction been promoted. While one instructor and one assistant may handle a class of 99 students in the SCALE-UP room, this setting requires one assistant at each laboratory plus the instructor that may float between labs or facilitate the class from the instrument room located in the middle of both laboratories. This is just an example of how facilities are used to work for us. Different settings have been used to promote the SCALE-UP format.

Curriculum Development

Due to the activity-driven nature of the SCALE-UP Chemistry format and its inquiry-guided approach, the instructional materials developed provide the instructor with a series of tools to help him/her facilitate activities in class. The heart of the curriculum lies in the activity table section, which provide the instructor with suggested instructional steps and rationale for following those steps. One hundred activities have been developed for the general chemistry curriculum and can be found at http://scaleup.ncsu.edu. Demonstrations, wet-chemistry laboratories, problem worksheets, and simulations/animations have all been sources used to create these activities. The template for these activities is shown in Figure 2 and a specific example of a conceptual activity is given in Figure 3.

Activity Template

TITLE

    Time: *time suggested for completing activity*
    Topic: *topics covered by activity*
    Type: *probe or investigation*
    Level: *introductory, intermediate, or advanced*
    Overview: *statement outlining the activity*
    Materials and Equipment: *items needed to complete the activity*
    Objective(s): *statements identifying the intended learning outcomes*
    Misconceptions: *common misunderstandings that conflict with scientific theory*
    Other Student Difficulties: *areas that should be given special attention*
    Prerequisites: *concepts or material needed to complete the activity*

    Activity Table   *outlines every step of the activity for instructors*

Task	Reason	Notes
Action to be taken by students or instructors	*Why the action is important*	*Helpful information for instructors*

    Related Activities: *activities that incorporate related concepts*
    References: *the resources used in developing the activity*
    Supplementary Material: *Discussion of concepts, explanation of demos and procedures*

Figure 2. Activity Template

A Conceptual Activity

Counting Equilibrium
Time: 30 minutes
Topic: Equilibrium and introduction to Le Châtelier's Principle
Type: Probe
Level: Introductory
Overview: Students will determine when a "penny reaction" reaches equilibrium and what happens when that equilibrium is disturbed.
Equipment and Materials: 30 pennies per group
Objective(s):

    Students will observe how a reaction comes to equilibrium.
    Students will be able to define/describe equilibrium.
    Students will construct graphs of concentration vs. time.
    Students will be able to define k_f and k_r for a reaction.
    Students will write equilibrium constant expressions.
    Students will be able to determine the effect of a perturbation on the reaction. **Misconceptions:** Equilibrium is in effect when [reactants] = [products].
Other Student Difficulties: Reading and interpreting equilibrium graphs.
Prerequisites: chemical equations

Activity Table

Task	Reason	Notes
Demonstrate how the simulation will work at t = 0, t = 1 min, and t = 2 min.	To clear up any confusion about the procedure.	Use this reaction $A \underset{\frac{1}{4}\,\text{min}^{-1}}{\overset{\frac{1}{3}\,\text{min}^{-1}}{\rightleftharpoons}} B$

Give each group 24 pennies and the reaction with $k_{forward}$ and $k_{reverse}$.	To spark interest of the students.	$A \underset{\frac{1}{4}\ min^{-1}}{\overset{\frac{1}{2}\ min^{-1}}{\Leftrightarrow}} B$
Ask students to collect data on the reaction at 1-minute intervals starting at zero.	To have students determine how the k_f and k_r work in the reaction.	Students will probably stop when they see the numbers don't change anymore.
Ask students when did they stop collecting data and why.	To define equilibrium as a dynamic process.	The reaction reaches equilibrium after 3 minutes.
Have students graph concentration of A and B vs time on the same plot.	To visualize and explain what is happening to the [ ]'s of reactants and products.	See data and plot in Supplementary Material.
Discuss what k_f and k_r mean.	To define k_f and k_r.	
Introduce the equilibrium constant, K_c.	To define the equilibrium constant.	$K_c = k_f / k_r$ = [products]/[reactants]
Give each group 6 more pennies. Ask them what happens when you add these to the reaction at equilibrium.	To illustrate the shift and how concentrations change.	
Ask students how long it took to reestablish equilibrium.	To determine the effect of a perturbation.	It takes 3 minutes. See data in Supplementary Material.
Have students graph this second data set.	To practice graphing and observe changes graphically.	
Have students determine whether the reaction "shifted" to the left or right.	To have them interpret the graphical data.	This is a prelude to teaching Le Châtelier's Principle.
Ask students to calculate K_c for comparison.	To show that K_c remains the same.	

Related Activities: Shifting Reactions
References: Harrison, John A.; Buckley, Paul D. *J. Chem. Educ.* **2000**, *77*, 1013-1014.

Discussion and Supplementary Material:

Many students have a difficult time understanding dynamic equilibrium in a conceptual manner. This probe will allow students to visualize what goes on in an equilibrium reaction. Use the following reaction:

$$A \underset{\frac{1}{4}\ min^{-1}}{\overset{\frac{1}{2}\ min^{-1}}{\Leftrightarrow}} B$$

Start with 24 pennies representing reactant A at time zero. ½ of reactant A, 12 pennies, is lost in the forward reaction in the first minute. During the second minute ½ of A and ¼ of B, 6 and 3 respectively, are lost to the opposite sides leaving 9 A and 15 B (sum must always equal 24). During the next minute values must be rounded down because pennies cannot be divided. See the reference for discussion of this issue. After three minutes the reaction reaches equilibrium. The data and graph of concentration vs. time are provided below.

Table 1. Concentration Data.

Time	[A]	[B]
0	24	0
1	12	12
2	9	15
3	8	16
4	8	16
5	8	16

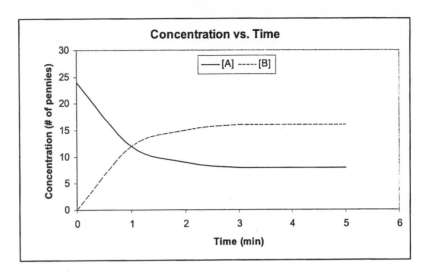

Table 2. Concentration Data before and after Perturbation.

Time	[A]	[B]
0	24	0
1	12	12
2	9	15
3	8	16
4	8	16
5	8	16
6	14	16
7	11	19
8	9	21
9	10	20
10	10	20
11	10	20

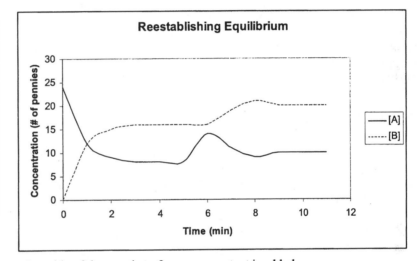

There is an overall shift to the product side of the reaction after more reactant is added.

Optional (Collaborative Group)

You may assign groups with different starting number of pennies and different values for k_f and k_r. Let them compare their results.

Figure 3. A Conceptual Activity

The development of these activities was a sequential process. We first developed and tested just 6 activities during one semester. From that experience we worked on additional ones to facilitate one activity per class period the following semester. Testing these activities was crucial in teaching us how to process the information, how to dissect it in reasonable chunks conducive of inquiry-guided approach, and how to facilitate the suggested steps. It was not until we felt comfortable with the strategies and pedagogical approach that we developed and incorporated additional activities to the point now where activities are the driving force of the time spent in class.

Instructional materials need not to be developed from scratch since there are a number of resources available. It is a matter of identifying these materials and modifying them to fit the content, teaching strategies and methodologies you want to incorporate. It must be pointed out that the methodology in using these activities is crucial. The SCALE-UP activities are designed to promote inquiry-guided instruction and not to be used as "verification" activities for the material "covered" in lecture. These SCALE-UP Chemistry activities are the main driving force of class time and they may complement any general chemistry textbook.

Technological Resources

Our SCALE-UP classrooms are equipped with computers and software as is the trend in laboratory settings nowadays. How we use these make the difference since the timing of each SCALE-UP Chemistry class is crucial to accomplish each day's goals. Certain tools help us keep students on task. We depend on a course management system to post detailed agendas and instructional materials for the day. We use an electronic homework system in class to submit group or individual work. This electronic system also allows us to monitor individual performance in homework. Access to computers allows the incorporation of simulations and animations into our activities as well as the use of the Internet for instructional Websites. Graphing skills can be promoted during activities in class using appropriate software. We use technological resources that permit us to manage these large enrollment sections in an effective way while demanding only a reasonable period of time.

Advanced technologies are not necessary but can make the management aspect easier especially for large enrollment classes. For example, a remote desktop control system allows the instructor to monitor and control all computers in the room. This system offers the instructor options such as projecting a particular screen to all others, distributing information to student computers, and even locking students out so that they can't wonder around cyberspace! Even though advanced technologies are nice to have, low-tech tools are even more important. For example, a simple digital clock projected on the screen remind students of the time left to work on a particular task keeping students on task. Round tables promote communication among students while whiteboards allow all students to discuss results from remote tables.

Classroom Management Techniques

A typical SCALE-UP Chemistry class may appear to the visitor as a chaotic environment. However, if the visitor happens to be an educator and he/she sits for a little while observing closely, the educator would soon realize that the apparent chaos is an amazing web of intricately connected techniques that work synergistically to manage effectively classes of up to 99 students. The common *modus operandi* involves doing hands-on wet activities, running and discussing simulations and animations, working individually and in groups to perform a demonstration or solve assigned problems, and constructing and debating ideas. Some of the management techniques developed for the SCALE-UP format have proven to be crucial for its success and they can be easily adapted to other formats of instruction.

The foundation of the classroom management techniques developed for the SCALE-UP format is capitalizing on students' learning as identified by Johnson, Johnson, and Smith (1991). These techniques include:
- Individual accountability
    i) *Reading prior to coming to class* – We all have experienced frustration as our students defy practicing their reading skills. Electronic homework systems provide a means to "motivate" students in doing so. For each class period there is an assignment due which consists of one-fourth reading material questions and three-quarters challenging questions from material already facilitated in class. The reading questions are very simple and straightforward, easy points for those who take the time to read the assigned pages. However, if reading is consistently neglected, the homework grade suffers considerably. In addition, these electronic systems allow the instructor to check, prior to coming to class, how the class as a whole has done in each question or how individuals have performed the assignment. The instructor can easily with a glance at the scores, identify those students who have failed the reading material questions. Measures taken may range from just pointing out to these students that their performance is been monitored to not giving these students credit for work done in class that day. These electronic homework systems allow us to monitor "individually" classes of large enrollment in a relatively fast and easy way.

    ii) *Individual submission of worksheets, quizzes, and exams* – All testing materials are performed individually. In addition, class work such as worksheets or problems may be collected individually or per group. Hands-on activities may be partition into individual and group tasks where the group performance or result would depend on individual tasks. This puts the responsibility of learning on individuals first.

    iii) *Roll of the dice* – More involved assignments usually consist of paragraphs written on reflective journals. It is impossible to grade such assignments for 99 students on a regular basis. The "roll of the dice" technique provides a solution by making every student responsible but only a handful accountable. The way it works is that the instructor rolls a die and the table that matches the lucky number hands in their journal answers. The instructor may roll the die as many times as he/she wants papers to collect. This portion of the homework grade is small, however, students quickly come to realize that if their number gets called once during the semester, that single assignment counts as the entire journal grade. If their lucky table gets called multiple times during the semester a particular assignment is not going to have that much weight. Since this is a matter of luck students quickly realize that each journal assignment is as important as any other.

- Positive interdependence
  - i) *Remuneration of group effort* – Group members receive extra bonus points on exams when the average of the individual exams in the group is above a certain minimum (usually 75/100). In SCALE-UP Chemistry our groups consist of three students and this technique have proven effective with highly structured cooperative groups. One criterion in our grouping is the results from a pre-test which measures basic content knowledge. Each group would consist of a high, an average and a low performance student. We have observed that the high performance student would start to pay attention to the other students because 100 points for them is not good enough if 105 points are available. In doing so, the opportunity to teach others and, therefore, to understand the material better becomes available. On the other hand, the lower performance student who consistently is 10 points below passing grade soon realizes that 4 or 5 points on his/her exam may bring the group average to the minimum and thus obtaining the bonus is reachable. The self-confidence these incremental goals may bring to these students is incalculable.

  - ii) *Debate and resubmission of answers* – Problems, portions of activity tasks, and predictions on demonstrations and simulations may be assigned individually. Answers collected via quick polls are acknowledged and then students are asked to discuss with fellow classmates in groups of three per table. A second poll usually reveals a higher number of correct answers after discussion. An important message is reminded each time: "Multiple minds may reach higher levels than one alone."

- Interpersonal skills
  - i) *Nametags* – Every student creates a nametag which is placed on holders on top of the tables and displayed at all times during class. These nametags allow the students at a table to quickly learn their classmates' names, the instructor to call on anyone at any table by name, and the class as a whole to familiarize with students sitting at even remote tables from their own. This simple technique brings a sense of community to the 99-student class.

  - ii) *Cooperative/collaborative groups* – Group work have shown to develop teamwork skills so necessary for our students entering the workforce. Even loosely structured grouping promotes interaction and conflict solution. Cooper (2005) and Johnson, et.al (1998) present overviews on the rationale, benefits, and research on group work.

- Self-assessment of group work
  - i) *Evaluations* – Students complete evaluation forms on a regular basis. Students evaluate each other as well as themselves on specific criteria. This exercise takes minimum time from class since the criteria are already specified for them. This provides the necessary accountabilty of each student's responsibilities and performanceas validated by peers. Figure 4 shows a portion of this evaluation form.

Evaluation Criteria

Write the names of all your team members, **INCLUDING YOURSELF**, and rate the degree to which each member fulfilled his/her responsibilities in completing the homework assignments. The possible ratings are as follows:

Excellent	Consistently went above and beyond -- tutored teammates, carried more than his/her fair share of the load
Very Good	Consistently did what he/she was supposed to do, acceptably prepared and cooperative
Satisfactory	Usually did what he/she was supposed to do, minimally prepared and cooperative
Ordinary	Often did what he/she was supposed to do, minimally prepared and cooperative
Marginal	Sometimes failed to show up or complete assignments, rarely prepared
Deficient	Often failed to show up or complete assignments, rarely prepared
Unsatisfactory	Consistently failed to show up or complete assignments, unprepared
Superficial	Practically no participation
No Show	No participation at all

Be honest with yourself and with your group members because credit should be given where credit is due. **A group which rates all its members "excellent" is expected to do well on assignments and on tests.** Ratings of unsatisfactory would explain why some groups are not doing as well. Please list any comments that you feel would be beneficial in making your group work better.

Figure 4. Evaluation Criteria

In addition to these classroom management techniques that capitalize on students' learning, the instructor faces class time management challenges to keep students on task and on time. To accomplish this the instructor and teacher assistants must stay engaged and very active while students are working on their activities by constantly monitoring group discussions, dynamics, and performance. From this close monitoring, adjustments are made to the time allotted for a particular activity (extend or cut the activity short), to the "mini-lecture" content (what will be discussed and pointed out to the class a whole), and to the sequence of activities for the day (some may be too advanced while others may be skipped). The allotted time for each activity is projected on the screens via a digital clock for students to manage their own time. During the "mini-lectures" students put laptop monitors down so that the instructor does not have to compete with Cybernet distractions.

Format Options

Two formats are currently in place at NC State for SCALE-UP general chemistry. One format totally integrates laboratory and lecture where the SCALE-UP class does not enroll in separate lecture and lab sections. In this format students meet three times a week for two hours at a time in the SCALE-UP room. Traditional laboratories have been modified and incorporated as "activities" in this format. This is the format of choice for the first semester of general chemistry. The second format uses SCALE-UP instruction for the "lecture" section of the course and the students attend a traditional laboratory setting for the lab section. In this format, students meet twice a week for two hours at a time in the SCALE-UP room and then attend a separate traditional laboratory session. This is the format of choice for the second semester general chemistry. It is important to note that in SCALE-UP "lectures" sections students are constantly engaged in activities, while instructors monitor the learning process and use mini-lectures to address main lessons to be learned and how to solve pedagogical "struggles". Activities are not used to verify concepts "covered" in class but to find out what those concepts entail.

Assessment of Student Achievement

As chemical educators we certainly aim at improving the teaching and learning processes because ultimately we want to make a positive impact on student learning. The SCALE-UP format was implemented in Chemistry because of my conviction that it would make a difference. To show others what we experience in class, three studies have been conducted so far that evaluated both cognitive gains and attitudinal changes that have resulted from the implementation of SCALE-UP in our chemistry classes (Oliver-Hoyo and Allen 2004; 2005; 2006).

The SCALE-UP Chemistry teaching practices (group work, inquiry-guided and activity-based instruction) and instructional materials (challenging problems, real-world situations, demonstrations, and discrepant events) constantly promote discussions, shake-up preconceptions, and bring thoughtful struggle into the learning process. These practices tend to promote the use of cognitive skills such as analysis, application, and evaluation. Such effect on SCALE-UP students was shown in a quantitative study that carefully controlled for variables including the instructor and contact time, time of day, time on task, and content coverage (Oliver-Hoyo and Allen 2004). SCALE-UP students routinely tackle more complex problems successfully, a practice I seldom try anymore in traditional lectures because of the frustration it brings upon the students and myself.

Hand-in-hand with student performance comes student attitudes. It is a well-accepted assumption that student achievement and attitudes are positively interdependent (Rennie and Punch, 1991) and research has shown that affective variables are as important as cognitive variables in molding student learning (Laforgia, 1988). We conducted two studies that monitored this dimension and these have indicated that the SCALE-UP format had a positive impact on student attitudes toward learning chemistry (Oliver-Hoyo and Allen, 2005) and specifically toward cooperative grouping and hands-on activity driven instruction (Oliver-Hoyo and Allen, 2006). It must be pointed out that these positive gains are not observed until the latter part of the semester. At the beginning of each semester there is resistance to this format where students expect to be given all pertinent information and have all questions answered by the instructor. The majority of students also resist working in groups, a skill so necessary to compete in the workforce. This resistance fades away as the benefits of cooperative grouping are experienced throughout the semester. Feedback from SCALE-UP students shows an appreciation not only for chemistry as a subject matter but also to the processes of learning, communication of ideas, and teamwork achievements. This is anecdotal evidence palpable every semester and in my view even more important that what we have been able to show with control studies.

Recommendations and Conclusion

The SCALE-UP Chemistry format provides guidelines and tools to assist students in the discovery of the true nature of learning. This format shifts the responsibility of learning from the instructor to the student and presents success as a partnership between instructor and student. The breath of what is taught expands beyond content coverage since this format promotes communication skills, teamwork, and a sense of learning responsibility in students. The practical lessons to share with readers considering educational change in their classrooms and at their institutions include:

- *Any initiative should start slowly, taking it one step at a time.*
  To bring changes into the classroom, the instructor should familiarize him/herself with a few things at a time, whether these are teaching strategies, methodology, or new instructional materials. After the instructor decides what to adopt, time is required to feel comfortable with the changes before expanding or adopting new others. This avoids frustration and consequently giving up on the process.

  For institutional changes, the best way to convince others of the benefits of active, inquiry-guided instruction is leading by example, documenting efforts, sharing results with the community of scholars, and extending seminar invitations to those that can provide data about the success of their efforts.

- *Flexibility and creativity are part of the process.*
  Even though physical facilities may be built to accommodate ideal settings, the philosophy behind SCALE-UP Chemistry can be practiced in a variety of physical settings. The activities and classroom management techniques developed can be incorporated into other settings and the inquiry-guided approach is not constraint to any specific one.

- *The teaching and learning processes demand time.*
The most difficult concept for students to understand is that struggle is part of the learning process. This format allows the instructor to show and sometimes convince students that it is not until they start asking themselves questions and reflecting upon the content information that learning starts to take place.

After all efforts to develop the instructional materials and to refine the educational approach, practice and reflection keep fine-tuning the process each semester. The most crucial element for any educational change to succeed lies in reflecting upon ones' practices.

In addition to the individual challenges instructors need to address, it is a fact that the institutions in which chemical educators work pose a second layer of challenges. Each institution is very unique with specific needs probably found in no other place. The most important issues to be addressed for implementation of a program like SCALE-UP are:

1) Identifying interested parties that must include faculty (who will take these initiatives into the classroom) and administration (who will make things happen).
2) Obtaining or developing instructional materials that complement the teaching methodologies and making these available to instructors.
3) Providing faculty development and TA training workshops to increase confidence levels of instructors in the classroom.
4) Selecting scheduling options and facilities that best accommodate institutional needs while remaining flexible and creative to incorporate changes.
5) Addressing hurdles one at a time and taking the lessons learned from one semester into the next to improve upon programmatic issues.

Suggested Readings

Inquiry-guided instruction, IGI, is at the heart of the SCALE-UP Chemistry format. The most meaningful exposure I have had to IGI came from an initiative led by Virginia Lee at North Carolina State University where faculty and administrators immersed in a two- year program comprised of seminars, workshops, retreats, and presentations that promoted the IGI philosophy. These efforts are well documented in an easy to read book entitled "Teaching & Learning Through Inquiry: A Guidebook for Institutions & Instructors" edited by Virginia Lee, Stylus Sterling Publishing LLC, Va. (2004).

The SCALE-UP project started at North Carolina State University in the physics department with Professor Robert Beichner leading the efforts. For a summary of the educational impact SCALE-UP Physics have had you may read "Introduction to the SCALE-UP Project", In Invention and Impact: Building Excellence in Undergraduate Science, Technology, Engineering, and Mathematics (STEM) Education by Robert Beichner and Jeffrey Saul. Am. Assoc. for the Advancement of Science (2005).

References

Birk, J.P. and Foster, J. (1993). The Importance of Lecture in General Chemistry Course Performance. *J. of Chemical Education*, 70, pp 180-182.

Cooper, M.M. (2005). An Introduction to Small-Group Learning. In N.J. Pienta, M.M. Cooper, and T.J. Greenbowe (Eds.), *Chemist's Guide to Effective Teaching* (pp 117-128). New Jersey: Pearson, Prentice Hall.

Domin, D.S. (1999). A Content Analysis of General Chemistry Laboratory Manuals for Evidence of Higher-Order Cognitive Tasks. *J. of Chemical Education*, 76, pp 109-111.

Education Commission of the States (1995). *Making quality count in undergraduate education.* Denver, CO: Education Commission of the States.

Fortenberry, N.L. (2000). An Examination of NSF's Programs in Undergraduate Education. *Journal of SMET Education*, 1/1 Jan-April, pp 4-15.

Johnson, D.W., Johnson, R.T. and Smith, K.A. (1991*). Cooperative Learning: Increasing College Faculty Instructional Productivity*. ASHE-ERIC Higher Education Report, No. 4. Washington, DC: George Washington University, School of Education and Human Development.

Johnson, D.W., Johnson, R.T., and Smith, K.A. (1998). Cooperative Learning Returns to College: What Evidence Is there That it Works?. *Change*, 30, pp 26-35.

Laforgia, J. (1988). The Affective Domain Related to Science Education and Its Evaluation. *Science Education*, 72, pp 407-421.

Lazarowitz, R. and Tamir, P. (1994). Research on Using Laboratory Instruction in Science. In D. Gable (Ed.), *Handbook of Research on Science Teaching and Learning* (pp 94-121). New York: MacMillan.

MacGregor, J., Cooper, J.L., Smith, K.A., Robinson, P., Svinicki, M.D. (Eds.) (2000). *Strategies for energizing Large Classes. New Directions for Teaching and learning*, No. 81, San Francisco: Jossey-Bass.

Meador, G. (1994). *National Science Education Reforms: Are We on the Road to a National Curriculum?* Retrieved September 8, 2005, from: ww.bartlesville.k12.ok.us/physics/sciref.pdf

Oliver-Hoyo, M.T. and Allen, D. (2004). Effects of an Active Environment: Teaching Innovations at a Research I Institution. *J. of Chemical Education*, 81, pp 441-448.

Oliver-Hoyo, M.T. and Allen, D. (2005). Attitudinal Effects of a Student-Centered Active Learning Environment. *J. of Chemical Education*, 82, pp 944-949.

Oliver-Hoyo, M.T. and Allen, D. (2006). The Use of Triangulation Methods to Validate Results of Qualitative Educational Research. *Journal of College Science Teaching*, Jan/Feb, pp 42-47.

Pickering, M. (1993). The Teaching Laboratory through History. *J. of Chemical Education*, 70, pp 699-700.

Rennie, L.J. and Punch, K.F. (1991). The Relationship Between Affect and Achievement in Science. *Journal of Research in Science Teaching*, 28, pp 193-209.

The Boyer Commission on Educating Undergraduates in the Research University, *Reinventing Undergraduate Education: A Blueprint for America's Research Universities*
Retrieved September 8, 2005 from: http://naples.cc.sunysb.edu/Pres/boyer.nsf/

Tobias, S. (1992). *Revitalizing Undergraduate Science: Why Some Things Work and Most Don't*, Tucson, AZ: Research Corporation.

11

Model-Observe-Reflect-Explain (MORE) Thinking Frame Instruction: Promoting Reflective Laboratory Experiences to Improve Understanding of Chemistry

Dawn Rickey
Department of Chemistry
Colorado State University

Melonie A. Teichert
Department of Chemistry
Colorado State University

Lydia T. Tien
Department of Chemistry & Geosciences
Monroe Community College

Abstract

The Model-Observe-Reflect-Explain (MORE) Thinking Frame is an instructional tool designed to guide students' thinking in the laboratory, and to encourage students to reflect upon their ideas and how they fit with empirical evidence. This framework promotes students' monitoring of their understandings before, during, and after laboratory sessions, and encourages students to connect macroscopic observations with molecular-level behavior to inform refinements of their personal models. This chapter provides guidelines for effectively implementing the MORE Thinking Frame in undergraduate laboratory courses. We focus on how to use MORE in conjunction with standard laboratory experiments, to enable instructors to begin using MORE within an existing laboratory course. We discuss how to scaffold students in constructing and evaluating personal models as well as how to lead reflective discussions in the laboratory. The chapter also includes information regarding the types of laboratory experiments that work particularly well with MORE. Throughout the chapter, we cite results from our research that support these implementation guidelines.

Biographies

Dawn Rickey is an Associate Professor in the Department of Chemistry at Colorado State University. Her research investigates relationships among metacognition, conceptual change, representational competence, and ability to apply ideas in new contexts, as well as applications to chemistry education, including the design and assessment of learning environments and associated instructor professional development experiences. Dawn completed a B.A. in Chemistry with a minor in Psychology at Rutgers University. She co-developed the Model-Observe-Reflect-Explain (MORE) Thinking Frame at the University of California at Berkeley as part of her graduate work, which included research in chemistry education as well as inorganic chemistry. Dawn then continued to research metacognitively-focused instructional tools as an NSF Postdoctoral Fellow in Science, Mathematics, Engineering, and Technology Education at UCLA. She is currently the principal investigator on the NSF-sponsored project "Expansion and Refinement of a Research-Based Laboratory Curriculum to Enhance Diverse Students' Abilities to Apply Chemistry Ideas Effectively in New Contexts."

Melonie A. Teichert is a research associate at Colorado State University, working with Dawn Rickey on research regarding the implementation of the MORE Thinking Frame. Prior to joining Dr. Rickey's research group, she taught general and honors chemistry and coordinated the general chemistry program at the United States Naval Academy. She completed a B.S. in Mathematics with minors in Chemistry and Music at the Massachusetts Institute of Technology and a Ph.D. in Chemistry at the University of California at Berkeley. Her dissertation focus was on both physical chemistry and chemistry education. The chemistry education part of her dissertation focused on improving students' conceptual understanding of thermodynamics topics through student explanation and the identification and integration of students' initial ideas.

Lydia T. Tien is currently an Assistant Professor of chemistry at Monroe Community College (MCC). She completed a B.A. in Chemistry at Cornell University and earned her M.S. in Chemistry and Ph.D. in Science and Mathematics Education from the University of California at Berkeley. As part of her graduate work, she co-developed the MORE Thinking Frame and investigated student beliefs and inquiry skills. Prior to joining the faculty full time at MCC, she was involved with the Peer-Led Team Learning project, in the training and development of peer leaders, and as an instructor in general chemistry. She continues to be interested in issues in teaching and learning, including the implementation, dissemination, and research activities of MORE.

Introduction

Too often, student learning of chemistry is shallow. In the general chemistry laboratory, students usually complete experiments in which they follow a set of procedures and calculate quantities using known algorithms, a format that does not encourage students to make sense of the underlying chemistry. Most experiments reach a predefined "correct answer". Research has shown that such verification experiments help students to learn laboratory techniques, but do not lead to better understanding of chemistry concepts (Lazarowitz and Tamir, 1994; Lunetta, Hofstein, and Clough, 2007). A survey of 203 college and university general chemistry programs in the United States found that the primary goal of laboratory instruction is to enhance students' conceptual understanding, followed by the development of laboratory skills and scientific processes (Abraham et. al., 1997). However, despite extensive use of the laboratory in undergraduate chemistry education with the purported goal of student understanding of concepts, there continues to be a strong emphasis on having students follow cookbook procedures and perform algorithmic calculations on the data they collect (Abraham et. al. 1997, Spencer, 1993-1994, Lloyd, 1992). An analysis of contemporary general chemistry laboratory manuals has also demonstrated that the majority of the laboratory programs do not promote higher-order thinking (Domin, 1999), and thus fail to encourage students to develop understandings of science concepts at a deep level. Students are typically given experimental protocols telling them *what to do* in the lab. It is far less common for students to be scaffolded in *how to think* during the inquiry process.

The Model-Observe-Reflect-Explain (MORE) Thinking Frame is an instructional tool designed to address the problem of shallow learning by guiding students' thinking in the laboratory, and encouraging students to reflect upon their ideas and how they fit with empirical evidence (Tien, Rickey, and Stacy, 1999). Unlike standard laboratory courses, MORE Thinking Frame instruction has been shown to improve students' conceptual understanding and problem-solving success (Rickey, 1999). The MORE Thinking Frame provides students with a model of scientists' thinking processes. Specifically, MORE prompts students to describe their current understanding of a chemical system prior to experimentation (model), conduct experiments to explore the experimental system (observe), think about the implications of their observations and use the experimental evidence as a basis for refining their initial ideas (reflect and explain). The MORE Thinking Frame promotes students' monitoring of their understanding before, during, and after laboratory sessions, and encourages students to connect their macroscopic observations with molecular-level behavior. Students become more aware of what they understand and how their ideas may need to be refined to be consistent with empirical observations. Thus, the MORE framework explicitly encourages metacognition (thinking about one's own thinking) which has been linked to improved understanding of ideas (Alexander and Judy, 1988; Garner and Alexander, 1989; White, 1992) and problem-solving success (Flavell, 1976; Schoenfeld, 1992; Rickey and Stacy, 2000).

Depending upon the context in which it is used, the term "model" could refer to an analogical model, a mathematical model, a computer model, a concrete three-dimensional model (e.g., ball and stick molecules), or a mental model that exists within the mind of an individual (Bodner, Gardner, and Briggs, 2005; Harrison and Treagust, 2000; Justi and Gilbert, 2002). The "model" aspect of the MORE Thinking Frame denotes a student's mental model of a particular chemical system, which he or she articulates in a written laboratory report. Such a model focuses on the student's understanding of the chemical system as described in words and/or pictures. One particular focus of MORE models is the connection between macroscopic observations and the molecular-level behavior of particles. Thus, a student's model represents that individual's ideas, integrates various modes of representation, and varies with respect to complexity, abstraction, and predictive power. Over the course of a laboratory module, students successively refine their personal models in light of experimental evidence, such that several iterations of MORE mimic the scientific process of constructing, evaluating, refining, and extending models to explain aspects of the world.

Studies comparing students participating in MORE laboratory courses with those participating in standard laboratory courses have shown that using the MORE Thinking Frame prompts students to be more reflective and enhances students' conceptual understanding and problem-solving success (Rickey, 1999; Tien, 1998). On a lecture-based final examination, MORE students performed significantly better than students in a matched control group both on questions that were isomorphic to those encountered previously in the course and on problems that required near transfer of knowledge, but larger differences were observed for near-transfer problems (Rickey, 1999). These data provide evidence that implementing MORE within the laboratory portion of a course improves students' overall understanding of chemistry ideas. After completing a laboratory course employing MORE, students are able to diagnose and correct their own misconceptions, construct meaningful conceptual frameworks, and close the gap between isomorphic and transfer problem-solving success (Rickey, 1999). These improvements in student learning appear to be the result of the explicit promotion of metacognition as students reflect upon and revise their understandings through use of the MORE Thinking Frame. Specifically, the use of the MORE Thinking Frame promotes three essential aspects of thinking that mediate improved understanding of chemistry in students: (1) engagement in reflection/metacognition, (2) making connections between macroscopic observations and molecular-level mechanisms, and (3) revising personal models for consistency in light of experimental evidence. Recent research has shown that laboratory experiments incorporating the MORE Thinking Frame prompt students to revise their models to be consistent with the experimental evidence and to progress toward more scientifically correct ideas (Tien, Teichert, and Rickey, 2007). Research has also identified instructional conditions that promote all three mediating behaviors mentioned above. Many of these instructional conditions are included in the guidelines that follow for the implementation of the MORE Thinking Frame.

Superimposing the MORE Thinking Frame on Existing Laboratory Experiments

The MORE Thinking Frame was originally implemented and assessed in a problem-based modular curriculum that incorporated the Thinking Frame as an essential part of the pedagogy (Rickey, 1999; Tien, 1998). For a detailed description of a problem-based laboratory module designed to complement the use of the MORE Thinking Frame, see Mattox, Reisner, and Rickey (2006). Since its original inception, the Thinking Frame has also been used to effectively promote metacognition and understanding of chemistry ideas in more traditional laboratory courses that employ standard, one-week experiments. Implementing MORE instruction by superimposing the Thinking Frame over standard experiments used in an existing curriculum requires relatively small changes in instructional methods and prepares instructors to teach MORE modules in the future. In this way, the MORE Thinking Frame has been implemented at a range of institutions (including high school, community college, primarily undergraduate institution, and research university) by individuals with varying levels of teaching experience (from undergraduate- and graduate-student instructors to seasoned veterans) for most of the chemistry topics covered in the standard one-year general chemistry curriculum.

To adapt one-week, stand-alone laboratory experiments for use with the MORE Thinking Frame, instructors need to develop "model assignments", incorporate reflective discussions into the laboratory sessions, and provide students with appropriate feedback. Here we describe in detail the adaptation of a one-week, stand-alone laboratory experiment for use with MORE. Specifically, the MORE Thinking Frame was introduced at a research university by superimposing it on the standard first-week experiment "Small Scale Techniques and the Absorption of Light"

(Thompson, 1990). The laboratory experiment (subsequently referred to as the "blue dye" experiment in the interest of brevity) introduced students to pipeting techniques, colorimetry, and factors that influence light absorption. Students explored factors that control the drop volume delivered from a microburet, prepared serial dilutions of a standard solution to be used as color standards, and investigated the effects of concentration and path length on light absorption.

Practical suggestions for how to create effective model assignments, lead reflective laboratory discussions, and provide feedback, along with supporting research results for a sample of 17 consenting students, are discussed in the following sections. The blue dye experiment is used throughout the discussion, and further examples are given to demonstrate the implementation principles for other chemistry topics.

Developing Model Assignments. The model assignments that guide students in describing and refining their ideas are central to the effective implementation of MORE Thinking Frame instruction. Students construct initial models of the chemical systems they will study for their pre-laboratory reports (rather than writing introductions and procedural flow charts, for example) and include model refinements in the conclusions of their post-laboratory reports. Figure 1 shows the initial model guidelines provided to students for the blue dye experiment. Students are asked to explain their initial understanding of the dye solutions they will study by describing both their macroscopic and molecular-level ideas.

Initial Model Guidelines
Based on your initial understanding, describe and/or represent the important characteristics of the dye solutions that you will prepare in this experiment. In formulating your model, include macroscopic-level (what is observable to the naked eye) and molecular-level descriptions (in words and/or pictures) of your most concentrated solution and your most dilute solution. Cite evidence from your everyday life to support your initial model.

Refined Model Guidelines
Present your refined model.
Develop a refined model of the dye solutions based on the information you currently possess. Describe your refined macroscopic model (your observations) and your refined molecular-level model that accounts for your observations.

Explain why your model has changed from initial to refined.
Discuss how your refined model is different from your initial model and explain why your model has changed from initial to refined (or why it has not, if your refined model is exactly the same as your initial model) by using experimental evidence (such as observations, data, calculations, and results) to support or refute the claims you made in your initial model. (Using evidence in this way is an important part of a good scientific explanation.)

Generalize your refined model.
Generalize your model so that the model could be used to understand new systems.

Propose a next experiment.
What questions do you have? Propose an experiment that could help you to answer one of your questions or to test your refined model.

Figure 1. Initial model and refined model assignments for the blue dye experiment.

Writing good model assignments is important. Our research has shown that the MORE Thinking Frame is most effective when used with fairly generic initial model assignments. We have found that very specific model guidelines or lists of questions in the initial model assignment cause students to respond only to those specific requests, limiting personal reflection; therefore, we recommend more generic initial model assignments. As seen in Figure 1, the following template can be used for constructing initial model assignments: "Based on your initial understanding, describe and/or represent the important characteristics of [system of study]. In formulating your model, include macroscopic- and molecular-level descriptions (in words and/or pictures) of the [system of interest] at these important stages of the experiment: [given stages of experiment; e.g. different points of a titration]." This template works well for most experiments, and makes writing and completing the model assignments easier due to the recognizable pattern for both instructors and students. [See Figure 2 for additional examples of initial model assignments for the topics of acid-base chemistry and thermochemistry.]

Figure 3 presents excerpts from the initial models submitted by students for the blue dye experiment, providing examples of what instructors can expect from such an assignment. Despite students' lack of experience with describing and representing phenomena at the molecular level, 88% of students included molecular-level representations in these first independent initial models.

Initial Model: What happens when an acid and base are mixed?

Based on your initial understanding, describe and/or represent the important characteristics of an acid-base titration in which a strong base (B) is added to an acid (HA). In formulating your model, include macroscopic- and molecular-level descriptions (in words and/or pictures) of the expected contents of your flask at the following stages of the experiment:

a)   just before you begin the titration;
b)   in the middle of the titration (halfway to the end point); and
c)   at the end point of the titration.

Indicate the approximate pHs of the relevant solutions and provide balanced chemical equations to indicate the reactions that will occur. In representing your molecular models, you may ignore the presence of the indicator in the flask.

Initial Model: How do chemical reactions transfer heat?

Based on your initial understanding, describe and/or represent the important characteristics of how chemical reactions transfer heat. Specifically, focus on the mixing of $NaOH(aq)$ and $HCl(aq)$ in the calorimetry experiment. In formulating your model, include macroscopic- and molecular-level descriptions (in words and/or pictures) before, during, and after the mixing process. Be sure to include information about what you think is responsible for any heat transfer from a molecular-level perspective.

Figure 2. Initial model assignments for acid-base and thermochemistry experiments.

In addition to helping the students become aware of their ideas, the MORE Thinking Frame is an invaluable tool for instructors to become aware of student conceptions prior to and following laboratory experiences. Student 10's model (Figure 3) illustrates how a student connects the visual appearances of solutions of different concentrations (macroscopic level) to the ratios of blue dye molecules to water molecules (molecular level); his verbal description reveals some incorrect ideas concerning the light-absorbing species. Student 14's model (Figure 3) exemplifies the misconception that the concentration of a solution is a function of the spacing of molecules, that is, as the concentration increases, the space between molecules decreases.

After each laboratory experiment, students complete a post-laboratory assignment that includes a refined model. The refined model guidelines prompt students to include four important components in their refined models. (See Figure 1.) First, students are asked to refine their models based on the experimental evidence they collected in the laboratory. Second, students are prompted to compare their refined models, both from macroscopic- and molecular-level perspectives, to their initial models and to explain why they refined their models (or did not make refinements) by using experimental evidence. Thus, the refined model guidelines explicitly encourage metacognition. In many cases, students' model refinements lead to models that are more scientifically correct, but this depends on the nature of the evidence and how it relates to students' ideas (particularly molecular-level ideas). We provide more detail on what characteristics of laboratory experiments are particularly effective for use with MORE later in the chapter. Third, students are asked to generalize their models; and finally, students propose experiments to answer any remaining questions they have or to test their refined models.

Goals of MORE instruction include helping students to engage in reflection, to make connections between the macroscopic and molecular levels for a chemical system, and to revise their personal models for consistency in light of experimental evidence. Our research indicates that students exhibit evidence of these behaviors in their model assignments, and analyses of students' laboratory reports capture the nature of students' reflection on molecular-level models. For example, 71% of students made connections between macroscopic observations and molecular-level mechanisms in their refined models for the blue dye experiment. Additional analyses of student learning has shown that the MORE Thinking Frame prompts students to revise their personal models for consistency in light of experimental evidence and to progress to more scientifically accurate ideas compared with the ideas expressed in their initial models (Tien, et.al., 2007).

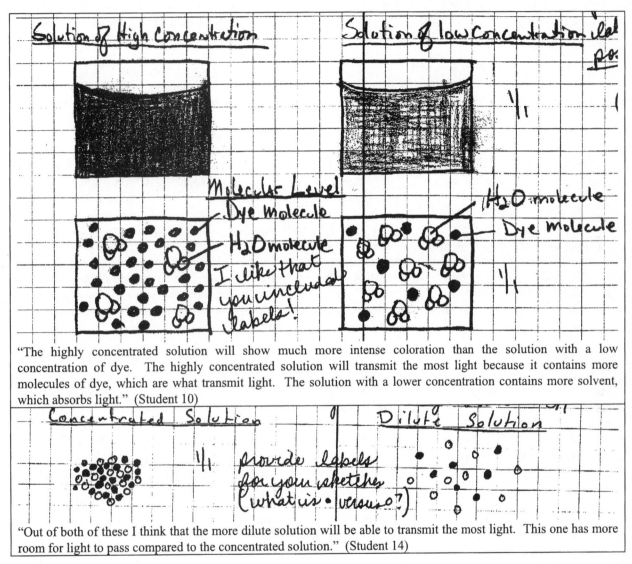

"The highly concentrated solution will show much more intense coloration than the solution with a low concentration of dye. The highly concentrated solution will transmit the most light because it contains more molecules of dye, which are what transmit light. The solution with a lower concentration contains more solvent, which absorbs light." (Student 10)

"Out of both of these I think that the more dilute solution will be able to transmit the most light. This one has more room for light to pass compared to the concentrated solution." (Student 14)

Figure 3. Excerpts from students' initial models for the blue dyes experiment. The students' written descriptions are typed verbatim; the students' drawings are scanned in directly from the students' laboratory reports. The graduate student instructor's written comments are in cursive.

Leading Reflective Discussions. In addition to the model assignments, another essential feature of implementing the MORE Thinking Frame is the facilitation of reflective discussions during the laboratory sessions. Students are guided through the "observe" and "reflect" parts of the framework through in-class discussions with their peers and with the instructor. At the beginning of the laboratory session, there is a presentation and discussion of the students' initial model ideas. This pre-laboratory discussion can take place in small groups and/or involve the whole class; it gives students the opportunity to present their ideas and hear the ideas of their peers. During the discussion, the instructor acts as a facilitator to bring out the students' ideas. The instructor is careful not to judge the correctness of the ideas through verbal or nonverbal cues. In doing so, the instructor establishes a learning environment in which students feel comfortable sharing what they think and are open to evaluating the ideas in light of empirical evidence that they will collect. For instance, the following is an excerpt of the graduate student instructor encouraging students to share their initial model ideas prior to beginning the blue dye experiment:

> *Well, okay, first of all, remember your initial models, your models, are never judged on whether they are correct or incorrect. Especially your initial models. I want to know what you are thinking right now before you go into the lab. And maybe you have never thought of this, this is really unfamiliar to you, but you do your best to represent what you think is going on. And so, first I want to squelch that fear, you know, that I did it correctly or incorrectly.*

The pre-laboratory discussion yields a number of student ideas, some of which may disagree with one another. Such differences provide an opportunity for the instructor to highlight differences among the initial models and encourage students to focus on how the observations they will make as they conduct experiments may or may not support the various ideas.

Initially, students are typically somewhat wary of sharing their initial model ideas in front of the class, not only because they may be shy or insecure about the correctness of their ideas, but also because, for the first MORE model assignment, students are uncertain of the instructor's expectations. One approach is for the instructor to ask for volunteers to share their ideas, with the understanding that all of the students will be expected to share their ideas at some point(s) during the semester. Since students are not always forthcoming, a second approach is to have students first share their ideas in a smaller group (2-4 students), constructing a "group" model on poster board, then having a whole-class discussion and sharing of ideas. An additional benefit of posting group models is that they can serve as a reference during later discussions. A third approach is to have multiple students put their initial models (or some aspects of them) on the board at the same time so that students can evaluate similarities and differences among the models. The first time students are asked to share their ideas may be the most challenging; in order to help students feel comfortable sharing their ideas, an instructor can scan through the student papers and select a few examples to jump-start the discussion and help students feel comfortable participating in the discussion.

Following the pre-laboratory discussion, the students make observations as they carry out experiments. In order to prompt students to reflect while they are in the laboratory, the instructor circulates through the lab asking questions such as: "How does what you are observing relate to your initial model? What do you think is happening on the molecular level?" (See Figure 4 for additional examples.) This is similar to Schoenfeld's (1987) approach to question-asking for the purpose of promoting metacognition. Asking open-ended questions in the vein of King's (1990) reflective questioning approach such as "How do you think...and...are similar? How do you think...affects...? How do you think...is related to...?" is also useful.

- What is the goal of this experiment?
- How does what you are doing contribute to the goal of the experiment?
- How does what you are currently observing relate to your initial model?
- Are your observations consistent with your initial model?
- Does your model fully explain your observations? How?
- What do you think is happening on the molecular level?
- What doesn't make sense to you?

Figure 4. Typical questions posed during a MORE laboratory to guide student reflection.

Encouraging students to engage in reflective discussion often represents a change in emphasis of instructor discourse in the laboratory. Instructors have commented that, with the use of MORE, the laboratory discourse becomes more focused on students' ideas about chemistry and shifts away from focusing on calculations. For instance, one high school instructor noted that he began to focus discussions more on the students' ideas.

> Instructor: *And before, we teach them the concepts, hand out a piece of paper, they would follow directions. Fill it out, you know, turn it in.*

Interviewer: *And you don't know if they got it?*
Instructor: *And you don't know. But now I am talking to the students and I can hear what they have to say. And it's worked out better.*

An instructor at a primarily undergraduate institution said, "I think the MORE framework gives you sort of a framework as an instructor. I can't think of a better word for just how you should be interacting with your students." Instead of focusing on students completing the computations, her focus shifted to "can they connect the calculations to the chemistry." This instructor shared in her journal:

> *When I reflect on my experiences on teaching lab, I realize that most of the time, I had considered my role as that of "babysitter" and technique demonstrator. Now that I'm making an effort to discuss chemistry in the lab, I feel that they may be the biggest change in my managing a laboratory. And mentally, during those three hours, it's a lot tougher than my former role.*

In addition, consider the following interview excerpt. The instructor was asked how the MORE Thinking Frame influenced her behavior in the lab:

Instructor: *... I feel like I have better questions to ask the students...*
Interviewer: *And where does that kind of thing come from? From knowing more about what their misconceptions are, or what would cause you to have -*
Instructor: *Having to write those model assignments beforehand.*
Interviewer: *Oh, huh. So you are thinking more about what they are going to be thinking about?*
Instructor: *Yeah.*

As a MORE implementer, the instructor works at prompting student reflection in the laboratory through instructor-student interactions. For instance, instead of answering a student's question immediately, the instructor can seize the opportunity for a "teachable moment" and guide students' thinking. However, it is not unlikely for an instructor to be bombarded with procedural concerns (e.g. answering students' procedural questions, developing students' laboratory skills). When the instructor is overwhelmed and/or the students are frustrated, it is a natural tendency to resort to giving the answers. To alleviate the burden on the instructor to prompt student reflection through open-ended questioning, some MORE instructors have distributed the reflection questions in Figure 4 to students and asked the students to be prepared to answer those questions as the instructor makes rounds to each laboratory group. In this way, students should always be thinking of how they would answer those questions even if the instructor does not get around to actually asking them.

Two additional approaches to prompting student reflection are embedding questions in the laboratory manual text and designating time for whole-class discussion. Both approaches have led to substantial student reflection during laboratory sessions as seen in video data of students working in the laboratory. Analysis of student-student interactions indicates that embedded reflection questions prompt student reflection/metacognition, such as making sense of observations and relating experimental evidence to their initial models. When the instructor is not able to engage in multiple reflective discussions with all of the laboratory groups, the embedded questions in the laboratory manual text target all students and serve as a springboard for laboratory groups to discuss and debate their ideas. MORE instructors will often create their own reflection questions for students, either embedded into the lab manual or handed out separately, depending on the logistics of printing out lab manuals at a particular institution. (See Figure 5 for examples of reflection questions.) Note that the reflection questions can be very specific, in contrast to the more generic initial model guidelines. If there are specific issues an instructor wants students to address, we have found that these work better as reflection questions rather than as questions within model assignments. Whole-class discussions also provide opportunities to share and evaluate data and ideas, discuss how observations relate to the initial models previously discussed, and make connections between macroscopic observations and molecular-level mechanisms.

The Importance of Students' Personal Models

We have stressed the importance of students expressing their own ideas and conceptions, particularly how they make macro-molecular connections, in their models. This is crucial both for student learning and to guide instruction, as instructors can use the students' expressed conceptions to tailor their instruction to the students' needs.

The emphasis on students' ideas can make seemingly simple experiments rich learning experiences, and instructors appreciate the learning value of MORE, especially its emphasis on macro-molecular connections. The graduate student instructor for the blue dye experiment wrote in her journal:

> *I was amazed, actually, at how the MORE framework added value even to this particular lab. I really wasn't that excited about teaching this lab, but when I had the opportunity to go around and help each group of students discuss their observations, whether their observations made sense, and help them to discuss their observations in terms of the blue dye molecules, I was very pleased with the students' responses. Normally, I would expect students to "get through" the lab, report their observations to me if I happened to walk by and ask how they're doing, and leave without really having considered how concentration and path length are related to transmission of light beyond strictly obvious relationships. I would probably expect students to state the relationships in terms of macroscopic observations ("the darker solution filters out more light" or "the higher the column of dye solution that the light has to travel through, the less light will get through it and it will look darker"), but not necessarily connect it to the molecular level, like they did in this week's lab (with some guidance of course).*

Reflection questions: Blue dye experiment

- Which solution do you think will transmit the most light? (How will you be able to detect which solution transmits the most light?)
- If two solutions are of equal concentration, but the path length differs, how do you think the transmittance will compare?

Reflection questions: What happens when an acid and base are mixed?

- What are the major species present before and at the end point?
- What species must be present to constitute a buffer solution?
- How could you distinguish an acid solution from a buffer solution at the same pH?

Reflection questions: What is occurring during "heat flow"?

- What is the relationship between heat lost and heat gained in a closed system?
- How are heat and temperature similar and/or different from one another?
- What is the specific heat of water? What does this *mean*?
- Which of these processes—bond breaking or bond formation—releases energy?

Figure 5. Examples of specific reflection questions embedded in the laboratory manual.

Because students are explicit about their ideas, instructors gain insights into students' understanding prior to and following an experiment. The student ideas presented in Figure 3 illustrate that students may come into the classroom with incorrect ideas. The initial and refined model assignments allow the instructor to be aware of students' ideas, correct as well as incorrect, thus allowing the instructor to be more informed in tailoring instruction to respond to such conceptions and assessing the impact of the learning experiences. One instructor commented in her journal:

> *Another realization that I had this week is that I'm learning more about my own students' misconceptions and how compartmentalized their learning is. Again, I think this stems from*

> *talking with them about their initial models and from reading their initial models. For instance, by reading their initial models this week I found that 85-90% of them believe that energy is released when bonds are broken (which I know is a reported misconception, but it's always more eye-opening to realize that your own students think this way).*

Later in the semester, the same instructor remarked:

> *I'm amazed at how much more I know about what my students **do** understand and **don't** understand regarding chemistry concepts by using the MORE Thinking Frame. I mean, I have taught labs for six years, I know the literature regarding misconceptions, and yet it's never been as evident to me that my students hold these same misconceptions. It's never been as evident to me how much they fragment their knowledge. Sure they "think ions" while we're doing the Solutions and Reactions lab, but then they drop it as soon as we move on to other labs… It's easy to fool yourself into thinking they really understand this when you don't have students model their thinking for you.*

Clearly, by focusing on students' personal ideas, an instructor is more prepared to facilitate discussions specifically tailored to those conceptions.

Because instructors are more aware of their students' conceptions, particularly at the molecular level, the MORE Thinking Frame often prompts a shift in the instructors' foci and discourse in the lecture as well. While MORE was intended as a tool for the laboratory, one college instructor noted that her use of the MORE Thinking Frame in the lab has impacted how she thinks about chemistry and how she teaches it to her students in the lecture. Specifically, she encourages students to think about and draw connections between the macroscopic and molecular levels throughout the course. For example, in introducing gases to the students during lecture, she gave various scenarios to her students to have them brainstorm their ideas (or, *model*) regarding the macroscopic and molecular level, while in previous years she had taught the topic using a more didactic approach.

Instructors also find that participating in MORE instruction has deepened their chemistry content knowledge. In prompting students to make macro-molecular connections and to explain their own understandings, the instructors are also compelled to reflect more on the chemical systems as part of the classroom preparation. One college instructor wrote in her journal that "I felt like I learned some chemistry in this lab" because once she started looking into the trends from a molecular-level perspective, she was excited to see how she could use the data to draw connections to the molecular level. A graduate student instructor commented in her journal:

> *This has also prompted me to question the depth of my knowledge. I think I've had more discussions with (a chemistry colleague) regarding things like what is actually happening in the flame during a flame test that gives off color. This was prompted by a student who really is perplexed that the flame seems to be an endless source of energy, so why would an excited electron come back down to the ground state and give off a photon…*

Grading and Scaffolding Students with the Model Assignments

As with any new assignment, students will at first be unsure of the instructor's expectations for initial model assignments. Thus, it is imperative that the instructor explain the expectations, guide the students in completing their model assignments, and give ample oral and written feedback throughout the process of implementing the MORE Thinking Frame. Instructors must take the time and effort to carefully grade students' models and provide explicit feedback on the different aspects of the models.

Typically, the instructor grades the initial model assignment on completeness, not correctness, making sure that each student addressed the macroscopic- and molecular-levels and responded to any other questions. For the first initial models of the semester, an instructor might choose to grade leniently, but give ample written feedback as to what changes the instructor would like to see in future models (e.g., more explicit molecular-level views or more detail about student's conceptions). In this way, students are not penalized early on as they learn how to construct models. With respect to the refined models, some instructors have used correctness as part of the grading criteria, but instructors should consider aspects such as those indicated in Figure 6, which presents the rubric used to grade students' revised models for the blue dye experiment. In our experience, students can earn a perfect score on a refined model even if the model is not entirely correct. As the rubric in Figure 6 demonstrates, students earn points for relating their evidence to their molecular-level models, and for explaining how and why their refined models may differ from their initial models. One focus of MORE instruction is to encourage students to refine their ideas to be consistent with their experimental evidence. Consequently, instructors tailor their feedback meet the goals of MORE rather than focusing on scientific correctness. For instance, if a student has an incorrect idea in the refined model that is not consistent with some of the student's observations, the instructor could comment "How does this (molecular-level idea) relate to your observations in the lab?" or "model not consistent with data" rather than simply correcting the idea.

We have also found that it can be difficult for students to be explicit about how and why their models progressed, for example, explaining why an idea in their refined model is different from what they expressed in their initial model. Sometimes students will not acknowledge that there was a change, in effect ignoring their initial model ideas. An important component of MORE is student reflection on how their conceptions change and why, and recent research results show that students' conceptual understanding is strongly correlated with their ability to explain their model revisions (Rickey, Teichert, and Tien, 2006). Therefore, instructors should assign a significant number of points to this component of the refined models and also provide written feedback to students.

Component	Points		
Relates light transmission to concentration:			
Uses evidence to support model	1.5	1	0
Connects macroscopic / molecular levels	1.5	1	0
Relates light transmission to path length			
Uses evidence to support model	1	0.5	0
Connects macroscopic / molecular levels	1	0.5	0
Relates calculations / equations to model (Beer's Law; $C_1V_1 = C_2V_2$)	0.5		0
Explicitly compares initial and refined models and explains changes	2	1	0
Generalizes refined model	1	0.5	0
Addresses confusion / proposes experiment	0.5		0
Overall clarity of model	1	0.5	0

Figure 6. Sample grading rubric for the blue dye experiment.

A common concern among MORE instructors is the time required to grade student models and provide ample written feedback. Depending on the format of the lab report that the instructor typically grades, evaluating model assignments may be a more daunting task. MORE instructors have graded holistically and used specific rubrics, such as that shown in Figure 6. Some find the rubrics helpful, particularly when new to MORE, while others find them restrictive and can grade more efficiently with a holistic approach. While ample feedback on every student paper is essential early in the semester, some instructors have found it helpful to give extensive feedback on only a fraction of the papers each week later in the term. This is especially useful for instructors with heavy teaching loads.

Grading is not the only way to scaffold the students in constructing their models. The instructor can also draw on his/her students as resources. For example, after students complete the first initial model assignment, the instructor can provide the class with exemplar models and discuss various aspects of these models, such as how students represented the molecular level, made macro/molecular connections, and used evidence in their models. It is useful to do this after the first model assignments are graded, so that each student can more clearly understand the expectations of the model assignments. In addition, instructors have found it useful to allow students to critique each others' initial and refined models and then permit revisions. Such a critique activity is useful in two ways: (1)

students have an opportunity to read a classmate's model and think about how to apply the instructor's grading criteria, and (2) each student receives individual feedback on his/her model.

Characteristics of Experiments that Work Well With the MORE Thinking Frame

Our research has shown that, when used with standard experiments, the MORE Thinking Frame is most effective when the following criteria are met. First, the experiment should employ simple chemical systems, procedures, and/or techniques. When an experiment contains laboratory concepts or procedures that are too cognitively demanding, students have less time and ability to reflect on their personal understandings. Simple aqueous systems and gaseous systems lend themselves easily to incorporating the MORE Thinking Frame. While it is possible to use the MORE Thinking Frame for nearly any chemical system, the instructor must keep in mind that students may have difficulty constructing and refining models for a very complex system.

Second, since the emphasis of the MORE Thinking Frame is on the students' personal understandings, it is essential that the textbook and/or pre-laboratory reading does not "give everything away". The laboratory manual and/or assigned readings that accompany many standard laboratory experiments explicitly state what students should expect to observe. Students will not be motivated to revise their models if they can accurately predict everything from the reading before they carry out the experiment. Furthermore, if students think they already know the "correct model," they will not see the need to relate their model to the experimental evidence. Generic model assignments help to avoid these pitfalls; while answers to specific questions can be researched by students, the generic assignment to describe one's understanding of a certain system requires individual thought and effort.

Third, it is helpful if an experiment yields macroscopic observations that inform the molecular-level behavior in a relatively straightforward way. For instance, when the MORE Thinking Frame was superimposed on a "Synthesis of an Alum" experiment (Thompson, 1990) for which there are many procedural details and observations of which to keep track (the multi-step synthesis involves oxidation-reduction, acid-base, and precipitation reactions), students found it extremely difficult to relate their observations to the molecular-level behavior. When evaluating refined models generated by the same class of students for the blue dye and alum experiments, 82% of the students presented molecular-level models for the blue dye experiment compared with only 29% for the alum experiment; and 71% of the students made at least one macro-molecular connection for the blue dye experiment compared with 29% for the alum experiment. In addition, results of the analysis of video of the same group of students who were studied in the blue dye experiment shows that, while the nature and frequency of instructor-student interactions are comparable, there was a lower proportion of reflective student-student interactions during the alum experiment despite the fact that the alum experiment was conducted one week later in the semester. Thus, it is evident that experiments such as the one involving the synthesis of an alum can be so cognitively demanding that students struggle to both keep track of procedural details and engage in reflective thinking.

Finally, we have found that instructors prefer using a modular approach that incorporates multi-week experiments. Modules, particularly those that are structured around an overarching problem for students to solve, also tend to be more effective for student reflection and learning. The use of modules avoids having new chemical systems and laboratory procedures to study every week such that the students are overloaded. The modular approach also gives students the opportunity to make multiple model refinements for a chemical system, thus developing progressively more sophisticated explanatory models, and provides more opportunity for class discussion of refined models. These findings prompted the development of "pseudo-modules" that group together multiple standard laboratory experiments with common themes (e.g., acid-base chemistry or thermochemistry) into a module. The acid-base module guidelines given in Figure 2 were used in a pseudo-module. The pseudo-modular approach influences the ways in which instructors introduce and teach various topics, emphasizing the connections from one week to the next, and integrating the different empirical observations. Pseudo-modules allow an instructor with a constrained laboratory syllabus of more traditional laboratory experiments to gain many of the advantages of a multi-week module designed for use with the MORE Thinking Frame.

Introducing the MORE Thinking Frame to Students

A successful introduction of the MORE Thinking Frame is essential to its effective use in the laboratory since it is likely very different from the students' other laboratory experiences. All of the implementation guidelines discussed above apply in particular to the first MORE experiment that students complete. Using MORE can be time-consuming for the student, and he/she might not immediately see the value of the approach. Thus, it is imperative to allow time for MORE to be used effectively as students get used to the idea of a "model" and how the grading of models is different from grading based largely on accuracy and precision. Furthermore, it is crucial that the first initial and refined model assignments be accessible to students. For their first models, it is easiest for students to describe chemical systems with which they are familiar from everyday life. The blue dye experiment described in this chapter and one of our MORE laboratory modules that asks students to describe salt and sugar solutions (Mattox, et.al., 2006) are examples of effective early model assignments due to their simple chemical systems and laboratory procedures. In addition, we have developed a one-week introductory activity to help students learn how to write and revise models. This activity is available upon request to the lead author. Once the students have experience writing personal models, they will be able to write models for more complex chemical systems that may come later in the semester.

At the beginning of the semester, MORE instructors usually give the students a handout explaining the MORE Thinking Frame in detail. This handout goes through each part of MORE: model, observe, reflect, explain, and model refinement, independent of a particular laboratory experiment, and serves to help students navigate their early model assignments and laboratory discussions. Instructors can create their own handouts, tailored to their students, institutions, and laboratory experiments. The handout used by our instructors is available for anyone interested by contacting the lead author.

Summary

The Model-Observe-Reflect-Explain Thinking Frame is an instructional tool that ameliorates the problem of shallow learning in the chemistry laboratory by guiding students' scientific thinking processes. Specifically, MORE encourages students to engage in reflection/metacognition, make connections between their macroscopic observations and the underlying molecular-level behavior, and revise their personal models of chemical systems for consistency in light of experimental evidence. In addition, MORE provides valuable insights into students' conceptions, focuses the laboratory discourse on molecular-level behavior (as opposed to calculations), and deepens instructors' understandings of chemistry. Although MORE is most effective when used with multi-week, problem-based laboratory modules, it also improves students' understanding when superimposed over standard laboratory experiments. In this chapter, we have presented instructional conditions that our research has identified to maximize the desired student learning behaviors in the context of MORE laboratory courses. Important aspects for instructors to focus on when implementing the MORE Thinking Frame in their general chemistry laboratories include developing effective, generic model assignments; facilitating reflective discussion throughout the laboratory experience via structuring initial- and refined-model discussions, prompting reflection while circulating among laboratory groups (in contrast to simply answering students' questions), and embedding open-ended questions in the laboratory manual or handouts; and providing students with appropriate feedback through grading and critiquing.

Suggestions for Further Reading

Collins, A., Brown, J.S., and Holum, A. (1991). Cognitive apprenticeship: Making thinking visible. *American Educator*. Winter, 6-11, 38-46.

Rickey, D. and Stacy, A. M. (2000). The role of metacognition in learning chemistry. *Journal of Chemical Education*. 77(7), 915-920.

Tien, L.T., Rickey, D., and Stacy, A. M. (1999). The MORE Thinking Frame: Guiding students' thinking in the laboratory. *Journal of College Science Teaching. 28*, 318-324.

References

Abraham, M.R., Cracolice, M.S., Graves, A.P., Aldhamash, A.H., Kihega, J.G., Palma Gil, J.G., and Varghese, V. (1997). The nature and state of general chemistry laboratory courses offered by colleges and universities in the United States. *Journal of Chemical Education.* 74(5), 591-594.

Alexander, P.A. and Judy, J.E. (1988). The interaction of domain-specific and strategic knowledge in academic performance. *Review of Educational Research.* 58(4), 375-404.

Bodner, G.M., Gardner, D.E., and Briggs, M.W. (2005). Models and modeling. In Pienta, N.J., Cooper, M.M., Greenbowe, T.J. (Eds.), *Chemists' Guide to Effective Teaching.* Upper Saddle River, NJ: Pearson Prentice Hall.

Champagne, A.B., Klopfer, L.E., and Anderson, J.H. (1980). Factors influencing the learning of classical mechanics. *American Journal of Physics.* 48, 1074-1079.

Domin, D.S. (1999). A content analysis of general chemistry laboratory manuals for evidence of higher-order cognitive tasks. *Journal of Chemical Education.* 76(1), 109-112.

Flavell, J.H. (1976). Metacognitive aspects of problem solving. In L.B. Resnick (Ed.), *The Nature of Intelligence* (pp. 231-235). Hillsdale, NJ: Lawrence Erlbaum Associates, Inc.

Garner, R. and Alexander, P.A. (1989). Metacognition: Answered and unanswered questions. *Educational Psychologist.* 24(2), 143-158.

Harrison, A.G. and Treagust, D.F. (2000). A typology of school science models. *International Journal of Science Education.* 22(9), 1011-1026.

Justi, R. and Gilbert, J. (2002). Models and modeling in chemistry education. In J.K. Gilbert, O. DeJong, R. Justi, D.F. Treagust, and J.H. Van Driel (Eds.) *Chemical education: Towards research-based practice.* Dordrecht: Kluwer Academic Publishers.

King, A. (1990). Enhancing peer interaction and learning in the classroom through reciprocal questioning. *American Educational Research Journal.* 27, 664-687.

Lazarowitz, R. and Tamir, P. (1994). Research on using laboratory instruction. In D.L. Gabel (Ed.), *Handbook of Research on Science Teaching and Learning* (pp. 94-128). NY: MacMillan.

Lloyd, B.W. (1992). The 20th century general chemistry laboratory. *Journal of Chemical Education.* 69(11), 866-869.

Lunetta, V.N., Hofstein, A., and Clough, M.P. (2007). Learning and teaching in the school science laboratory: An analysis of research, theory, and practice. In S.K. Abell and N.G. Lederman (Eds.), *Handbook of Research on Science Education* (pp. 393-441). Mahway, NJ: Lawrence Erlbaum Associates.

Mattox, A.C., Reisner, B.A., and Rickey, D. (2006). What happens when chemical compounds are added to water? An introduction to the Model-Observe-Reflect-Explain (MORE) Thinking Frame. *Journal of Chemical Education. 83(4).*

Rickey, D. (1999). *The Effects of Laboratory Curriculum and Instruction on Undergraduate Students' Understanding of Chemistry.* Ph.D. Thesis, University of California, Berkeley, CA.

Rickey, D. and Stacy, A.M. (2000). The role of metacognition in learning chemistry. *Journal of Chemical Education. 77(7),* 915-920.

Rickey, D., Teichert, M.A., and Tien, L.T. (2006, July). *Investigating instructional conditions that promote reflection, macro-molecular connections, and model revision in the general chemistry laboratory.* Paper presented at the 19th Biennial Conference on Chemical Education, West Lafayette, IN.

Schoenfeld, A.H. (1987). What's all the fuss about metacognition? In A. H. Schoenfeld (Ed.), *Cognitive Science and Mathematics Education.* Hillsdale, NJ: Lawrence Erlbaum Associates, Inc.

Schoenfeld, A.H. (1992). Learning to think mathematically. Problem solving, metacognition, and sense making in mathematics. In D.A. Grouws (Ed.), *Handbook of Research on Mathematics Teaching and Learning: A Project of the National Council of Teachers of Mathematics* (pp. 334-370). New York: Macmillan.

Spencer, J.N. (1993-1994). The general chemistry curriculum: Different times, different students, same course. *Journal of College Science Teaching.* 23(3), 159-161.

Thompson, S. (1990). *Chemtrek: Small-scale experiments for general chemistry.* Upper Saddle River, NJ: Prentice-Hall, Inc.

Tien, L.T. (1998*). Fostering Expert Inquiry Skills and Beliefs about Chemistry through the MORE Laboratory Experience.* Ph.D. Thesis, University of California, Berkeley, CA.

Tien, L.T., Rickey, D., and Stacy, A.M. (1999). The MORE Thinking Frame: Guiding students' thinking in the laboratory. *Journal of College Science Teaching. 28,* 318-324.

Tien, L.T., Teichert, M.A., and Rickey, D. (2007). Effectiveness of a MORE laboratory module in prompting students to revise their molecular-level ideas about solutions. *Journal of Chemical Education. 84(1), 175-181.*

White, R.T. (1992). Implications of recent research on learning for curriculum and assessment. *Journal of Curriculum Studies. 24*(2), 153-164.

12

Technology Based Inquiry Oriented Activities for Large Lecture Environments

Michael R. Abraham
Department of Chemistry and Biochemistry
The University of Oklahoma

John I. Gelder
Department of Chemistry
Oklahoma State University

Abstract

Dissatisfaction with the instructional strategies typically used in large lecture settings has led us to explore more inquiry-oriented approaches. Guided by instructional theory and research on instructional strategies, and aided by recent advances in technology, we have been developing and implementing course materials based on the learning cycle approach that can be conveniently used in large lecture settings. This approach is based on linked activities that students would do before, during, and after a class meeting.

Biographies

Michael R. Abraham is David Ross Boyd Professor of Chemistry and director of freshman chemistry at the University of Oklahoma. He received a B.A. in Chemistry at Grinnell College, a Masters of Arts in Teaching from Emory University, and a Ph.D. in Science Education from Florida State University. He has taught science at all academic levels from elementary school to college. His research interests are in the field of science/chemical education; specifically instructional strategies, student misconceptions, and the use of computers in helping students visualize atomic and molecular behavior. He has developed curriculum materials using inquiry-oriented instructional strategies at the high school and university levels. At present, he directs the Ph.D. program in Chemical Education at the University of Oklahoma. Email: mrabraham@ou.edu.

John I. Gelder is Professor of Chemistry at Oklahoma State University. He is widely known in the chemical education community for his expertise in computer applications in chemistry. He has been active in the development of computer animations since 1978. He has integrated the WWW into his class instruction using PHP and MySQL. He was the Chief Faculty consultant in AP Chemistry for the College Board and the Educational Testing Service from 2001 – 2005 and has chaired the CLEP Examination in Chemistry committee for the Education Testing Service. He is a member of the Board of Publications for the Journal of Chemical Education. Email: john.gelder@okstate.edu.

Introduction

For many years we have been concerned about the instructional effectiveness of the general chemistry courses taken primarily by freshman science majors in large universities. We, like many other faculty members involved in these courses, have become increasingly concerned by the lack of motivation of our students: their refusal to read the textbook, their poor performance on tests, and their shoddy attendance in our classes. Some may argue that the root of these ills can be found in the quality of available textbooks, instructors, or the nature of students. We believe the lack of engagement on the part of our students may be the result of traditional instructional approaches that no longer appeal, if they ever did, to these students. Science education research has shown that a student centered inquiry-based instructional approach develops a positive attitude towards learning, increases student understanding of concepts and improves the ability to use scientific processes (Abraham & Renner, 1983; Lawson, Abraham, & Renner, 1989).

Currently, however, there is a lack of learning materials that support such an approach in a practical manner in the large class setting typical of large universities. As a consequence, instructors are left to their own devises to develop instructional materials that are consistent with effective approaches. To partially address this issue, we propose an instructional approach that supports an inquiry-based instructional strategy (using the Learning Cycle Approach, (Lawson et al., 1989)) that can conveniently and practically be used in large class settings. Specifically, this approach would consist of instructional activities for "before", "during", and "after" class meetings of the large beginning class settings typical in universities. These before, during, and after class activities would be linked together and address a specific learning objective(s) for the course.

Before, During, and After Class Activities

In our approach, students are asked to go to an assigned web site before class and either answer 5 to 7 questions that assess what the student knows or thinks he/she knows about the subject being studied, or generate data using a simulation of a typical laboratory experiment. Responses and data are automatically submitted to the instructor for review before class meets. These Before Class Explorations (BCEs) are designed to require 10 to 15 minutes of a student's time to complete. BCEs can be used to: pool data to be used to invent concepts in lecture, identify student misconceptions to be addressed in lecture, and/or review concepts needed as prerequisite knowledge for a lecture topic. The instructor can access student responses to BCEs and use them to customize their lecture, to address specific students' misconceptions, to assess students' prerequisite knowledge, and to develop charts and graphs of student-generated observations that can be used to invent concepts. One of the goals of BCEs is to encourage students to come to the lecture already thinking about the topic to be discussed. Large lecture classes can be a passive experience for students and BCEs are one method for more actively involving them. Upon submission of the BCE, students receive a copy of the questions and their responses, and where appropriate, an expert's response to the same questions for comparison. Students are advised to bring the response page to class.

The During Class Invention (DCI) develops/invents the concepts or ideas introduced by the BCE. It poses questions/problems that are focused on a course learning objective and are designed to be done in a class setting by small cooperative groups (Johnson, 1991). The questions/problems are presented in a handout or as a class presentation by the instructor (see for example ConcepTests: Landis et al., 2000; Mazur, 1997). Students are expected to have a group discussion and come to a consensus in response to the questions/problems. Students can report their consensus response for the instructor's consideration using a student response system (H-IIT, Educue, eLearning, Interwrite PRS (Duncan, 2005)) and/or by turning in a written response. A class discussion can then be based on the DCI.

The After Class Application (ACA) is a web-based set of questions that will allow students to apply their knowledge and/or practice using concepts introduced by the BCE and invented during the DCI. Both the BCE and ACA are web-based and student responses are stored in a relational database.

The Learning Cycle Approach

The BCE/DCI/ACA approach can be shown to be an application of an inquiry-oriented instructional strategy called the learning cycle approach. The learning cycle approach is a student centered inquiry-oriented approach that is research-based (Abraham, 1998). Instruction using the learning cycle approach can be seen as being divided into phases of instruction (Renner, 1982). First, students are exposed to data or questions (called the Exploration Phase) from which concepts can be derived (called the Invention Phase). Students can then apply the concept to other phenomena (called the Application Phase). In contrast to traditional instructional approaches, this inquiry-oriented approach is based upon data and the use of questions/problems. This difference has several consequences to the role played by various instructional activities. Data and question generating activities play a central role in introducing concepts. Classroom activities are focused on using these data and questions to generate concepts rather than informing students of the concepts. Follow up questions can be used to apply, reinforce, review, and extend concepts. This approach encourages more active learning by students. This instructional strategy can be applied to the "before", "during", and "after" class activities described in the previous section. The "before" class activity can be used to explore the concept, the "during" class activity can be used to invent the concept, and the "after" class activity can be used to apply the concept.

Technology and Large Classes

The learning cycle approach has been successfully used in class settings where the student to teacher ratio allows for the direct monitoring of student responses to questions followed by feedback to the students (Lawson et al., 1989). However, for this approach to be viable in large class settings, methods for dealing with the large number of student responses must be developed. Instructional technology offers a solution for this problem. We devised a system for collecting all the student responses into a relational database (MySQL) through PHP-scripted dynamic web pages that are accessible via any standard web browser. This web page/relational database environment also allows an instructor to access student responses to the BCE/ACA questions. Although limited, the use of widely available standard course management systems (Blackboard, WebCT, and Desire2Learn) can also be used. Readers interested in applying this approach can refer to the implementation section at the end of this chapter.

Rationale for the Approach

A pilot trial of the BCEs and ACAs has been carried out at Oklahoma State University and the University of Oklahoma over the past several years. Students have been asked on an end-of-class survey if they would rather do a BCE or read a selection from a textbook. For the past three semesters that we have used BCEs, above 90% of our students prefer the BCEs. After a recent semester, students were asked about their attitudes towards the ACAs they were doing. Again a majority of students responded positively (72%). Students who responded negatively frequently commented that an ACA was just one more thing to do.

The BCE has several similarities to Just in Time Teaching, JIIT (Novak, Patterson, Gavrin, & Christian, 1999). Just-in-Time Teaching uses a combination of a pre-lecture web component and an active learner classroom to enhance learning when students and teacher are in the classroom. The pre-lecture web components fall into three categories. The first includes both WarmUps and Puzzles. These two web activities typically consist of three questions, two of which are based on a reading assignment. The second category consists of Enrichment Pages. This category stresses reading but also provides links to URLs with additional related materials that provide connections between course content and relevant applications. The last category includes stand-alone instructional materials such as simulations and spreadsheet activities.

While the structure of our approach and JITT are similar in that they both use web-based questions before class, our approach uses an instructional strategy that does not require students to read a section in their textbook and use that knowledge to answer the questions. Rather we want students to use the BCE to generate and use data and their own ideas to explore the concept(s) to be invented in class. By doing this we can gauge students' preconceptions about concepts that they are bringing to class so that they can be effectively addressed during class. In our approach, the textbook plays the role of supporting the invention of concepts, which takes place during class using DCIs, and its role after class to support the application of concepts during ACAs.

Gregor M. Novak and Evelyn T. Patterson have implemented Just-in-Time Teaching in their physics classrooms at Indiana University Purdue University Indianapolis, and the United States Air Force Academy. Over thirty other institutions use Just-in-Time Teaching in many subject areas. Their research results demonstrate improvements in retention rates and cognitive gains. Further evidence for the viability of this approach lies in the large amount of research concerning the Learning Cycle since its origins in the 1960s. Most of the research supporting the Learning Cycle approach is discussed in detail in Lawson, Abraham, & Renner (Lawson et al., 1989). It supports the conclusion that the Learning Cycle approach can result in greater achievement in science, better retention of concepts, improved attitudes toward science and science learning, improved reasoning ability, and superior process skills than would be the case with traditional instructional approaches (see, for example, Abraham & Renner, 1986; Ivins, 1986; McComas III, 1992; Raghubir, 1979; Renner, Abraham, & Birnie, 1985). This is especially true with intermediate level students where instructional activities have a high level of intellectual demand (Lott, 1983). The Learning Cycle Approach is an inquiry oriented instructional strategy that has great promise for chemistry instruction. The Learning Cycle Approach gives guidance to instructors as to how to interact with students during instruction, how to design activities for classroom use, and what to emphasize as the goal of instruction. A wide variety of proven instructional tactics can be utilized within its format (Abraham, 2005).

Cooperative learning and other small group tactics are also an excellent research-proven replacement for more formal teacher-led discussions and lectures (Johnson, 1991; Johnson, Johnson, & Holubec, 1993; Johnson, 1976). Cooperative procedures can also be used in laboratory settings (Abraham & Pavelich, 1999; Cooper, 2003). Cooperative learning activities can be used in many of the phases of the learning cycle approach. As "Exploration Phase" activities, they can be used by students to explore the "what did you observe?" question (for a non-laboratory example see (Moog & Farrell, 2008); as "Concept Invention Phase" activities to organize their data and begin to address the "what does it mean?" question (Abraham, Gelder, & Greenbowe, 2008a: 2008b), and as "Application Phase" activities to address extensions of their concept (Gosser, Strozak, & Cracolice, 2001). In large class settings the use of student response systems make using cooperative learning groups during DCI activities much more viable (Duncan, 2005).

The tactic of exposing students to information questions and data sources as an introduction to concepts (i.e., BCEs) is supported by the "advanced organizer" research of David Ausubel (Ausubel, 1960; Ausubel, 1963; Ausubel, Novak, & Hanesian, 1968). Advanced organizers are presentations/questions/visuals given prior to instruction around which students can organize subsequent knowledge.

Examples of BCE/DCI/ACA Activities

<u>Calorimetry Example:</u> This set of activities is used to establish the variables necessary for measuring heat ($Q=mC\Delta t$) (Abraham & Gelder, 2008). The BCE in Figure 1 is used as an activity to introduce the variables associated with the $Q=mC\Delta t$ equation. Students are asked to complete this BCE before the first lecture/discussion on the subject. Students were not required to read ahead in their texts and our experience has been that most do not do so. The students accessed the BCE on a web site and responded to the questions in the spaces provided.

Question 1 (see Figure 1) is used to establish an inverse relationship between mass and change in temperature. Students are shown a graphic of two containers of water at 25°C. One contains 25mL and the other 50mL. They are heated with the same source for the same amount of time. The students are asked, which sample has the higher final temperature? In a typical semester, 80% of the students correctly selected the beaker on the left. Reasons for selecting the beaker on the right included: "... because as it heats there will be more water evaporating ..." (or similar evaporation responses), "... because there is more there because of the higher volume." (or similar higher volume responses), "... because they had the same amount of heat" (or initial temperature, substance, or same final temperature responses). Other students choose the beaker on the right because of its having more molecules, a larger mass, or higher density. This misconception can be addressed in class using the DCI.

Question 2 establishes a direct relationship between heat and mass. Students are shown a graphic of two containers with different amounts of water at 25°C. They are both heated with the same source. After heating, the final temperature of both samples is the same. Students are asked, which sample absorbed the greater amount of heat? About 12% choose the wrong answer. In the third question students are shown two containers of water at 25°C. They can't see the amount of water in each beaker. The students are asked if twice as much heat is added to one of the beakers, and if that beaker has a lower final temperature, which beaker has more water? About 13% choose the wrong answer and 4% could not answer the question.

1. Consider the two beakers containing water, both at the same initial temperature, say 25 degrees Celsius.

The beaker on the left has 25 mLs of water and the beaker on the right has 50 mLs of water. Both have the same initial temperature. If I add the same amount of heat to both beakers, using a Bunsen burner, does the beaker on the right or the beaker on the left have the higher final temperature? Explain?

2. Consider the two beakers containing water, both at the same initial temperature, say 25 degrees Celsius.

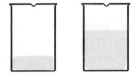

If the final temperature of the water in both beakers is identical, is the greater amount of heat added to the beaker on the right or the beaker on the left? Explain.

3. Consider the two beakers containing water, both at the same initial temperature, say 25 degrees Celsius.

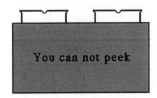

If twice as much heat is added to the beaker on the right compared to the beaker on the left, and the final temperature of the beaker on the right is lower than the beaker on the left, which beaker has more water? Explain.

4. Identical candles are used to add heat three different samples all having the same mass. The three samples are heated for a short period of time (so the wood does not catch on fire.) The three different substances are wood, glass and copper. Each is a cube. Each of the three substances is heated for the same amount of time with its candle. Based on your experience/intuition order the three substances as to its final temperature.

lowest final T..........highest final T

5. Where would water fit in your order? Explain.

6. Suppose you had in view two samples of helium and you could see the atoms of helium at the atomic level. One of the samples of helium is at 25 degrees Celsius and the other is at 50 degrees Celsius. Assuming you were not told which sample was at which temperature, explain how you would identify which sample was at which temperature.

7. Is there anything about the questions that you feel you do not understand? List your concerns/questions.

8. If there were one question you would like to have answered in lecture, what would that question be?

Figure 1. Calorimetry Example BCE

Questions 4 and 5 introduce the idea that different substances absorb different amounts of heat. Students are asked to compare equal masses of wood, glass, and copper. Each is heated for the same time and students are asked to compare the final temperature of the three samples. 55% had the correct order. Most of the students who had the wrong order were correct concerning the wood sample but not with glass and copper.

Question 6 attempts to link the macroscopic and submicroscopic views of heat and temperature. Surprisingly, almost 22% of the students said they could not answer this question. Only 48% stated that the molecules at a higher temperature would be moving faster. The most common response was that hotter particles would be farther apart. Many of the students who gave wrong answers still had a basic understanding of the relationships between heat, temperature, and mass. The following DCIs and ACAs were designed to solidify this understanding.

After the students respond to these questions, they submit their answers to a database that can be accessed by the instructor. They are also given a copy of the questions with their answers and an expert's answer to the questions for comparison. The answers to these questions point out that our students often lack ideas about chemical phenomena that we often take for granted. These are issues that make for good discussions in class.

DCI – In class, students are provided with an activity sheet (see Figure 2) (Abraham, Gelder & Greenbowe, 2008a) that asks students to respond to questions that are a follow-up to the BCE. This activity can be done in cooperative groups. Student responses can be collected using "clickers." The responses to the questions can then be used for class discussion resulting in the invention of the mathematical relationship Q=mCΔT.

Table 1 contains the responses from 191 students who participated in the DCI. The majority of the students were able to transfer their qualitative understandings of mass, heat and temperature relationships from the BCE and the expert responses that were provided to the quantitative questions of the DCI. The students who missed questions 1 and 2 probably didn't realize that the critical issue was temperature change rather than just temperature. The concept of specific heat content (Question 6) was not understood by 48% of the students, but 23% got it right and 29% saw there was an issue with using ethanol instead of water but didn't know how to handle it. This question provides a way to introduce the concept of specific heat capacity into the relationship (q α mass·ΔT) they used to answer Questions 4 and 5.

As a follow up to the in-class discussion students are directed to an after class application (ACA) of what they have learned about the Q=mC$_s$Δt as a self-test (see Figure 3). After submitting their answers to the questions they are given expert answers to the questions.

1.   Two containers of water are at 20 °C initially. One contains 50 mLs and the other 100 mLs. They are each heated with the same source of heat for the same amount of time. If the final temperature of the 50 mLs sample were 50 °C what would be the final temperature of the 100 mLs sample?

      A.   50 °C
      B.   80 °C
      C.   25 °C
      D.   100 °C
      E.   35 °C

Explain:

2.   Two containers each have 50 mLs of water at 20 °C initially. They are each heated with the same source of heat. One is heated for ten minutes and the other for five minutes. If the container that was heated for five minutes has a final temperature 30 °C what would be the final temperature of the other sample?

      A.   35 °C
      B.   40 °C
      C.   60 °C
      D.   25 °C
      E.   30 °C

Explain:

3. Two containers of water are at 20 °C initially. One contains 50 g of water and is heated by a source for a specified time to a final temperature of 30 °C. The second container has an unknown amount of water and is heated with the same source to 30 °C. However, it takes twice as long to get to this final temperature. How much water is in this container?

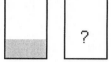

    A.   100 g
    B.   25 g
    C.   30 g
    D.   50 g
    E.   75 g

Explain:

4. 50 mLs of water at 80 °C is added to 50 mLs of water at 20 °C. What would be the final temperature?

    A.   60 °C
    B.   40 °C
    C.   30 °C
    D.   20 °C
    E.   50 °C

Explain:

5. 50 mLs of water at 80 °C is added to 100 mLs of water at 20 °C. What would be the final temperature?

    A.   70 °C
    B.   40 °C
    C.   30 °C
    D.   60 °C
    E.   50 °C

Explain:

6. 50 g of water at 80 °C is added to 50 g of ethyl alcohol at 20 °C. What would be the approximate final temperature?

    A.   60 °C
    B.   40 °C
    C.   30 °C
    D.   20 °C
    E.   50 °C

Explain:

Figure 2. Calorimetry Example DCI (Source: Abraham, Gelder & Greenbowe, 2006, pp. 37-38)

Responses to DCI

Response	Question 1	Question 2	Question 3	Question 4	Question 5	Question 6
A	2%	0.5%	95%*	5%	0.5%	23%*
B	0.5%	76%*	1%	0.5%	84%*	6%
C	41%	23%	0	0	5%	5%
D	0.5%	0.5%	0.5%	0	2%	0
E	55%*	0	10.5%	94%*	4%	36%
Blank	0.5%	0	10.5%	0.5%	5%	29%

    * Correct Answer

Table 1. Responses to DCI

1. How much heat (in joules) is required to change the temperature of 200.0 grams of H_2O from 23.2°C to 87.3°C? (Remember the specific heat of $H_2O(l)$ is 4.184 J g^{-1} °C^{-1} and that q(heat) = mass*specific heat*T.)

2. How much heat (in joules) is required to change the temperature of 200.0 grams of Cu from 23.2°C to 87.3°C? (Remember the specific heat of Cu(s) is 0.384 J g^{-1} °C^{-1}.)

3. Calculate the final temperature when 25.0 grams of H_2O at 23.5°C are added to 27.0 grams of H_2O at 63.5°C.

4. Calculate the final temperature when a 58.0 gram sample of Cu, initially at 98.5°C, is added to 205.0 grams of H_2O at 24.0°C.

5. Is there anything about the questions that you feel that you don't understand? List your concerns/questions.

6. If there were one question you would like to have answered in lecture, what would that question be?

Figure 3. Calorimetry Example ACA

An alternative ACA activity or subsequent BCE activity is based on Figure 4. Students are shown a graphic depicting a container of water being heated by a candle. The original mass of the candle and temperature of the water is given. After a period of time, the final mass of the candle and temperature of the water is given. Students are asked to calculate the heat transferred in this exercise. Given the equation for the combustion of candle wax (2 $C_{28}H_{58}$ + 85 O_2 → 58 H_2O + 56 CO_2 + q), students are then asked, "What is the value for q in this equation?" This can be used as an introduction for the determination of ΔH_{rxn}.

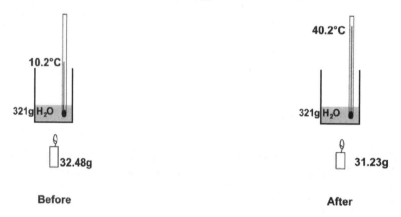

Figure 4. Alternative ACA/BCE

<u>Activities of Metals Example:</u> A second BCE/DCI/ACA example shows a set of activities designed to introduce the idea of an activity series, half reactions, and to introduce oxidation-reduction reactions. It uses a Flash animation of metal/metal ion interactions developed by Tom Greenbowe (Greenbowe, 2008). On a web site students are shown a macroscopic laboratory simulation of possible reactions between series of metals with corresponding metal ions. Students are randomly assigned to collect data on one of three sets of metals/metal ions and to rank the metals and metal ions from most to least reactive. They are then asked to bring their activity series to class.

DCI – In a class discussion based on the BCE activities, students are asked to enter their data into a form that shows a comparison between each metal and metal ion (see Figure 5).

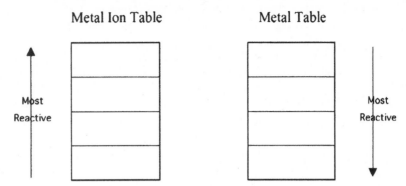

Figure 5. Ordering Metal/Metal Ion Reactivity

This table is used to invent the idea of a half reaction by relating the left and right hand side of the table by adding electrons to balance the relationship. Students in their cooperative groups are then asked to generate a rule for using the table (now a reduction half reaction table) and to predict what combinations will react and what combinations will not. They are also asked to predict what the products of the reactions are and how they can use the half reactions to confirm these predictions. Finally they are asked to combine their activity series of metal/metal ions with the other two developed by other students into a larger activity series. They will be able to do this because the three sets of metals/metal ions have overlapping examples.

ACA –Students are asked to return to the metal/metal ion simulation and do an activity showing the reaction of the metals of their previous activity interacting with acid (hydrogen ion). Using this data they are asked to include hydrogen ion in their reduction table.

Implementing the Approach

There are three options for implementing BCEs and ACAs in your own classroom. A large sample of activities that can be used as DCIs can be found in an activity manual published by Hayden-McNeil (Abraham, Gelder & Greenbowe, 2008a; Abraham, Gelder & Greenbowe, 2008b) and Wiley (Moog and Farrell, 2008).

Option I. Using existing course management systems: Course management systems such as WebCT, Blackboard, and Desire2Learn (D2L) are widely used. These systems have the facility for grading and storing student responses to questions. As such, they could be used to present the BCEs and ACA to students and store their responses. Accessing these responses for review, however, is limited. Blackboard and D2L will grade the responses and assign grades to students, but will only allow the review of the actual responses one student at a time. If you have several hundred students, you could only randomly select students to get a feel for what your class knows about a topic. There is no way to download the students' responses into an Excel database for rapid perusal. These course management systems are being constantly updated and may allow for downloading student responses into a database in the future. WebCT will allow the download of student responses in quiz mode, but only for multiple-choice questions. WebCT will allow open-ended responses to be downloaded in survey mode. However, in survey mode providing expert answers for student to compare with their answers is not an option. Constructing the actual questions and embedding simulations and other visuals into these course management systems can be tedious.

Option II. Using the existing BCE Web site: Contact the author JIG for information about using the existing set of BCEs or ACAs in your classroom. We have approximately 100 BCEs and ACAs for a first year introductory chemistry course for your review and/or use in your class.

Option III. Using IT expertise at your institution: Contact JIG for information about setting up a server to support Web, PHP and MySQL services. This option offers the greatest flexibility. However, it requires a moderate level of technical support on both the software and hardware side. More information regarding this option is available (Abraham and Gelder, 2008).

In comparing the three options, option I is the easiest to set up, if you're familiar with the course management system, but has the most administrative limitations. Option II requires the least set-up, but you can't customize the questions to your class. Option III is the most flexible and powerful, but requires expert help in setting up the system. However, no matter which option is used, a moderate knowledge of web based systems and tools is useful. Following is a discussion of some of the basics.

All BCEs and ACAs that we have developed use HTML and PHP scripting languages and MySQL query language. (These are defined below.) A web page written using HTML (HyperText Markup Language) is a text file that contains markup tags that tell the computer how to present the page over the web. There are a large number of books/manuals that are available that summarize the set of markup tags, their function and their attributes (Pence, 2003; Pfaffenberger, Karow, White, & Schafer, 2004). As of this writing the current release of HTML is version 4.01. Version 5 has been published in a draft form. Since an HTML page is just a text file, with an .htm or .html extension, HTML pages are very easy to generate. Any text editor, such as TextEdit (Mac OS) or WordPad (Windows), can be used to write an HTML page, but there are also very good web development tools such as Dreamweaver™ (by MacroMedia) that provide easy access to all the markup tags, their definition, attributes and other important features. Dreamweaver is particularly useful, as it will allow the user to enter the text of a document and automatically format the page into HTML. You can also save Word documents as HTML files.

PHP is a scripting language that runs on a web server, so it is referred to as server side language. PHP is used to generate dynamic, interactive web pages. Like HTML there are many reference books that are available to introduce the scripting language (e.g. Converse & Park, 2004; Welling & Thomson, 2003; Lerdorf, Tatroe, & MacIntyre, 2006). For an online PHP reference link to http://php.net. The language is not based on markup tags like HTML, but it is as easy to learn. One additional important feature of PHP is that it supports the inclusion of query language commands that allow access to data in most popular relational databases.

MySQL is a relational database server software package that is also open source like PHP. MySQL, like PHP, is very versatile in that it runs on any platform under the more popular operating systems and is free. A database is several things but first and foremost it is a collection of data. In general a relational database consists of a set of tables into which the data is organized. The real trick to using a relational database is the design of the tables. Considerable effort is required to determine the data that is stored in each table to maximize the efficiency of the storage and retrieval of the data. However, we have found that a less than efficient database design has had no effect on the speed with which students send or receive information from the database. Retrieval of the data from the database involves the use of a query language that is embedded into a browser page using PHP scripting language. More information regarding HTML, PHP and MySQL is available (Abraham and Gelder, 2008). A sample of HTML, PHP and MySQL query code is available from JIG (Abraham and Gelder, 2008).

Summary

Involving students to take a more active role in their learning is a challenge in large lecture settings. Using advances in technology and instruction, a strategy based on before, during, and after class activities can be utilized. These activities encourage students to think about chemistry content before class, to explore concepts during class, and to test their comprehension after class thus extending their learning beyond the classroom setting.

Suggested Readings

Abraham, M. R. (2005). Inquiry and the learning cycle approach. In N. J. Pienta, M. M. Cooper & T. J. Greenbowe (Eds.), *Chemists' Guide to Effective Teaching* (pp. 41-52). Upper Saddle River, N. J.: Prentice Hall. This article discusses the rationale for inquiry instruction and gives guidelines for constructing activities for teaching chemistry concepts.

Novak, G. M., Patterson, E. T., Gavrin, A. D., & Christian, W. (1999). *Just-in-time teaching: Blending active learning with web technology.* Upper Saddle River, NJ: Prentice-Hall. This is a primer on web teaching and using pre-lecture activities.

References

Abraham, M. R. (1998). The learning cycle approach as a strategy for instruction in science. In K. Tobin & B. Fraser (Eds.), *International handbook of science education, Part 1* (pp. 513-524). The Netherlands: Kluwer.

Abraham, M. R. (2005). Inquiry and the learning cycle approach. In N. J. Pienta, M. M. Cooper & T. J. Greenbowe (Eds.), *Chemists' guide to effective teaching* (pp. 41-52). Upper Saddle River, N. J.: Prentice Hall.

Abraham, M. R. and Gelder, J. I. (accessed April, 2008). Before, During and After Class Project. http://genchem1.chem.okstate.edu/CCLIEMD05/BCE.html.

Abraham, M.R., Gelder, J.I., & Greenbowe, T.J. (2008a). *During class inventions and computer lab activities Volume I,* (3rd ed.) *Plymouth, MI: Hayden-McNeil.*

Abraham, M.R., Gelder, J.I., & Greenbowe, T.J. (2008b). *During class inventions and computer lab activities Volume II,* (3rd ed.) *Plymouth, MI: Hayden-McNeil.*

Abraham, M. R., & Pavelich, M. J. (1999). *Inquiries into chemistry 3rd ed, Teacher's Guide* (3rd ed.). Prospect Heights, IL: Waveland Press.

Abraham, M. R., & Renner, J. W. (1983). *Sequencing language and activities in teaching high school chemistry: A report to the National Science Foundation.* Norman, OK: Science Education Center, University of Oklahoma (ERIC Document Reproduction Service No. ED 241 267).

Abraham, M. R., & Renner, J. W. (1986). The sequence of learning cycle activities in high school chemistry. *Journal of Research in Science Teaching, 23*(2), 121-143.

Ausubel, D. P. (1960). The use of advanced organizers in the learning and retention of meaningful verbal material. *Journal of Educational Psychology, 51*, 267-272.

Ausubel, D. P. (1963). *The psychology of meaningful verbal learning.* New York: Grune & Stratton.

Ausubel, D. P., Novak, J. D., & Hanesian, H. (1968). *Educational psychology: A cognitive view* (2nd ed.). New York: Holt, Rinehart and Winston.

Cooper, M. M. (2003). *Cooperative chemistry: Laboratory manual, 2nd Ed* (2 ed.). Boston: McGraw Hill.

Converse, T. & Park, J. (2004). *PHP5 and MySQL bible.* Indianapolis, IN: Wiley.

Duncan, D. (2005). *Clickers in the classroom: How to enhance science teaching using classroom response systems.* San Francisco, CA: Benjamin Cummings.

Gosser, D. K., Strozak, V. S., & Cracolice, M. S. (2001). *Peer-led team learning: General chemistry.* Upper Saddle River, NJ: Prentice Hall.

Greenbowe, T. (accessed April, 2008) . Computer animations and computer simulations: Reactions of metals and metal ions. http://www.chem.iastate.edu/group/Greenbowe/sections/projectfolder/flashfiles/redox/home.html.

Ivins, J. E. (1986). *A comparison of the effects of two instructional sequences involving science laboratory activities.* Unpublished doctoral dissertation, University of Cincinnati.

Johnson, D. W. (1991). *Active learning: Cooperation in the college classroom.* Minneapolis, MN: Burgess.

Johnson, D. W., Johnson, R. T., & Holubec, E. J. (1993). *Cooperation in the classroom.* Minneapolis, MN: Burgess.

Johnson, R. T. (1976). The relationship between cooperation and inquiry in science classrooms. *Journal of Research in Science Teaching, 13*(1), 55-63.

Landis, C. R., Ellis, A. B., Lisensky, G. C., Lorenz, J. K., Meeker, K., & Wamser, C. C. (2000). *Chemistry concepTests: A pathway to interactive classrooms.* Upper Saddle River, NJ: Prentice Hall.

Lawson, A. E., Abraham, M. R., & Renner, J. W. (1989). *A theory of instruction: Using the learning cycle to teach science concepts and thinking skills [Monograph, Number One].* Kansas State University, Manhattan, KS: National Association for Research in Science Teaching.

Lerdorf, R., Tatroe, K., & MacIntyre, P. (2006). *Programming PHP, 2nd ed.* Sebastopol, CA: O'Reilly Media.

Lott, G. W. (1983). The effect of inquiry teaching and advanced organizers upon student outcomes in science education. *Journal of Research in Science Teaching, 20*(5), 437-451.

Mazur, E. (1997). *Peer instruction: A users manual.* Upper Saddle River, New Jersey: Prentice Hall.

McComas III, W. F. (1992). *The nature of exemplary practice in secondary school science laboratory instruction: A case study approach.* University of Iowa.

Moog, R. S., & Farrell, J. J. (2008). *Chemistry: A guided Inquiry,* (4th ed.). New York: Wiley.

MySQL. (accessed April, 2008). http://www.mysql.com .

Novak, G. M., Patterson, E. T., Gavrin, A. D., & Christian, W. (1999). *Just-in-time teaching: Blending active learning with web technology.* Upper Saddle River, NJ: Prentice-Hall.

Pence, J. H. (2003). *How to do everything with HTML and XHTML.* Emeryville, CA: McGraw-Hill Osborne Media.

Pfaffenberger, B., B. Karow, C. White, & S. M. Schafer. (2004). *HTML, XHTML, and CSS bible (Bible), 3rd ed.* Indianapolis, IN: Wiley.

Raghubir, K. P. (1979). The laboratory-investigative approach to science instruction. *Journal of Research in Science Teaching, 16*(1), 13-18.

Ray, J. and Ray, W. (2005). MacOSX tiger unleashed. Indianapolis, IN, SAMS Publishing.

Renner, J. W. (1982). The power of purpose. *Science Education, 66*(5), 709-716.

Renner, J. W., Abraham, M. R., & Birnie, H. H. (1985). The importance of the form of student acquisition of data in physics learning cycles. *Journal of Research in Science Teaching, 22*(4), 303-325.

Welling, L. & Thomson, L. (2003). *PHP & MySQL web development.* USA: Sams Publishing.

13

Using Visualization Technology and Group Activities in Large Chemistry Courses

James P. Birk
Department of Chemistry and Biochemistry
Arizona State University

Richard C. Bauer
Department of Chemistry and Biochemistry
Arizona State University

Debra E. Leedy
Department of Chemistry
Glendale Community College

Abstract

Reforms were implemented in lecture for a two-semester general chemistry course and in laboratories for five different first-year college chemistry courses. Reforms fell into five categories: (1) The course focus was changed to a molecular-level conceptual understanding of chemical phenomena instead of a more algorithmic-based approach of mathematical descriptions. (2) A variety of multimedia was incorporated into the lecture courses to support a more molecular and conceptual approach. (3) The quantitative portion of the lecture course was refocused on an understanding of chemical behavior rather than on manipulating numbers. Students work out their own procedures for solving problems rather than following algorithms modeled by the instructor. (4) Lecture time is used for various types of cooperative learning exercises. (5) All first-year chemistry laboratory courses were converted to inquiry labs in which students solve problems in a student-directed environment using cooperative groups. These changes were evaluated by examining student outcomes as follows: exam performance, student attendance at lecture, student persistence in the courses, student success in the courses, student persistence and success in organic chemistry, and student attitude surveys. In each case, the reformed courses have a higher level of the desired outcome.

Biographies

James P. Birk is Emeritus Professor of Chemistry and Biochemistry and a faculty member in the Center for Research on Education in Science, Math, Engineering, and Technology at Arizona State University. He received a B.A. degree in chemistry from St. John's University (Minn.) and a Ph.D. in physical chemistry from Iowa State University. After a post-doctorate at the University of Chicago, he started his academic career at the University of Pennsylvania, where he was appointed to the Rhodes-Thompson Chair of Chemistry. Initially doing research on mechanisms of inorganic reactions, he switched to research on various areas of chemical education after moving to Arizona State University as Coordinator of General Chemistry. His teaching responsibilities have been in General Chemistry, Introductory Chemistry, Chemistry for Engineers, Inorganic Chemistry, Methods of Teaching Chemistry, and graduate courses on Inorganic Reaction Mechanisms, Chemical Education, and Science Education. He has received several teaching awards, including Awards for Distinction in Undergraduate Teaching, Teaching Innovation

Awards, the National Catalyst Award, and the President's Medal for Team Excellence. He has been a feature editor for the Journal of Chemical Education, editing the columns: Filtrates and Residues, The Computer Series, and Teaching with Technology. Recent research has focused on visualization (such as Dynamic Visualization in Chemistry and The Hidden Earth), on inquiry-based instruction, and on misconceptions (Chemistry Concept Inventory).

Richard C. Bauer completed his B.S. degree in chemistry at Saginaw Valley State University. While pursuing his undergraduate degree he worked at Dow Chemical as a student technologist. He pursued Masters and Ph.D. degrees in Chemistry Education at Purdue University. He then spent two years at Clemson University as a visiting assistant professor. He presently serves as General Chemistry Coordinator at Arizona State University, where he has implemented an inquiry-based laboratory program. He has taught Introductory and General Chemistry courses for 12 years, and also teaches a Methods of Chemistry Teaching course. In addition to general chemistry lab development, he has interests in student visualization of abstract, molecular-level concepts; TA training; and methods of secondary school chemistry teaching.

Debra E. Leedy received a B.A. degree in mathematics and chemistry from Texas Christian University, an M.S. degree in chemistry from Arizona State University, and a Ph.D. degree in science education from Arizona State University. After doing postdoctoral work in geology education at Arizona State University, she has joined the chemistry faculty at Glendale Community College. She has done extensive work in science visualization, having worked on the Dynamic Visualization in Chemistry and the Hidden Earth projects. She has taught courses in Introductory Chemistry, General Chemistry and Methods of Teaching Chemistry.

Introduction

We wish to report here on efforts to improve introductory courses in chemistry (and other sciences) taken by pre-service teachers and science majors (Wyckoff 2001). These courses were reformed to better serve as models of effective teaching methods in the expectation that the prospective teachers would then be more likely to adopt these methods for their own teaching. The chemistry reforms were initiated during Spring 1996 for the first semester of a two-semester sequence in general chemistry (CHM-113) and were continued into the second semester of this sequence (CHM-115) during Spring 1997. These courses are taken primarily by science majors, including pre-med students, and to a lesser extent, by engineering majors. In each course, the reforms were piloted with a small group of students by the senior author, then scaled up to full-size during the second offering of the reformed course, and have now been expanded to multiple sections of the courses.

Nature of Reforms

Lecture sessions make use of group activities, with an emphasis on atomic/molecular explanations and multimedia presentations to initiate student-instructor interactive exchanges and student group discussions. Problem solving, which has traditionally been a significant part of these courses, is now presented in a non-algorithmic format, with little instructor modeling of problem solving strategies. Laboratory experiences make use of group work in an inquiry format, in part using calculator-based laboratory (CBL) probes (Holmquist, Randall, Volz 1995; Bauer, Birk, Sawyer 2004).

Modify Role of Students in Lecture

Previous research has shown that lecture is ineffective in promoting student learning in general chemistry (Birk, Foster 1993). To modify the lecture environment, we now have students participate in classroom discussions and activities in permanently established groups of four. Lecture time is limited to about half the class period and is used largely for multimedia presentations that help initiate student discussions. The student groups are assigned so that groups will be as heterogeneous as possible (Nurrenbern 1995). Group activities are used to make lecture an active learning environment. Short activities of 5-10 minutes are used 3 to 6 times per class period. Lab groups consist of the same students as the lecture groups.

Multimedia Presentations to Initiate Discussion

Because the focus of these courses is on developing atomic or molecular level explanations for chemical phenomena, we make extensive use of molecular modeling software such as Rasmol (Sayle, Milner-White 1995). Other software involving molecular explanations has been developed at ASU (Birk, Leedy, Lihs, Morgan, Nickoles, Drake, McKelvy 2003; Birk 1997, 1998). Any software that is not copyrighted to others is made available to the students to use in a computer laboratory or to take home, if they wish. In addition, many molecular animations developed for the course have been published as interactive CD-ROMs (Birk 1998; Birk, Marks 2000, 2002). The general format of our lecture courseware involves visualizations once available on videotape or videodisk, along with QuickTime movies and computer software, merged into PowerPoint presentations to give seamless access to all the visualization tools that we have assembled. During the development of our reform efforts, we have converted much of the video to QuickTime format to reduce the amount of required hardware and to make the material more easily accessible. While much of this multimedia is on the hard drives of Pentium laptop computers, we also use numerous CDs available from *Journal of Chemical Education: Software* and various textbook publishers, along with CDs prepared in our lab containing animations coupled with microscopic and macroscopic video (Birk, Leedy, Lihs, Morgan, Nickoles, Drake, McKelvy 2003).

Student Reactions to Multimedia

Students are favorably inclined toward the use of multimedia and group discussions. Although the learning environment is initially strange to most students, they adapt quickly and there is very little resistance to the changes we have made. Initially there was some dismay that the classroom had to be kept only dimly lighted, but this problem disappeared as brighter projectors became available. After becoming accustomed to the reformed classroom, student reaction is typified by the following comment: "Thanks for putting together all the computer animations. This is the first time chemistry has made any sense to me. Seeing the molecules moving around made things click for me."

Problem Solving

We have substituted group explorations for algorithmic problem solving. The focus is now on understanding the underlying principles rather than on manipulating numbers. The course instructor no longer models how to solve numerical problems. Instead, instruction on numerical problem solving is done by peers in cooperative groups. After conceptual development of the background, students are given problems to solve during class time. When most of the students have completed the problem, groups are asked to compare their answers. Additional discussion ensues if the groups do not agree on the solution to the problem. The course instructor and any teaching assistants who are present circulate among the groups, listen to the discussions, and serve as resources as needed.

Example of Lecture Activities

As an example of typical classroom activities, chemical reactions are introduced in the following manner. As a demonstration, two beakers containing clear colorless liquids are poured together, with no visible effect other than volume change. Students are asked whether a chemical reaction occurred. They respond in the negative based on the absence of any visible change. The mixed liquid is then demonstrated to be hot, at which point they change their conclusion. The students are then asked to work in their groups to compose a list of clues that nature might offer that can be used to conclude that a reaction had occurred. The lists are shared with the class and are illustrated with images or videos that the instructor has pre-assembled in Powerpoint format. These lists are usually much richer than the few clues that are usually mentioned in textbooks.

Students are then asked how we might predict whether a chemical reaction would occur and what the products would be. The discussion is guided to the use of periodicity and classification. Students are then presented with a set of labeled atomic/molecular models:

They are asked to work with these representations in their small groups to draw pictures of all the different types of atomic-molecular changes these substances could undergo. Discussion results are summarized on the board for the class. The groups are then asked to examine these results to create the smallest possible number of classes. This discussion results in the classical four classes of reactions: decomposition, combination, single displacement, and double displacement. The class then is asked to assign suitable names for these classes and they generally come up with those mentioned. Examples of each class are presented in the form of molecular representations to further illustrate the features of each class (Figure 1). Students are then asked to work in their groups to classify about 20 chemical reactions on a worksheet. This entire sequence of activities takes about one class period. These and related activities are elaborated in more detail elsewhere (Bauer, Birk, Marks 2006).

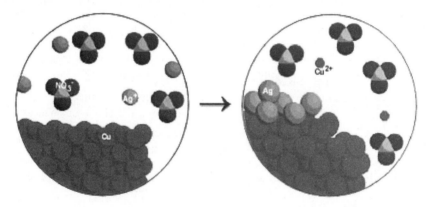

Figure 1. A typical molecular diagram used in CHM-113 to illustrate single-displacement reactions was created with Rasmol and Photoshop. Students are told that the water was omitted to simplify the images. Molecular art was originally rendered in color.

How do we accommodate group work in large lecture halls?

Most work on the use of cooperative learning has involved a restructuring of the classroom so students can work around a table in small groups. After the initial pilot group of 24 students, this was not possible. Our large lectures (150-200 students) are situated in ramped lecture theaters with fixed seats, which cannot be remodeled to provide a more suitable environment. Nor were there other facilities available to us that were more appropriate. This situation inappropriately prevented us from trying these reforms at an earlier date. During Fall 1995, it was decided to try group activities a few times in a large classroom to see how students would cope and how they would react to these activities. As a result of positive reactions from the students, we developed a fully reformed course during Spring 1996. Students are directed to become acquainted with their assigned group members during their lab period during the first week of class. Students are then expected to sit in the lecture hall with their group members by the end of the first week. The most appropriate configuration of seating to allow the students to work in their groups is left up to them. In most cases, they sit next to one another and those sitting on the outside lean in to talk with those sitting in the middle of the four seats. Some groups choose to sit in two rows, which requires the front students to turn around in their seats or the rear students to lean over the front seats.

How do we find time for group work?

A common objection to spending time on multimedia and group activities arises from skepticism about the possibility of covering all the course material. In fact, the reformed course covers all the major topics and most of the minor ones that were covered before. How is this possible? Several timesaving strategies are incorporated into the reformed courses. Based on former lecture notes, it was estimated that about 30% of class time in the past was spent working problems at the board to model problem solving for students. Problem solving is no longer modeled for students; they spend this time working on problems in groups instead. Considerable time was previously spent at the blackboard to transfer notes from the lecturer's paper to the students' papers. Use of multimedia frees up this time. All the class notes are presented with PowerPoint. Students are provided with a set of the class notes so they do not have to attempt to copy all the text on the PowerPoint slides. Although pre-organized notes prevent spontaneity in the lecture to some extent, it is relatively easy to make instantaneous changes by adding PowerPoint slides during the lecture period, and the PowerPoint notes are primarily bulleted lists, which allow for considerable spontaneity in the discussions. Students still have to add details of discussion results to their notes. In addition, the PowerPoint slides contain many images of chemical phenomena and molecular-level explanations, as well as links to video and animations that can be activated with a click of the mouse. More links are included than are typically used to provide additional flexibility to illustrate concepts during discussions. Images of the PowerPoint slides themselves are available on a course web site (http://www.public.asu.edu/~jpbirk/).

Copyright Issues. Much of the art used in these slides was produced locally, especially the molecular art, which is readily created with Rasmol and an image-editing program such as Photoshop. Although we took photographs ourselves if they were not otherwise available, most photographs were taken from images supplied with the textbook used in the course. Posting these copyrighted images requires permission of the textbook publisher. Such permission is generally granted, although it may be necessary to restrict the web site to local use only, depending on the wishes of the publisher. Negotiations of this sort would probably be quite sucessful if made at the time of textbook adoption decisions. Alternatively, the image on the website slide could be replaced with a reference to location of the textbook image.

Inquiry Labs

Students work in cooperative groups of four to develop their own procedures to solve chemical problems. These problems are kept simple enough that the students are likely to develop meaningful solutions. Students are generally given more than one lab period to plan and complete their experiment, giving them the opportunity to try several ideas and pursue the most promising. They are also able to collect preliminary data and then return the next week to improve their lab techniques after preliminary data analysis. When appropriate, the students use calculator-based laboratory (CBL) probes. Data are collected into the memory of TI-82 or TI-83 Plus graphing calculators and then transferred to floppy disks by means of computers located in each laboratory room, using GraphLink software and cables (Wyckoff 2001). This allows for faster data collection and analysis. The emphasis of these experiments is on inventing ways to solve experimental problems, rather than on getting an answer that matches a preconceived conclusion. Student instructions are very brief (Bauer, Birk, Sawyer 2004), usually only one page. Students write complete reports and are required to rewrite them until they are acceptable. Grading is based on the number of rewrites required to produce an acceptable report rather than on matching their answer to a predetermined result.

Reform Outcomes

The reformed courses have been offered continuously since 1996. We collected data on course outcomes for a six-year period. We stopped collecting data when all sections were using active learning techniques, since we no longer had sections to use as a control. Not every section uses active learning techniques every semester, depending on the particular faculty that are teaching the courses during a given semester, but these techniques have been maintained in some sections up to the present. Lab reforms were implemented over a period of two years and now include all sections of these courses, as well as all other first-year courses in our program (about 3000 students per year). In the following comparisons, a single instructor (the senior author) taught all the reformed courses and sections taught by several other instructors are combined as a control.

Persistence. Students stay in the course to a greater extent. Typical withdrawal rates from these courses in the past have been in the 20-30% range. In the reformed courses, the average withdrawal rate has decreased to 3.2% (Table 1). The reformed sections have significantly fewer withdrawals than the control sections. The sections taught by the senior author prior to the reforms (Fall 1994 and Fall 1995) had about the same withdrawal rates as the control sections. Thus, the lower withdrawal rates cannot be attributed to the instructor, but rather to the teaching style of the instructor. When all sections of CHM-113 were reformed, we had withdrawal rates around 3% for the entire course. Over the past 4 years, with a mixture of reformed and unreformed sections, the overall withdrawal rate has been in the range of 6-8%, still a considerable improvement over what we saw before these reforms were initiated.

Student Success and Persistence in Reformed Courses

Course	Semester	Year	Students	Grades: D	E	W
CHM-113	Spring	1996	24	1	0	1
CHM-113	Summer	1996	73	1	0	2
CHM-115	Spring	1997	47	0	0	1
CHM-115	Spring	1998	157	5	0	3
CHM-113	Fall	1997	186	7	1	12
CHM-113	Fall	1998	187	12	1	6
CHM-115	Spring	1999	161	3	3	3
CHM-113	Fall	1999	191	8	6	7
CHM-115	Spring	2000	153	2	0	3
		Overall Percent of 1179 students:		3.3%	0.9%	3.2%

Table 1. Student Success and Persistence in Reformed Courses

Course Grades. Students succeed in the course to a greater extent. During the pilot offering of CHM-113, 9 of 24 students were repeating the course because of poor grades (D or E; Note: E is our grade for failing); all 9 received grades of A or B. Since the reforms started, very few students have received grades of D or E (see Table 1). Upon examination of grade files for all our courses over a period of time, it was determined that our multiple instructors generally used similar cutoff points for grades of D and E. (The reformed sections use pre-established grade cutoffs.) Thus, we decided to do a comparison of students who did not complete the course with a grade of C or better. The combination of D, E, and W grades is 7.4% in the reformed courses, so over 92% of those students are now completing and passing the reformed courses with a grade of C or better. These results are compared with results for the control sections in CHM-113 in Figure 2. Again, note the dramatic difference between reformed and control sections, and the higher rate of failure for the reform section prior to reform. Results were similar for CHM-115. In both cases, the grade pattern improved for the sections taught by the senior author after reforms were instituted.

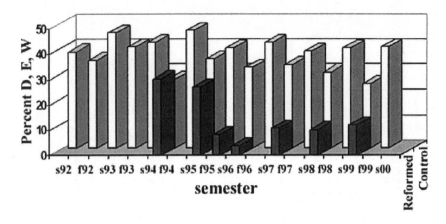

Figure 2. Course grades of D, E, and W for CHM-113. No course reforms were implemented during Fall '94, some course reforms were tested during Fall '95, and the reforms were adopted fully in Spring '96.

Lecture Attendance. Our earlier research showed that lecture was ineffective in promoting student learning in general chemistry (Birk, Foster 1993). In these studies we saw little difference in performance between students who attended or did not attend lecture. In addition, there was no correlation between performance in a later course and the identity of the instructor who taught an earlier course in the sequence. In these studies, we found that attendance at lectures averaged between 30% and 70%, depending on the lecturer. Attendance at lecture in the reformed courses, measured by occasional counts and from the number of unannounced in-lecture quizzes that were turned in, has increased to 90% or more. In the earlier study, we examined the correlation between exam performance and self-reported attendance at lecture. In Figure 3, we compare this to a study done for the Fall 2000 reformed class based on the number of in-class quizzes taken by each student. In the original study, we found no correlation between performance and attendance; the correlation coefficient was -0.297, but with a two-tailed significance of 0.302. A fit of the data has a slope of -0.086 ± 0.080, which also indicates there is no significant correlation. In contrast, data for the reformed class has a correlation coefficient of 0.828, with a two-tailed significance of 0.003. The slope is 0.26 ± 0.06. In the reformed class, exam performance does correlate with class attendance.

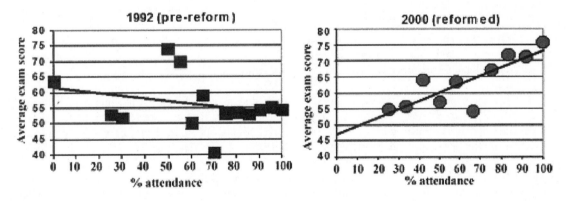

Figure 3. Comparison of the correlation between exam performance and class attendance before and after reforms in CHM-113.

Exam Performance. Since the various instructors each write their own exams, it is not possible to compare exam performance for reformed and control sections of classes. Instead, a comparison was made for the reformed sections before and after initiation of reform. Selected exam questions were used in the reformed course that had been used during previous years and for which reasonable statistics were available. Scores on these exam questions were 17% higher on hour exams and 10% higher on the final exam in the reformed courses. Of the 103 repeated questions, 82 had higher scores in the reformed sections and 20 were higher in the control sections (Figure 4). A t-test indicated the differences in scores on these questions were significant with p <0.01.

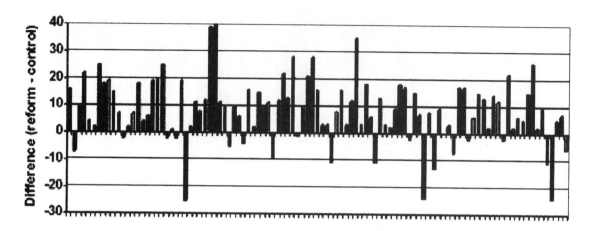

Figure 4. Difference in exam scores for each question. Positive values represent improved average scores for a question in the reformed section. Negative values represent better scores for the control sections. Values are arranged in the order the questions were asked during the semester.

Although we are not using as many numerical problems on exams as in the past, student performance on identical numerical problems used before and after reform increased from 57% to 68% correct. In no numerical question did the reform group perform significantly less well than the previous students, in spite of the absence of formal instruction on problem solving.

Laboratory Reforms

Inquiry/discovery investigations differ significantly from traditional general chemistry labs. Students are presented with a scenario, a problem (or problems) to solve, a materials list, and a very general procedure. Within their group, students design experiments to solve the problems posed, collect data, analyze the data, and write a report. They do all this without the "recipes" that usually accompany general chemistry experiments. In comparison with traditional labs, we have found that students completing inquiry-based investigations rely more on fellow group members, depend less on their teaching assistant, and learn to use the text as a reference. Reports from the organic chemistry laboratory instructors indicate that the students are now better able to carry out independent lab work in this more advanced course. However, students sometimes take more time than they did before because they want to discuss procedures with other students so they understand the procedures before they carry them out.

Satisfaction with lab has increased significantly. Student complaints about lecture and lab not being connected are rarely heard anymore, probably because students now have to research lecture material to develop the discussion section of their lab reports. Many students recognize that they are doing real science in the laboratory and appreciate the opportunity to develop their own experiments.

Cheating in lab has decreased, but unfortunately it did not disappear completely. Lawson, Lewis, & Birk (1999) did a study prior to the lab course reforms, when recipe-type experiments were used. They found that 81.5% of the students in general chemistry admitted to changing lab data on their reports. A survey of one class of about 200 students after lab reforms indicated that this had decreased to less than 20%.

Laboratory Poster Session. The laboratory program in general chemistry culminates with student group presentations of their findings. Each group presents one of their lab investigations in the form of a poster at the end of the semester. Students present their results orally in a presentation to their lab section. They then display their procedure and results during a poster session. Chemistry faculty members participate in the poster sessions by wandering through the labs asking students to comment on their work. The poster session and presentation activities have been successful in providing students with experience to develop their communication skills in various forms. Their presentations and posters have been very creative and are often insightful.

Laboratory Group Work. During the first semester of full implementation of inquiry-based labs, students were surveyed about their reactions to cooperative learning elements of the investigations on a Likert scale. For nearly all the statements that addressed group function, students reacted favorably, often in excess of 85% responding "agree" or "strongly agree", as shown in the following list:

- Groups effectively delegate duties: 87%

- Groups resolve conflicts: 87%

- Comfortable sharing ideas with groups: 92%

- Group members offer insightful recommendations: 85%

- Individual is included in discussions and activities: 93%

- Confident in group members' abilities: 81%

- Individual offers help to group members: 93%

- Groups equally share lab duties: 87%

- Students come to lab prepared: 90%

- Groups meet outside of lab to discuss lab report: 53%

Success in Organic Chemistry

We carried out a longitudinal study of student success in chemistry after completion of general chemistry. CHM-331 is first-semester organic chemistry, taken after CHM-113 and CHM-115. We examined the performance of students over a three-year period, during which CHM-331 was taught each semester by the same instructor using a traditional lecture format. We included only those students who took the three courses in consecutive semesters to cancel out other variables. The SAT scores for the students who took reform sections or non-reform sections of CHM-113/115 were nearly identical. What about their CHM-331 grades? As shown in Figure 5, the only significant differences were among students who received grades of A in CHM-331 or who withdrew from the course. Students from reformed sections of CHM-113/115 received grades of A at twice the rate of those from non-reform sections, and they withdrew from CHM-331 at about half the rate. Thus, we conclude that students who study general chemistry in a reformed class are more successful in organic chemistry than those who were enrolled in the traditional sections of general chemistry.

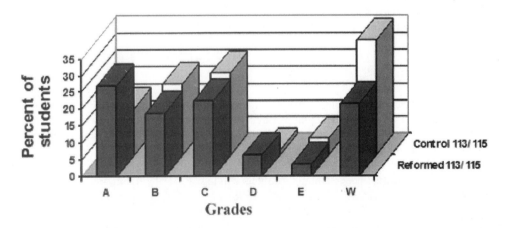

Figure 5. Course grade distribution in organic chemistry (CHM-331) for students who had participated in reform sections of CHM-113 and CHM-115, compared to that for students who had participated in control sections.

What causes the lecture improvements?

Since we have made several changes in our courses at one time, we are unable to determine what caused the desirable outcomes. Two components in particular, the use of multimedia and the use of small-group activities, might be expected to cause the improvements. Increased student performance has been reported for an astronomy course that incorporated a conceptual approach and small-group discussions (Bisard, Zeilik 1998; Zeilik, Schau, Mattern, Hall, Teague, Bisard 1997; Zeilik, Schau, Mattern 1999). The use of small-group activities in both small lecture and large lecture settings in introductory chemistry helped with retention of at-risk students (Mason, Berdel 2001). Retention rates increased for organic chemistry students upon incorporation of small-group activities during lecture (Hagen 2000). Incorporation of small-group quizzes and problem-solving assignments during large lectures in introductory biology led to improved student performance (Klionsky 2002). A meta-analysis of 15 studies of the use of cooperative learning techniques in high school and college chemistry courses indicated that student performance increased significantly over traditional lecture courses (Bowen 2000). The use of multimedia has also had beneficial effects. Several studies have shown that the use of multimedia, especially molecular animations, develops better conceptual understanding of chemical processes at a particulate level (Sanger, Phelps, Fienhold 2000; Williamson, Abraham 1995; Sanger, Greenbowe 1997). Modification of an introductory biology lecture by using multimedia, with no small-group activities, resulted in increased attendance, retention, and course performance (Moore, Miller 1996). Thus, we find studies that support both multimedia and small-group activities as causal agents for improved attendance, retention, and performance. We could delete one of these features from our courses and measure the outcome, but it is difficult to justify experiments that are expected to have a negative impact on student learning. We suspect that the small-group activities are most influential in attendance and retention, while the multimedia probably has an impact on conceptual learning of molecular topics. As described earlier, the use of multimedia also enables the ability to fit small-group activities into the allotted time. Although we have not isolated specific changes that caused the improvements, it can be noted that all the changes we made supported the incorporation of active learning into our large lecture courses, which was the primary reason for making the changes.

New Culture for Learning

With the implementation of cooperative learning techniques in some lecture courses coupled with the use of inquiry-based investigations in the lab, we have noticed a significant change in the study behavior of chemistry students. The students are now frequently found working together with their groups all over the building outside of scheduled class hours. They work together in small classrooms, study rooms, laboratories, hallways, and the Chemistry Learning Resource Center. Prior to our reforms the Resource Center was open weekdays from 8:30 am until 4:30 pm. As a result of increased usage, we have had to hire additional personnel to keep the facility open until 9:30 pm. Students are now working as part of a learning community as a result of the formation of groups, consistent with the findings of Towns, Kreke, and Field (2000).

Teaching Assistant Training

Successful implementation of changes in general chemistry at ASU depends largely on the quality of the teaching assistants (TAs). Most teaching assistants come from instructional backgrounds similar to ours. We all learned our university-level chemistry through lectures and recipe-style laboratories. We now offer a three-week TA orientation in late summer. This TA orientation program provides us an opportunity to model inquiry-oriented teaching with those chemistry graduate assistants who are charged with guiding students through conceptual understanding, problem solving, and critical thinking. An early version of this program has already been described (Birk, Kurtz 1996).

Orientation instructors do very little talking during the training period. Instead they model cooperative learning techniques. In addition, new teaching assistants complete many of the investigations that their students will do during the semester. Like their students, they develop procedures to solve the problems posed, sometimes with mixed success. An experienced graduate student models inquiry-based teaching techniques and leads post-lab discussions highlighting the various techniques that students have used to solve the problems.

The orientation helps prepare TAs for problems they will encounter while teaching the inquiry-based labs. Many TAs develop excellent skills in helping students overcome some of the frustration that often accompanies scientific work. TAs learn to provide students with hints, help build student confidence, suggest text references, ask students leading questions, and value students' creativity. In general, TAs develop skills to guide students during the investigations without telling them exactly what to do. New TAs also learn to accept students' proposals for solving the lab problems even if the student-designed experiments have little or no merit. Although the first inclination of a novice TA is to fix students' procedural problems before allowing them to proceed, teaching assistants rapidly begin to appreciate the educational value of letting students learn from mistakes.

Considerable TA camaraderie develops as a result of the three-week orientation. During the semester TAs usually run their own staff meetings, offering insights about problems students might encounter while completing the inquiry investigations. In addition, we have found that teaching assistants depend less on lecturing to students. Instead, they use student-centered teaching techniques such as cooperative learning during the 50-minute discussion periods. In addition, some former general chemistry TAs, with the help of the faculty in charge, are incorporating elements of inquiry into the upper level courses they now teach.

Institutionalization

Initially only one section of our two-semester sequence was subjected to reforms. As the reforms proved to be a successful improvement, efforts were made to expand the number of sections and instructors. The first approach was a one-month summer workshop supported by the National Science Foundation, involving faculty from our university and from local community colleges. This workshop involved both aspects of learning theory supporting the reforms (along with our own data) and practical issues of curriculum materials production. This workshop created a small core of university faculty who initiated reforms in their own sections of CHM-113 or other courses, such as introductory chemistry. Over a period of years, other faculty adopted some or all aspects of the reforms as a result of peer-to-peer discussions with this small core of faculty. To assist faculty who were interested in reforming their sections, all course materials were made available to them. Although they modified these materials, having a set of Powerpoint slides available considerably reduced the effort involved in adopting the reforms. Sharing of materials has enabled the reform of other courses in our program as well.

Acknowledgments

This material is based upon research partially supported by the National Science Foundation, DUE Award No. 9453610 and the U. S. Department of Education under grant no. OPE P336B990064. Any opinions, findings, and conclusions or recommendations expressed in this publication are those of the authors and do not necessarily reflect the views of the National Science Foundation or the Department of Education.

Suggested Reading

Piburn, M. D., McAuliffe, C., Reynolds, S. J., Johnson, J. K., Birk, J. P., & Leedy, D. E. (2005). The Role of Visualization in Learning from Computer-Based Images. *Intl. J. Sci. Educ.*, *27*, 513-527.

Cooper, M. M. (2005). An Introduction to Small-Group Learning. In N. J. Pienta, M. M. Cooper, T. J. Greenbowe (Ed.), *Chemists' Guide to Effective Teaching* (pp. 117-128). Upper Saddle River, NJ: Pearson Prentice Hall.

Varma-Nelson, P. & Coppola, B. P. (2005). Team Learning. In N. J. Pienta, M. M. Cooper, T. J. Greenbowe (Ed.), *Chemists' Guide to Effective Teaching* (pp. 155-171). Upper Saddle River, NJ: Pearson Prentice Hall.

Tasker, R. (2005). Using Multimedia to Visualize the Molecular World: Educational Theory into Practice. In N. J. Pienta, M. M. Cooper, T. J. Greenbowe (Ed.), *Chemists' Guide to Effective Teaching* (pp. 195-211). Upper Saddle River, NJ: Pearson Prentice Hall.

References

Bauer, R.C., Birk, J.P., and Marks, P.S. (2006) *A Conceptual Introduction to Chemistry*. Dubuque, IA: McGraw-Hill.

Bauer, R.C., Birk, J.P., & Sawyer, D. (2004) *Laboratory Inquiry in Chemistry* (2nd ed.). Pacific Grove, CA: Brooks/Cole.

Birk, J. P. & Foster, J. (1993). The importance of lecture in general chemistry course performance. *J. Chem. Educ.*, *70*, 180-182.

Birk, J. P. & Kurtz, M. J. (1996). Using Cooperative Learning Techniques to Train New Teaching Assistants. *J. Chem. Educ.*, *73*, 615-616.

Birk, J. P. & Marks, P. (2000). *Electronic Companion for General Chemistry* [CD-ROM]. San Francisco: Cogito Learning Media.

Birk, J. P. & Marks, P. (2002). General Chemistry (1 of 5 CDs). In *CollegePro Science*. Renton, WA: Topics Entertainment.

Birk, J. P. (1997). In *Interactive Chemistry* (Version 2.0) [CD-ROM]. Boston: Houghton-Mifflin Co.

Birk, J. P. (1998). In *Interactive Chemistry* (Version 3.0) [CD-ROM]. Boston: Houghton-Mifflin Co.

Birk, J. P., Leedy, D.E., Lihs, F., Morgan, R., Nickoles E.J., Drake, M., & McKelvy, M.J. (2003). Dynamic Visualization in Chemistry [CD-ROM]. *J. Chem. Educ.: Software*, Special Issue 31.

Bisard, W. & Zeilik, M. (1998). Restructuring a Class, Transforming the Professor: Conceptually Centered Astronomy with Actively Engaged Students. *Mercury*, *27*(4) 16-19.

Bowen, C. W. (2000). A Quantitative Literature Review of Cooperative Learning Effects on High School and College Chemistry Achievement. *J. Chem. Educ.*, *77*, 116-119.

Hagen, J. P. (2000). Cooperative Learning in Organic. II. Increased Retention on a Commuter Campus. *J. Chem. Educ.*, *77*, 1441-1444

Holmquist, D.D., Randall, J., & Volz, D.L. (1995). *Chemistry with CBL*, Portland: Vernier Software.

Klionsky, D. J. (2002). Constructing Knowledge in the Lecture Hall. *J. Coll. Sci. Teaching*, *31*, 246-251.

Lawson, A. E., Lewis Jr., C. M., & Birk, J. P. (1999). Why Do Students "Cook" Lab Data? A Case Study of the Tenacity of Misconceptions. *J. Coll. Sci. Teaching*, *28*, 191-198.

Mason, D. & Verdel, E. (2001). Gateway to Success for At-Risk Students in a Large-Group Introductory Chemistry Class. *J. Chem. Educ.*, 78, 252-255.

Moore, R. & Miller, I. (1996). How the use of multimedia affects student retention and learning. *J. Coll. Sci. Teaching*, *25*, 289-293.

Nurrenbern, S.C. (1995). *Experiences in Cooperative Learning: A Collection for Chemistry Teachers*. Madison, WI: Institute for Chemical Education.

Sanger, M. J. & Greenbowe, T. J. (1997). Students' Misconceptions in Electrochemistry Regarding Current Flow in Electrolyte Solutions and the Salt Bridge. *J. Chem. Educ.*, *74*, 819-823.

Sanger, M. J., Phelps, A. J., & Fienhold, J. (2000). Using a Computer Animation to Improve Students' Conceptual Understanding of a Can-Crushing Demonstration. *J. Chem. Educ.*, *77*, 1517-1520.

Sayle, R.A. & Milner-White, E.J. (1995). RasMol: Biomolecular graphics for all. *Trends in Biochem. Sci.*, *20*, 374-376.

Towns, M. H., Kreke, K., & Fields, A. (2000). An Action Research Project: Student Perspectives on Small-Group Learning in Chemistry. *J. Chem. Educ.*, *77*, 111-115.

Williamson, V. M. & Abraham, M. R. (1995). The effects of computer animation on the particulate mental models of college chemistry students. *J. Res. Sci. Teach.*, *32*, 521-534.

Wyckoff, S. (2001). Changing the culture of undergraduate science teaching. *J. Coll. Sci. Teach.*, *30*, 306-312.

Zeilik, M., Schau, C., & Mattern, N. (1999). Conceptual Astronomy. II. Replicating Conceptual Gains, Probing Attitude Changes Across Three Semesters. *Am. J. Phys*, *67*, 923-927.

Zeilik, M., Schau, C., Mattern, N., Hall, S., Teague, K. W., & Bisard, W. (1997). Conceptual Astronomy: A Novel Model for Teaching Post-Secondary Science Courses. *Am. J. Phys*, *65*, 987-996.

14

Computer Animations of Chemical Processes at the Molecular Level

Michael J. Sanger
Department of Chemistry
Middle Tennessee State University

Abstract

Many recent high school and college-level introductory chemistry textbooks come with CD's containing computer animations of chemical processes at the molecular level. But many chemistry instructors still have questions regarding the use of these animations in their classroom. Why should we use them? How should we use them? Do they improve student learning? Do they hamper learning? This chapter was written as a series of questions that chemistry instructors would ask about computer animations and answers from a chemical educator who designs and uses them. This chapter discusses the work of Paivio, Mayer, Piaget, and Johnstone as the theoretical framework for the use of computer animations in the chemistry classroom. It also provides a brief overview of the chemical education research on the effectiveness of using computer animations of chemical processes at the molecular level in the classroom.

Biography

Michael J. Sanger is a Professor of Chemistry at Middle Tennessee State University. He received his B.S. in Chemistry, with Highest Honors, from the University of California, Davis (1989), and his M.S. in Inorganic Chemistry (1994) and his Ph.D. in Chemistry and Education (1996) from Iowa State University. He has performed chemical education research studies aimed at identifying and dispelling student misconceptions, often using particulate drawings, computer animations, and electron density plots. This research have been published in the *American Biology Teacher*, *The Chemical Educator*, the *International Journal of Science Education*, the *Journal of Chemical Education*, and the *Journal of Research in Science Teaching*, and he has received the Distinguished Research Award in 2006 from the MTSU Foundation for this work. He has served on two national committees of the Division of Chemical Education: The Committee for Computers in Chemical Education since 1999, and the Committee for Research in Chemical Education (where he currently serves as the committee chair) since 2007. He has also received two teaching awards—the Award for Innovative Excellence in Teaching, Learning and Technology (International Conference on Teaching and Learning) and the Outstanding Achievement in Instructional Technology Award (MTSU Foundation)—for his use of technology in the chemistry classroom.

What is a Computer Animation?

According to the Merriam-Webster Online Dictionary (www.merriam-webster.com), an animation is "a motion picture that is made from a series of drawings, computer graphics, or photographs of inanimate objects (as puppets) and that simulates motion by slight progressive changes in each frame". Britannica Online (www.britannica.com) states that "the basis of all animation is the building up, frame by frame, of the moving picture by exact timing and choreography of both movement and sound". A computer animation is an animation that was created using (and often shown via) a computer (Burke et al. 1998).

What's the Difference Between a Computer Animation and a Computer Simulation?

Computer simulations, which are discussed in greater detail in Chapter 6 of this book, are a specific kind of computer animation. Rieber (1989) proposed a taxonomy of animations to differentiate between animations based on their instructional goal. This taxonomy includes six levels: Cosmetic, attention-gaining, motivation/reinforcement, presentation, conceptualization, and interactive dynamics.

Cosmetic animations have no direct instructional intent; they are simply intended to look attractive and be flashy. Unfortunately, these can be very distracting (as any audience member who has viewed a PowerPoint presentation with random and miscellaneous animated text motions can attest to). *Attention-gaining* animations are used to direct the learner's attention to relevant information, such as moving or flashing arrows pointing toward key words or concepts. *Motivation/reinforcement* animations are used as reinforcement or feedback to students' responses. Unfortunately, much like cosmetic animations, these animations can be distracting, and if different animations are provided for correct and incorrect responses, then students will often purposefully choose wrong answers so they can see the 'incorrect' animations, and this could inadvertently reinforce incorrect answers in the students' minds. *Presentation* animations are used to present new information or to elaborate on previously presented information by providing examples, non-examples, or elaborations of a concept or procedure. *Conceptualization* animations are closely related to presentation animations, but here the animation is used to develop students' conceptual understanding without providing any new information. These animations are used to demonstrate relationships through visual means and to provide a concrete representation of processes involving complex and abstract relationships. *Interactive dynamics* animations represent computer simulations, in which the animation mimics real-world situations and continually changes based on students' input.

Most computer animations of chemical processes at the molecular level fall in the presentation or conceptualization levels. What is important about these animations is that they are primarily created to help students understand the motions and interactions of atoms, molecules, and ions (i.e., kinetic molecular theory, collision theory, etc.).

Why Should We Expect Computer Animations to Help Our Students?

The theoretical basis for the effectiveness of computer animations stems from the work of two educational researchers. First, Paivio (1986) proposed his dual coding theory to explain educational research performed using words and static pictures. Mayer (2001) adapted Paivio's theory to explain the results of educational research based on computer animations, and developed a cognitive theory of multimedia learning. Interested readers are directed to Tasker's description of how he adapted the theoretical models developed by Mayer and Johnstone (1997) to describe a multimedia information-processing model for learning chemistry from audiovisual information (Tasker, 2005).

Paivio's Dual Coding Theory. Paivio's theory of dual coding (1986) is based on the results of large amount of experimental evidence in perceptual, memory, and language-processing tasks. His theory assumes that learners store information received in working memory as either verbal or imaginal (pictorial) mental representations in long-term storage. These two coding methods are assumed to be independent and additive, and information stored using both coding methods can be retrieved from either code. A comparison of the recall of words and pictures shows a 2:1 preference of pictures over words (a picture is worth two words?). This discrepancy is explained by the assumption that learners will spontaneously supply word labels to pictures and thus dually code pictures, while learners are less likely to spontaneously provide pictures to words (especially abstract words), which causes words to only be coded verbally. While the dual coding theory focuses on verbal information as single words and imaginal information as static pictures, Paivio states that represented imaginal information includes "not only static appearance but dynamic and variable properties as well" (1986, pp 59-60).

Mayer's Cognitive Theory of Multimedia Learning. Mayer's cognitive theory of multimedia learning (2001) assumes that the human information processing system includes dual channels, and that each channel has limited capacity for processing. The dual channel assumption asserts that humans process and store information using two different modalities; these modalities can be viewed based on the learner's senses (what the learner sees versus what the learner hears) or based on the presentation modes (whether the stimulus is verbal or imaginal). The first scheme is consistent with Braddeley's model of working memory (1999) while the second scheme is consistent with

Paivio's dual coding theory (1986); these two schemes are clearly related and almost interchangeable. The limited capacity assumption asserts that humans can only process a certain amount of information in each channel at one time, and that if this limit is exceeded, learning may be slowed or stopped.

In addition, Mayer's cognitive theory of multimedia learning includes seven corollaries based on educational research using computer animations performed by Mayer and his group. The *multimedia principle* asserts that students learn better from words and pictures than from words alone and is consistent with Paivio's dual coding theory (1986). Mayer reported that students who viewed animations and narrations performed better on tests of retention and transfer than learners who received narration alone. The *spatial contiguity principle* states that students learn better when word and pictures are presented close together than far away from each other on the screen. The *temporal contiguity principle* asserts that students learn better when word and pictures are presented simultaneously rather than successively in time. The *coherence principle* asserts that students learn better when extraneous material is excluded rather than included in an animation. The *modality principle* states that students learn better from animation and narration than from animation and on-screen text. The *redundancy principle* asserts that students learn better from animation and narration than from animation, narration, and text. In this case, the repetition of words in both auditory and visual displays interfered with each other; another way to explain this is that by presenting both words and pictures as images, the imaginal channel can become overloaded. Finally, the *individual differences principle* states that design effects are stronger for low-knowledge and high-spatial students than for high-knowledge and low-spatial students.

Why Should We Use Computer Animations in the Chemistry Classroom?

The simple answer to this question is that computer animations depicting chemical processes at the molecular level help students learn chemistry. Specifically, these animations help students develop their conceptual understanding of the molecular-level processes occurring in chemical reactions. Most of the questions students are asked to answer in chemistry classes involve mathematical calculations (algorithms). It wasn't until recently that chemical education researchers discovered that students who were successful at solving numerical chemistry problems did not necessarily understand the molecular concepts underlying these mathematical problems (Nurrenbern & Pickering, 1987; Sawrey, 1990; Pickering, 1990; Nakhleh, 1993). Before this time, many instructors believed (and perhaps still do) that students who were successful at mathematical assessments had a sound understanding of the underlying molecular concepts. Subsequent studies have shown that the use of computer animations can improve students' abilities to answer molecular questions (Williamson & Abraham, 1995; Russell et al., 1997; Sanger & Badger, 2001; Kelly et al., 2004).

As an example, consider the study performed by Sanger, Phelps, and Fienhold (2000). In this study, they compared students' molecular-level explanations of a can-crushing demonstration (Bodner et al., 1985), in which a soda can filled with a small amount of water was heated to boil the water, removed from the heat, and sealed. Some of these students viewed a computer animation depicting this process at the molecular level (Figure 1), while others saw static drawings created by their instructor on the chalkboard. The computer animation (and the static drawings) depicted the water molecules leaving the liquid phase in the bottom of the can and entering the gas phase inside the can, driving most of the nitrogen and oxygen molecules out of the can. When the can was capped and cooled, the gaseous water molecules started moving slower until they condensed back to the liquid phase as droplets of water. Then, the can was crushed by the imbalance of molecular collisions inside and outside the can (i.e., the decreased inner pressure could no longer prevent the collisions of air molecules on the outside of the can from crushing the can).

Although the two sets of students would probably have performed similarly on a mathematical gas law question, students who did not view the animation showed more misconceptions regarding the chemical processes occurring in this demonstration when asked to explain what has happened to the can at the molecular level. These students were more likely to blindly quote gas laws ("$V \propto T$, $V \propto 1/P$"), were more likely to suggest gas particles change sizes when heated ("...gas molecules when heated are expanded and when they cool they 'shrink' back..."), and were less likely to recognize the importance of the decreased pressure inside the can and the condensation of the water vapor compared to students who viewed the animation. The students who viewed the animation were also more likely to provide a correct explanation (similar to the description in the last paragraph).

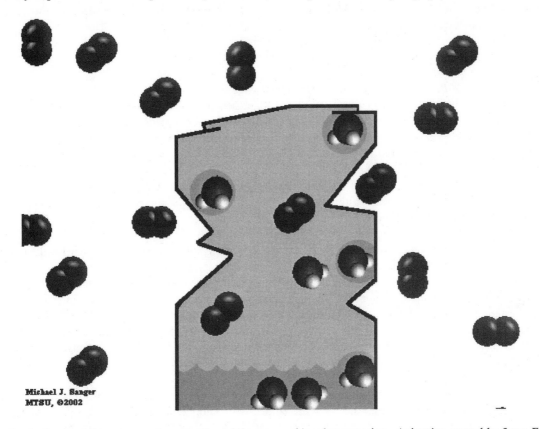

Michael J. Sanger
MTSU, ©2002

Figure 1. Static visual from a computer animation of the can-crushing demonstration. Animation created by Jason Feinhold (under the supervision of Michael J. Sanger).

Is There Any Theoretical Basis for Why Computer Animations Should Be Used in the Chemistry Classroom?

Chemistry courses require students to collect data and make real-world observations and relate them to the properties and interactions of atoms, molecules, and ions that they cannot actually see. So, part of the problem comes from asking students to think about abstract objects that they cannot directly see (Piaget's model of intellectual development); the other part of the problem comes from asking students to relate their data and observations to these abstract particles (Johnstone's three representations of matter).

Piaget's Model of Intellectual Development. In his work studying the intellectual growth and development of children, Piaget proposed four levels of intellectual growth that represent a developmental continuum (Nurrenbern, 2001): Sensorimotor, pre-operational, concrete operational, and formal operational. Most students in high school or college chemistry classrooms have reached the concrete operational level, so the biggest concern for chemistry instructors is the difference between students at the concrete operational and formal operational levels.

Herron (1975, 1978) introduced many chemists to Piaget's work and how it directly applied to the chemistry classroom. In particular, he listed a series of tasks that students who were formal operational thinkers could do, but students who were concrete operational thinkers could not do. These tasks included: Controlling variables, proportional logic ("if... then..." statements), proportional reasoning (based on ratios), and molecular-level thinking. Although the first three tasks make the quantitative aspects of chemistry classes difficult, it is the last task where computer animations can have an effect.

Although concrete operational thinkers may not be cognitively developed enough to understand chemical concepts at the formal operational level, Herron (1975) described some instructional methods that could be used to help concrete operational thinkers acquire "surrogate concepts" which can substituted for the formal operational concepts and enable them to interact in situations where formal operational concepts are needed. These methods include the use of concrete "hands-on" models of molecules and films that provide models of the molecular systems. Computer animations of chemical processes at the molecular level also represent models that can be used to facilitate the growth of these "surrogate concepts". Like most models (and analogies), care must be taken to ensure that the model doesn't lead to incorrect conceptions (Orgill & Bodner, 2005).

Johnstone's Three Representations of Matter. When chemists think about chemical processes, they use three interrelated but distinct representational levels: Macroscopic, microscopic, and symbolic representations (Johnstone, 1993; Gabel, 2005). *Macroscopic* representations involve qualitative observations made by chemists using their five senses: color changes, bubbles, precipitations, odors, sounds, heat changes, etc. *Symbolic* representations involve the use of symbols to stand in the place of other more abstract objects. One of the most common symbol systems used in chemistry is chemical symbols (H for hydrogen, O for oxygen, etc.). To chemists, the symbol 'Na' represents a soft metal that reacts explosively with water and prefers the +1 oxidation state; but to many students, 'Na' could just as easily stand for 'not applicable'. Another symbolic representation used by chemists is balanced chemical equations. In these equations, chemical symbols, subscripts, coefficients, electronic charges, and states of matter designations are used to describe chemical reactions. Chemists also use mathematical symbols and equations in their descriptions of chemical systems. For example, the mathematical formula for the ideal gas law ($PV = nRT$) contains mathematical symbols representing the gas pressure, volume, amount, temperature, and the gas constant; the formula itself also represents the mathematical relationship between these five symbols. Finally, graphical depictions of data (e.g., a plot of the pressure versus volume of a gas sample) are also symbolic representations. *Microscopic* representations describe chemical processes in terms of the properties and interactions of atoms, molecules, and ions. This representation often poses a problem for students because they cannot directly see or touch atoms, molecules, and ions in the classroom. Improving students' abilities to visualize these microscopic interactions is also discussed in Chapter 6 of this book.

With experience, chemists see the inherent connections and relationships among the three representations and use them interchangeably; they recognize that the representations are simply three different ways of explaining the same chemical processes from three different but related perspectives. Unfortunately, if students don't recognize that these representations are all attempting to explain the same chemical processes, then they will view the three representations as three different sets of unrelated information that must be memorized. This problem can be exacerbated by the way traditional chemistry lectures and labs are taught. Traditional chemistry lectures tend to focus almost exclusively on symbolic representations (balanced chemical equations, mathematical formulas and manipulations, and problem solving) with the occasional chemical demonstration thrown in (macroscopic). Traditional labs tend to focus on the symbolic representations discussed in lectures and on the macroscopic representation of data and observations collected during the lab. Traditional chemistry courses do not focus much of their students' attention on the microscopic representation—not because the instructor believes it to be unimportant but because it is difficult for instructors to show these interactions to students in the classroom. This is where computer animations can be particularly useful. Computer animations of chemical processes at the molecular level are powerful tools for helping instructors model how they think using the microscopic representation for students.

How Can I Use Computer Animations to Teach Students Using the Three Representations of Chemistry?

As an example of the interconnectedness of the three representations, consider an instructional lesson on the topic of precipitation reactions. The lesson begins with a chemical demonstration. A sample of aqueous silver nitrate (which appears clear and colorless) is added to a sample of aqueous sodium chloride (which is also clear and colorless). Immediately, the solution appears milky white and eventually (after a few minutes) a white solid has settled to the bottom, leaving a clear colorless solution. The instructor reviews the macroscopic data—when two clear colorless solutions are mixed, a white precipitate forms and eventually separates from the clear colorless solution.

To describe this reaction at the symbolic level, the instructor writes a balanced chemical equation. The aqueous solution contains silver ions, Ag^+(aq), and nitrate ions, NO_3^-(aq). Silver nitrate must be neutral overall, so the formula for silver nitrate must be 1:1 and is written as $AgNO_3$(aq). For the aqueous sodium chloride, the ions are

$Na^+(aq)$ and $Cl^-(aq)$ and the formula is also 1:1 and is written as $NaCl(aq)$. When the two solutions mix together, positive ions are attracted to negative ions and vice versa, so it is possible that the Ag^+ ions may react with the Cl^- ions and the Na^+ ions may react with the NO_3^- ions. Those products would be $AgCl$ and $NaNO_3$ (both 1:1 ratios). Finally, the instructor consults the solubility rules to determine that $AgCl$ will form a solid while $NaNO_3$ remains dissolved in water (aqueous). Now, the balanced equation can be written and the instructor emphasizes that the macroscopic data and the symbolic equation are telling us exactly the same thing: When two aqueous solutions are mixed, a solid forms while the other ions remain dissolved in the water.

$$AgNO_3(aq) \; + \; NaCl(aq) \; \rightarrow \; AgCl(s) \; + \; NaNO_3(aq)$$

Finally, a computer animation depicting the microscopic view of this chemical process is shown. The animation first shows a microscopic depiction of an aqueous sodium chloride solution, in which there is a 1:1 ratio of Na^+ to Cl^- ions, which are independent of each other (i.e., not attached to each other as ion pairs). Then, the animation shows the independent Ag^+ and NO_3^- ions in a 1:1 ratio. The instructor also reminds the students what the formula for NO_3^- means: 1 nitrogen atom in the middle (blue), 3 oxygen atoms around the outside (red), and a negative charge. Finally, the animation shows what happens when the ions are allowed to mix. In the animation, when the Ag^+ and Cl^- ions collide, they combine to form solid silver chloride, which settles to the bottom of the container, and the Na^+ and NO_3^- ions remain dissolved in the solution. The animation is shown two or three times in succession, with the instructor narrating and pointing out relevant reactions/interactions using a long wooden pointer aimed at the screen. Static visuals from two different animations of this same process appear in Figure 2. The instructor then emphasizes that all three representations tell us the same thing: when the two aqueous solutions mix, a solid and another aqueous solutions are formed.

These animations are also extremely useful in teaching students about ionic equations, net ionic equations, and spectator ions. Students should notice a discrepancy between the animations and the balanced chemical equation: The animations show the aqueous ions moving independent of one another, while the balanced equation includes "molecular" formulas of ionic compounds which may suggest to the students that neutral ion pairs exist (i.e., aqueous silver nitrate written as $AgNO_3(aq)$ instead of independent $Ag^+(aq)$ and $NO_3^-(aq)$ ions). These animations provide chemistry instructors with an opportunity to explain that although chemists write "molecular" formulas of aqueous ionic compounds for simplicity, the actual ions and their behaviors are better described using ionic and net ionic equations.

The Second Animation in Figure 2 Looks More Realistic Than the First One. Does That Mean It's Better?

Not necessarily. Mayer's coherence principle (2001) states that students learn better when extraneous material is excluded from an animation. This principle stems from Mayer's assumption that the dual channels used by learners to encode information into long-term storage each have a limited capacity, and when this capacity is exceeded, learning may be slowed or stopped. This principle is supported by several research studies (Garner et al., 1989; Mayer et al., 1996; Moreno & Mayer, 2000; Harp & Maslich, 2005), including Dwyer's classic experiment (1972). Dwyer found that students viewing abstract line drawings of the human heart performed better when asked to draw and label the parts of the heart than students who viewed detailed shaded drawings, photographs of a heart model, or

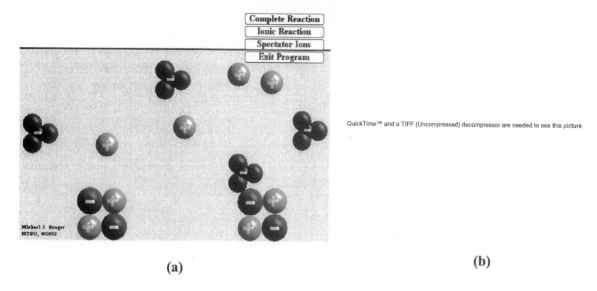

(a)   (b)

Figure 2. Static visuals from computer animations depicting the precipitation of silver chloride: (a) Animation created by Michael J. Sanger; (b) VisChem animation created by Roy Tasker (© University of Western Sydney, 1995).

realistic photographs of an actual heart. Dwyer concluded that since the type of learning measured did not require realistic detail, the additional detail in the other drawings may have distracted the students from the relevant learning cues and hindered their efficient acquisition and retention of the intended information.

Both animations have their advantages and disadvantages. While the animation by Sanger is less realistic than the animation by Tasker (2-dimensional vs. 3-dimensional), if the learning task does not require a high level of detail, this animation may be more appropriate. For example, this animation would be good for looking at the stoichiometry of the reaction and of the spectator ions. While the viewer can see the 1:1 reacting ratio of Ag^+ to Cl^- ions in both animations,[1] the one by Sanger shows that there must be equal amounts of spectator ions in solution (i.e., a 1:1 ratio of Ag^+ to NO_3^- and a 1:1 ratio of Na^+ to Cl^-). In addition, this animation shows that the spectator ions do collide with other ions; they simply do not react but instead stay dissolved in the solution. Since the ions in Sanger's animation are labeled with + and – signs, students can also compare the relative sizes of the cations and anions (in Tasker's animation, it could be difficult for students to determine which ion in the crystal is Ag^+ and which is Cl^-). Sanger's animation also has its shortcomings. It completely ignores the water particles and their role in the precipitation (for simplicity), it shows a solid particle with no motion, and the size of the ions compared to the distances between them is incorrect for ionic solutions with concentrations normally seen in chemistry classes.

Since Tasker's is more realistic, it can more correctly depict complex concepts than Sanger's animation. For example, Tasker's depiction of solid AgCl is more correct and shows a 3-dimensional crystal with silver and chloride ions that are still moving within the crystal. In addition, this animation would be better to help students realize that aqueous solutions normally used in the chemistry classroom are made up of mostly water. This animation also shows the attractions of water particles to cations and anions (and could be used when the fact that water is a polar molecule is introduced to students) and also demonstrates water's role in the formation and growth of insoluble ionic crystals from aqueous solutions. Tasker's animation also has its shortcomings. The ions are not labeled with + or – charges, very few spectator ions are shown in the animation, and the animation is very visually dense (and instructor narration would be essential when using this animation in class).

When I introduce the concept of precipitation in my chemistry classes, I actually use both of these animations. I start with Sanger's animation (two or three times, with instructor's narration) because it is less complex. I use this animation to discuss the stoichiometric reacting ratios, the relative size of ions, and spectator ions and their role in this reaction (as charge balancers). Then, I show Tasker's animation (two or three times, also with instructor's narration), using it to discuss the real nature of a crystalline ionic solid, the fact that aqueous solutions consist mostly of water particles, and the role of the water particles in the formation and growth of insoluble crystals.

How Can I Help My Students Focus on the Important Aspects of a Complex Computer Animation?

One way would be to create another computer animation that minimizes or eliminates the extraneous material. This is consistent with Mayer's coherence principle (2001). Another way would be to provide students with cues or prompts to help them pay attention to the relevant information within the animation (Rieber, 1989). These prompts can include sound effects, visual cues, or verbal cues. For example, the animation in Figure 3 uses visual 'flashes' to depict the important collisions in a Charles's Law experiment. While the particles inside and outside the container are hitting all of the walls of the container, it is only the collisions with the movable piston that can change the container's volume. The animation also verbally tabulates the number of collisions of the inner and outer particles with the piston. When the collisions are balanced the piston does not move, but when the collisions are unbalanced the piston is moved in the direction away from the colliding particle.

Since most instructors do not create their own animations, they must rely on computer animations that have already been created by others. If an instructor finds multiple animations of the same topic, he or she can choose to use the animation that has less irrelevant information depicted in it. Otherwise, the easiest way to focus students' attention on the relevant information within a computer animation is to verbally narrate the animation while students are watching it (Mayer, 2001).

Are There Any Guidelines For How I Should Use Computer Animations in My Classroom?

Mayer's seven corollaries (2001) provide excellent suggestions for the design and use of computer animation in the chemistry classroom. In fact, anyone designing computer animations for the chemistry classroom would do well to read and follow these guidelines. Since most chemistry teachers will probably use existing computer animations, these corollaries provide a list of suggestions for implementation. For example, the multimedia principle suggests that using narrated animations (words and pictures) is better than verbal descriptions (lectures). The temporal contiguity principle suggests that animations should be narrated; if you are using a non-narrated animation in your classroom, then you should provide a verbal description of the animation *while* students are watching it. The coherence

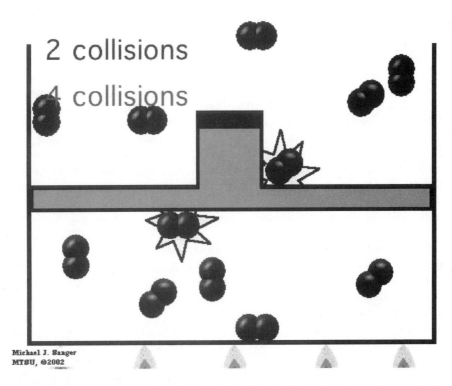

Figure 3. Static visual from a computer animation depicting Charles's Law that shows the use of visual and verbal cues (animation created by Michael J. Sanger).

principle suggests that you should try to find animations that do no have a lot of extraneous information. So, what should you do if an animation includes written text within the animation? The modality principle says that students learn better from narrated animations than ones with written text; however, if you narrate this animation in class, the redundancy principle says that the text and narration can interfere with each other. One solution would be to narrate the animation in class, but tell students to ignore the written text; another solution would be to show the animation without narration.

Chemical education research has shown that while students may initially have difficulty answering conceptual questions at the microscopic level, students' performance on these questions greatly improves with practice (Pickering, 1990; Russell et al., 1997; Sanger et al., 2007). In other words, if the instructor believes that it is important for students to be able to think at the microscopic level, then the instructor needs to find ways to incorporate microscopic-level pictures into the learning environment. This not only means consistently using static particulate drawings and molecular-level computer animations in the lecture, but also consistently incorporating them into the homework assignments and examination questions. Instructors who have never had experience writing (or even answering) microscopic-level questions can find examples of these types of questions in several different places. Most introductory college-level chemistry textbooks use microscopic drawings in the text and in the homework problems (McMurry & Fay, 2004; Hill et al., 2005; Olmsted & Williams, 2006). In addition, the *Journal of Chemical Education* publishes papers that have microscopic-level pictures and the ConcepTests website (www.jce.divched.org/JCEDLib/QBank/collection/ConcepTests/) contains hundreds of conceptual questions, some of which involve microscopic-level pictures (Landis et al., 2001).

Is There Any Evidence That Computer Animations Are Useful in the Chemistry Classroom?

Several researchers have shown that the use of computer animations can positively affect students' abilities to answer particulate questions at the microscopic level. These studies used statistical analyses in which the responses from students in the control and treatment groups were compared to answer their research questions. They differ primarily in the group of students used as the control group for the students who viewed the computer animations. Because these studies are making different comparisons, they are also answering different research questions.

Pre-Test vs. Post-Test for the Same Students. The first set of studies compared the responses of the same students (before animation vs. after animation). These studies were able to answer the question: *Do computer animations improve student learning compared to no instruction at all?* The disadvantage of these studies is that the control group is rather artificial—few instructors actually decide to do nothing at all if they don't use computer animations. Russell et al. (1997) noted that the proportion of correct statements to a microscopic-level question increased and the proportion of misconceptions decreased after students viewed computer animations showng synchronized pictures of gas equilibrium reactions at the macroscopic, symbolic, and microscopic levels. Unfortunately, no comparison was made to students who did not use the animation, so it is difficult to determine whether student gains were attributable to the animation or other instructional methods. Sanger et al. (2007) found that students' answers to a microscopic-level multiple-choice question concerning Gay-Lussac's Law improved significantly after students viewed an animated version of the question. Since the pre- and post-tests were administered at the same time, these effects can be attributed to the use of the computer animation.

Animations vs. Traditional Instruction. The second set of studies compared responses from students who viewed computer animations with those from students who received chemistry instruction that did not include static particulate drawings. These studies were able to answer the question: *Do computer animations improve student learning compared to traditional instruction?* These studies are more relevant because their control groups are more realistic, and while they show that the use of the computer animations can improve student learning, they cannot demonstrate that the animated motions were necessary for learning (i.e., the use of static pictures may also have improved student learning). Sanger and Greenbowe (1997) asked students to answer three conceptual questions regarding current flow in aqueous solutions after viewing microscopic-level computer animations of electrochemical cells. Their responses were analyzed to determine whether students consistently demonstrated the misconception that electrons flow in aqueous solutions and were compared to the responses of students who did not view animations (Ogude & Bradley, 1994). Students who viewed the animations were less likely to always choose answers consistent with the misconception and more likely to never choose answers consistent with the misconception than students who did not view the animation. Sanger (2000) asked students to decide whether several microscopic-level pictures contained solids, liquids, or gases; pure substances, homogenous mixtures or heterogeneous mixtures; and elements or compounds. One group received traditional instruction, while the other received instruction including microscopic-level computer animations. Students who viewed the animations were better able to identify microscopic pictures of liquids, pure compounds, heterogeneous mixtures, homogeneous mixtures, elements, and compounds and were more likely to use a correct classification scheme than students who did not view the animations. Sanger et al. (2001) compared students' responses to the Diffusion and Osmosis Diagnostic Test. (Odom & Barrow, 1995). Students who viewed microscopic-level animations of osmosis and diffusion in biology lab were less likely to demonstrate the misconception that particles stop moving when a system reaches equilibrium, and were less likely to attribute molecular motions to anthropomorphic "desires" of the molecules than students who did not view the animation.

Animations vs. Static Pictures. The third set of studies compared the responses of students who viewed computer animations with those from students who received chemistry instruction including static particulate drawings. These studies were able to answer the question: *Do computer animations improve student learning compared to static pictures?* These studies not only show that the use of computer animations can improve student learning, they also demonstrate that the animated motions were necessary for student learning. The study by Sanger, Phelps, and Fienhold (2000) described earlier falls into this category. Williamson and Abraham (1995) compared the responses of three sets of students; all three groups received instruction using static particulate drawings, while two groups viewed computer animations of chemical processes at the microscopic level (both groups viewed animations in lecture and one group viewed animations in their discussion sections as well). Both animation groups performed better than the 'no animation' group but there were no difference between the two animation groups based on the additional exposure to the animations in the discussion sections. These results suggested that brief exposure to the animations was capable of helping students develop "surrogate concepts" and additional exposure did not lead to additional learning (Herron, 1975). Kelly et al. (2004) asked two sets of students to explain the can-crushing demonstration used by Sanger et al. (2000). Both groups received similar instruction, but one group saw a computer animation of the can crushing demonstration while the other group saw static images drawn on the chalkboard. The researchers reported that students who viewed the animation not only showed a more complete microscopic understanding of the demonstration, but their macroscopic- and symbolic-level understandings were also more complete compared to the students who did not see the animation.

Is There Any Evidence That Computer Animations Can Cause Problems in the Chemistry Classroom?

While most chemical education research studies have reported positive effects for computer animations, some have shown either negative or no effects for animations. Sanger and Greenbowe (2000) saw no effects for computer animations on students' conceptions of current flow in aqueous solutions. They argued that because the control group received instruction involving static drawings that were updated throughout the study, the updated pictures could be viewed as crude animations, and since both groups viewed animations no effect should be expected. Sanger et al. (2001) noted that students who viewed computer animations of diffusion and osmosis were less likely to demonstrate the misconception of static equilibrium. However, these students did exhibit a misconception regarding why these particles do not stop moving: They believed that if the particles stopped moving they would settle out of solution. In addition, viewing the osmosis animation led to another misconception that sugar does not dissolve well in water. Informal student interviews demonstrated that students misinterpreted the animation.

Assessment Difficulties: One major difficulty in performing research on the effect of computer animations is designing appropriate microscopic-level assessments to measure students' conceptual understanding. Several studies have demonstrated that students often misinterpret these microscopic drawings. Sanger and Greenbowe (2000) noted that their microscopic pictures concerning electrode reactions could not adequately distinguish between two common misconceptions and the correct conception. Sanger (2000) also noted that some students misinterpreted his microscopic-level pictures. Although these students categorized the picture of a heterogeneous mixture as a pure substance, student interviews revealed that they had a correct conception of pure substances and mixtures but simply misinterpreted the microscopic picture. Pickering (1990) suggested that students have difficulty answering microscopic questions not due to a lack of student ability, but rather to a lack of experience in answering these questions. This is consistent with Sanger and Greenbowe's study (2000) where they found that students who did not attend lectures or recitations performed similarly on verbal questions, but had much more difficulty with microscopic-level questions than students who did attend classes.

So When Should We Use Computer Animations to Teach Chemistry Concepts?

In his review of animation research in computer-based instruction, Rieber (1989) concluded that animation should be incorporated into instruction only when its attributes are congruent to the learning task. He noted that if the lesson requires students to understand concepts involving visualization, motion, or trajectory, then the existing research supports the use of computer animations. If not, then the animations can distract students from learning the concepts. Some examples of chemistry topics that require students to develop their visualization skills are classification of matter (states of matter, elements/compounds, pure substances/heterogeneous mixtures/homogeneous mixtures) and VSEPR theory. Instruction involving chemistry concepts with a distinct time dependence ("before and after" reactions) can also benefit from the use of computer animations. These topics include (but are not limited to) acid-base reactions and buffers, electrochemistry, equilibrium, gas laws, kinetics and mechanisms, miscibility reactions, and precipitation reactions.

Much of the chemical education research described above has demonstrated that instruction including the use of computer animations of chemical processes at the molecular level can improve students' conceptual understanding at the microscopic level (which requires students to develop their visualization skills). In addition, Sanger and Greenbowe (2000) reported that students who received instruction involving computer animations of electrochemical cells and conceptual change strategies performed worse on verbal questions than students who only received instruction involving conceptual change. Since the questions were verbal and not visual, they theorized that the visual nature of the animations had a distracting effect on students' responses, consistent with Rieber's assertion (1989).

Where Can I Find Chemistry Animations to Use in My Classroom?

Many high school and college-level chemistry textbooks come with a wide array of ancillary materials, including CD's that contain computer animations of chemical processes at the molecular level, and there are several sites on the web that contain chemistry animations. The real trick is evaluating these animations and finding ones that teach the concepts well, have limited "bells and whistles" that can be distracting, and don't have glitches that prevent them from working. One place to look for computer animations in chemistry is the MERLOT (Multimedia Educational Resources for Learning and Online Teaching) website (www.merlot.org/merlot/index.htm). Examples of animations created by Greenbowe (1994), Sanger (Sanger et al., 2000, 2001, 2007), and Tasker (2005) can be found at the websites listed below.

Greenbowe's animations: www.chem.iastate.edu/group/Greenbowe/sections/projectfolder/animationsindex.htm
Sanger's animations: www.mtsu.edu/~mjsanger
Tasker's animations: bcs.whfreeman.com/chemicalprinciples4e

Suggested Readings

Robinson, W. R. (2004). Cognitive theory and the design of multimedia instruction. *Journal of Chemical Education*, *81*, 10-13.

Sanger, M. J., Phelps, A. J., & Fienhold, J. (2000). Using a computer animation to improve students' conceptual understanding of a can-crushing demonstration. *Journal of Chemical Education*, *77*, 1517-1520.

Tasker, R. (2005). Using multimedia to visualize the molecular world: Educational theory into practice. In N. J. Pienta, M. M. Cooper, & T. J. Greenbowe (Eds.), *Chemist's Guide to Effective Teaching* (pp 195-211). Upper Saddle River, NJ: Pearson.

References

Bodner, G. M., Schreiner, R., Greenbowe, T. J., Dirreen, G. E., & Shakhashiri, B. Z. (1985). Collapsing Can. In Shakhashiri, B. Z. (Ed.), *Chemical Demonstrations: A Handbook for Teachers of Chemistry*, Vol. 2 (pp. 6-8). Madison, WI: University of Wisconsin Press.

Braddeley, A. D. (1999). *Human memory*. Boston, MA: Allyn & Bacon.

Burke, K. A., Greenbowe, T. J., & Windschitl, M. A. (1998). Developing and using conceptual computer animations for chemistry instruction. *Journal of Chemical Education, 75*, 1658-1661.

Dwyer, F. M. (1972). The effect of overt responses in improving visually programed science instruction. *Journal of Research in Science Teaching, 9*, 47-55.

Gabel, D. (2005). Enhancing students' conceptual understanding of chemistry through integrating the macroscopic, particle, and symbolic representations of matter. In N. J. Pienta, M. M. Cooper, & T. J. Greenbowe (Eds.), *Chemist's Guide to Effective Teaching* (pp 77-88). Upper Saddle River, NJ: Pearson.

Garner, R., Gillingham, M., & White, C. (1989). Effects of seductive details on macroprocessing and microprocessing in adults and children. *Cognition and Instruction, 6*, 41-57.

Greenbowe, T. J. (1994). An interactive multimedia software program for exploring electrochemical cells. *Journal of Chemical Education, 71*, 555-557.

Harp, S. F., & Maslich, A. A. (2005). The consequences of including seductive details during lecture. *Teaching of Psychology, 32*, 100-103.

Herron, J. D. (1975). Piaget for chemists. *Journal of Chemical Education, 52*, 146-150.

Herron, J. D. (1978). Piaget in the classroom. *Journal of Chemical Education, 55*, 165-170.

Hill, J. W., Petrucci, R. H., McCreary, T. W., & Perry, S. S. (2005). *General Chemistry* (4th ed.). Upper Saddle River, NJ: Pearson.

Johnstone, A. H. (1993). The development of chemistry teaching. *Journal of Chemical Education, 70*, 701-705.

Johnstone, A. H. (1997). ...And some fell on good ground. *University Chemistry Education, 1*, 8-13.

Kelly, R. M., Phelps, A. J., & Sanger, M. J. (2004). The effects of a computer animation on students' conceptual understanding of a can-crushing demonstration at the macroscopic, microscopic, and symbolic levels. *The Chemical Educator, 9*, 184-189.

Landis, C. R., Ellis, A. B., Lisensky, G. C., Lorenz, J. K., Meeker, K., & Wamser, C. C. (2001). *Chemistry ConcepTests: A Pathway to Interactive Classrooms*. Upper Saddle River, NJ: Prentice-Hall.

Mayer, R. E. (2001). *Multimedia Learning*. New York, NY: Cambridge University Press.

Mayer, R. E., Bove, W., Bryman, A., Mars, R., & Tapangco, L. (1996). When less is more: Meaningful learning from visual and verbal summaries of science textbook lessons. *Journal of Educational Psychology, 88*, 64-73.

McMurray, J. & Fay, R. C. (2004). *Chemistry* (4th ed.). Upper Saddle River, NJ: Pearson.

Moreno, R., & Mayer, R. E. (2000). A coherence effect in multimedia learning: The case for minimizing irrelevant sounds in the design of multimedia messages. *Journal of Educational Psychology, 92*, 117-125.

Nakhleh, M. B. (1993). Are our students conceptual thinkers or algorithmic problem solvers? *Journal of Chemical Education, 70*, 52-55.

Nurrenbern, S. C. (2001). Piaget's theory of intellectual development revisited. *Journal of Chemical Education, 78*, 1107-1110.

Nurrenbern, S. C., & Pickering, M. (1987). Concept learning versus problem solving: Is there a difference? *Journal of Chemical Education, 64*, 508-510.

Odom, A. L., & Barrow, L. H. (1995). Development and application of a two-tier diagnostic test measuring college biology students' understanding of diffusion and osmosis after a course of instruction. *Journal of Research in Science Teaching, 32*, 45-61.

Olmsted, III, J., & Williams, G. M. (2006). *Chemistry* (4th ed.). New York, NY: Wiley.

Ogude, A. N., & Bradley, J. D. (1994). Ionic conduction and electrical neutrality in operating electrochemical cells. *Journal of Chemical Education, 71*, 29-34.

Orgill, M. K., & Bodner, G. M. (2005). The role of analogies in teaching chemistry. In N. J. Pienta, M. M. Cooper, & T. J. Greenbowe (Eds.), *Chemist's Guide to Effective Teaching* (pp 90-105). Upper Saddle River, NJ: Pearson.

Paivio, A. (1986). *Mental representations: A dual coding approach*. New York, NY: Oxford.

Pickering, M. (1990). Further studies on concept learning versus problem solving. *Journal of Chemical Education, 67*, 254-255.

Rieber, L. P. (1989, February). A review of animation research in computer-based instruction. Paper presented at the Annual Convention of the Association for Educational Communications and Technology, Dallas, TX.

Russell, J. W., Kozma, R. B., Jones, T., Wykoff, J., Marx, N., & Davis, J. (1997). Use of simultaneous-synchronized macroscopic, microscopic, and symbolic representations to enhance the teaching and learning of chemical concepts. *Journal of Chemical Education, 74*, 330-334.

Sanger, M. J. (2000). Using particulate drawings to determine and improve students' conceptions of pure substances and mixtures. *Journal of Chemical Education, 77*, 762-766.

Sanger, M. J., & Badger, II, S. M. (2001). Using computer-based visualization strategies to improve students' understanding of molecular polarity and miscibility. *Journal of Chemical Education, 78*, 1412-1416.

Sanger, M. J., Brecheisen, D. M., & Hynek, B. M. (2001). Can computer animations affect college biology students' conceptions about diffusion & osmosis? *American Biology Teacher, 63*, 104-109.

Sanger, M. J., Campbell, E., Felker, J., & Spencer, C. (2007). Concept learning versus problem solving: Does particle motion have an effect? *Journal of Chemical Education, 84*, 875-879.

Sanger, M. J., Phelps, A. J., & Fienhold, J. (2000). Using a computer animation to improve students' conceptual understanding of a can-crushing demonstration. *Journal of Chemical Education, 77*, 1517-1520.

Sanger, M. J. & Greenbowe, T. J. (1997). Students' misconceptions in electrochemistry: Current flow in electrolyte solutions and the salt bridge. *Journal of Chemical Education, 74*, 819-823.

Sanger, M. J., & Greenbowe, T. J. (2000). Addressing student misconceptions concerning electron flow in aqueous solutions with instruction including computer animations and conceptual change strategies. *International Journal of Science Education, 22*, 521-537.

Sawrey, B. A. (1990). Concept learning versus problem solving: Revisited. *Journal of Chemical Education, 67*, 253-254.

Tasker, R. (2005). Using multimedia to visualize the molecular world: Educational theory into practice. In N. J. Pienta, M. M. Cooper, & T. J. Greenbowe (Eds.), *Chemist's Guide to Effective Teaching* (pp 195-211). Upper Saddle River, NJ: Pearson.

Williamson, V. M., & Abraham, M. R. (1995). The effects of computer animation on the particulate mental models of college chemistry students. *Journal of Research in Science Teaching, 32*, 521-534.

15

Symbolic Mathematics in the Chemistry Curriculum: Facilitating the Understanding of Mathematical Models used in Chemistry

Theresa Julia Zielinski
Department of Chemistry, Medical Technology, and Physics
Monmouth University

Biography

Theresa Julia Zielinski is a Professor of Chemistry in the Department of Chemistry, Medical Technology and Physics at Monmouth University. She received her M.S. and Ph.D. in Physical Chemistry from Fordham University in New York City. Prior to joining Monmouth University she was Professor of Chemistry at Niagara University in Western New York for eighteen years and held a tenured faculty position at the College of Mount Saint Vincent in Riverdale, Bronx, NY for nine years. She served as Chair of the Department at Monmouth University from September 1998 till May 2002. She has taught a variety of chemistry courses for chemistry majors and non-science majors. Zielinski has authored or co-authored over 70 papers and in the past 10 years organized several symposia and presented over 35 talks at American Chemical Society national and regional meetings. She is a member of the Chemical Education, Computational Chemistry, Biological Chemistry and Physical Chemistry divisions of the American Chemical Society. She served on the Computers in Chemical Education and Physical Chemistry Examination committees of the American Chemical Society Division of Chemical Education. She is the feature editor for the SymMath column of the Journal of Chemical Education. She also is the curator for collection of peer reviewed and open review Symbolic Mathematics documents based on Mathcad, Mathematica, and Maple programs as part of the Journal of Chemical Education National Science Digital Library project as well as curator for the JCE Living Textbooks in Chemistry Physical Chemistry collection of teaching resources. Zielinski is also a member of the Editorial Board for The Chemical Educator, an Electronic Journal for Chemical Education and serves as the Education Section Editor for Reports in Computational Chemistry published by the ACS division of Computational Chemistry. Her work has been supported by grants from the National Science Foundation.

Abstract

The physical chemistry curriculum is grounded in the use of models of physical systems and the mathematical development of those models into equations that can be applied to examination of the properties of physical systems. However, students in their first physical chemistry course are challenged by the mathematics required to study the physical systems and often lack the ability to merge the physical system to the mathematical model for understanding experimental phenomena. This paper presents an over view with examples of how a Symbolic Mathematics Engine (SME) such as Mathcad can help students learn about models and explore the models as they build their understanding of physical chemistry concepts

Introduction

Symbolic Mathematics Engines (SMEs) have been around since the 1980's. These engines are calculation tools used by professionals, educators, and students. These tools make a calculation visible in a format that appears like a printed page, i.e. equations, data, and plots, intermingled with interpretive text. In spite of the simple appearance of the working interface (Figure 1) these tools are powerful mathematical packages that put the power of advanced programming into the hands of even a beginning user. Figure 1 displays the Mathcad page for the calculation of the Boltzmann distribution for Helium at two temperatures. Such a document would be useful for chemistry students at all levels of a college curriculum. This single example has the potential to increase learning when instructors use custom designed instructions for student self study. Alternatively files of this type can be used by the instructor during a lecture on a topic.

SMEs have been around for over 20 years. Maple's initial copyright is 1981, with Mathcad following in 1986, and Mathematica in 1988. The first SME to start using a user friendly interface was Mathcad. This interface let users enter equations and data into a template that resembled a printed page. There was syntax to learn but what you saw on the screen is what one would expect to see in a text book. More recently both Maple and Mathematica have included this feature to stand beside their traditional programming style input streams. The balance of this paper will primarily focus on Mathcad use in the Physical Chemistry Curriculum. Since the pedagogical significance is the same for all SMEs what is said about the usefulness of Mathcad in the curriculum applies to the other software packages as well. SME use depends on the instructor and the campus instructional support for that instructor. Student and instructor user friendly documents are essential for moving SME usage into the physical chemistry and other numerically intense parts of the chemistry curriculum.

History

Journal of Chemical Education published the first Mathcad documents for the physical chemistry curriculum (Coleman, 1990; Zdravkovski, 1991). These papers described the power of SME in computing overlap integrals, plotting radial distribution functions, solving cubic and differential equations, and taking derivatives. The following year Rioux (Rioux, 1992) described numerical solutions to the Schrödinger equation, an application of the linear variation method, and the one electron hydrogen molecule ion while another paper (Zdravkovski, 1992) presented a method for spectroscopic multicomponent analysis based on the Beer-Lambert law and regression analysis of kinetic data. These authors were the first to emphasize the importance of SME as tools for teaching physical chemistry concepts because of the way the software frees students of the tedium required when exploring more complex chemical mathematical models with hand calculations. The authors of these papers emphasized putting computational tools in the hands of students in their first physical chemistry courses.

Documents based on Mathematica also became available in the 1990s. Cooper and Casanova (Cooper & Casanova, 1991) applied this SME to the presentation of atomic and molecular orbital shapes, including hybrid orbitals. They considered Mathematica to be a powerful tool for undergraduate instruction. The following year Noggle described the use of a Mathematica notebook to determine vapor pressures (Noggle & Wood, 1992). Then Smith and Missen published an early example of using Maple in 1997 (Smith & Missen, 1997). It was Rioux who published the most extensive sets of templates for Mathcad (Rioux, 1994, 1995, 1997, 1998). This was followed by a description of a Maple notebook for obtaining chemical equations (Smith & Missen, 1997). Some useful Maple notebooks can be found at the Maple applications center, http://www.maplesoft.com/applications/index.aspx (accessed March 2008).

Physical chemistry applications for Mathematica and Mathcad also became available in book form (Atkins & de Paula, 2002; Cady & Trap, 2000; Cropper, 1998; Noggle, 1996, 1997). Maple IV & V notebooks are available on CD (Scarlete, 1999). A new four volume physical chemistry resource provides content supported by Mathematica and Mathcad appeared in 2006 (Metiu, 2006; Madura & Metui, 2005). Although all of these books are valuable resources with excellent expository material, they fall short of the goal of being pedagogically focused educational resources with emphasis on student learning. Although each book provides complete development of individual topics, the content seems to be written for the practicing physical chemist more than for the beginning student. With these books it is up to the instructor to provide the context and enabling pedagogical framework to make these resources student friendly.

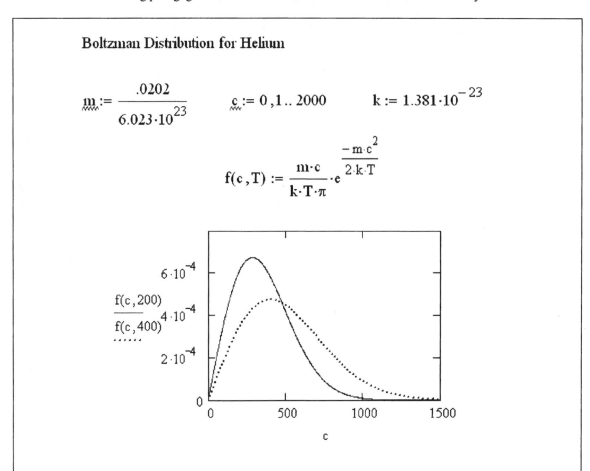

Figure 1. The Boltzmann distribution Mathcad template starts with the definition of constants required in the calculation. The distribution is written as a function of temperature and speed. Plots at 200 K (solid line) and 400 K (dotted line) appear below the equation. Students can manipulate the temperature independently and discuss their observations or the teacher can do the manipulations in class or assign this for group discussion during class.

At the New Traditions (NT) physical chemistry curriculum planning session in Madison, Wisconsin (February 1995, http://bluehawk.monmouth.edu/~tzielins/UW_Pchem.htm), physical chemists recognized that students think that physical chemistry is just an applied mathematics course. The participants also felt that it would be more appropriate for students to develop greater intuitive understanding of physical chemistry rather than focus on the mathematical details and that modern technology should be incorporated into all levels of the course. The group expressed an interest in using SMEs to advance student learning and felt that when SMEs are used appropriately, they will also increase mathematical abilities and intuition while increasing students' understanding of chemistry. Use of SMEs would also allow students to tackle problems that can not be solved by hand calculations. This would free the student to explore chemical models and construct greater understanding of how these models are used for interpreting structure, function, and the physical and spectral properties of molecules. There was some discussion about which SME was most appropriate to use in physical chemistry. The conclusion was that while all of the SME software types had strengths, Mathcad seemed most appropriate for the physical chemistry course because of its less steep learning curve and attractive GUI which permits interweaving of text graphics and mathematical processes on a screen that resembles the typical page in a book. An outcome of the NT project was the creation of a Mathcad web site in 1996 which grew into Mathcad in the Chemistry Curriculum feature column in the *Journal of Chemical Education* (*JCE*) (Theresa Julia Zielinski, 1998). In 2004 this feature column changed its name to JCE SymMath: Symbolic Mathematics in Chemistry (Theresa Julia Zielinski, 2004). The mission of this feature column is to promote the dissemination of quality SME documents using Mathcad, Maple, or Mathematica.

Two Examples of Using SME for Instruction

Two examples illustrate why more SME materials should be used in teaching. Both of these come from physical chemistry and they give an inkling of how learning can be deepened through the use of the SME materials.

Example 1: The Harmonic Oscillator

It is standard to find the equation for the solutions to the quantum mechanical harmonic oscillator Schrödinger equation and corresponding wavefunctions plots in physical chemistry and quantum chemistry textbooks. What is missing is the detailed examination of the components, i.e. exponential part, polynomial parts, and normalization factor.

$$\Psi_v(x) = N_v H_v(x) e^{-\frac{x^2}{2}}$$

It is not feasible to have students do a detailed analysis of these components by hand calculation. While teachers can prepare plots of the functions and show them as support for a discussion of the components, it is better, in my opinion, to let students use an SME template to examine the components for themselves and to create their own plots de novo. Figure 2 (a, b, c, d, e, and f) shows the Mathcad steps for this. Figure 2a sets up the calculation declaring constant values and performing preliminary calculations. Figures 2b, c, and d permit students to examine the three components of the wave functions. The three components of the wave function merge in Figure 2e to form the final wave functions. The exercise 2f. The complete template was can be found at the *JCE DLib* site (Zielinski,2007).

Using the harmonic oscillator template permits students to explore and deepen their understanding of the wavefunctions and other properties of the harmonic oscillator. After completing the exercises they should be able to:

- draw harmonic oscillator wave functions for the first few energy levels,

- discuss how the results of the quantum mechanical harmonic oscillator approach the classical oscillator results at high quantum number,

- relate the number of nodes in a wave function to the energy level described by that wave function, and

- Explain the reason for each component of the harmonic oscillator wave function in terms of the properties of well behaved wave functions.

Plank 's constant

The force constant for H_2

$$h := 6.62608 \cdot 10^{-34} \cdot J \cdot s$$

$$k := 520 \cdot \frac{N}{m}$$

$$hbar := \frac{h}{2 \cdot \pi}$$

$$xe := 74.16 \cdot 10^{-12} \cdot m$$ Equilibrium bond length in H_2

$$m1 := \frac{.001}{6.023 \cdot 10^{23}} \cdot kg$$ $$m2 := \frac{0.001}{6.023 \cdot 10^{23}} \cdot kg$$

$$mu := \frac{m1 \cdot m2}{m1 + m2}$$ Compute the reduced mass.

$$Bsq := \frac{hbar}{\sqrt{mu \cdot k}}$$ $$Bsq = 1.605 \times 10^{-22} m^2$$

$$B := \sqrt{Bsq}$$ $$B = 1.267 \times 10^{-11} m$$ **The magnitude of B indicates the range for the plots.**

$$x := \frac{-7.10 \cdot 10^{-11}}{B} \cdot m, \frac{-6.99 \cdot 10^{-11}}{B} \cdot m .. \frac{7.10 \cdot 10^{-11}}{B} \cdot m$$

Figure 2a. A Mathcad template first sets up the initial constants and preliminary calculations. Units can be used throughout a Mathcad document. x is the range for the calculations and plots. The range is divided by B to permit integer values on the abscissa of the plot.

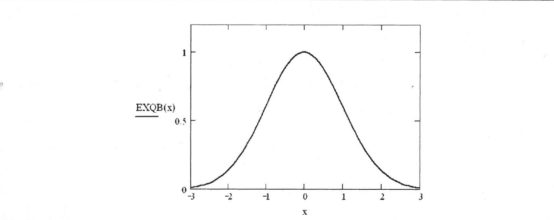

Figure 2b. The Exponential Component The exponential function is the same for all harmonic oscillator wavefunctions.

$$N_V(v) := \frac{1}{\left(2^v \cdot v!\right)^{\frac{1}{2}}} \cdot \left(\frac{1}{\pi}\right)^{\frac{1}{4}}$$

$N_v(3) = 0.108$

Figure 2c. The Normalization Factor. Specifying v automatically generates the normalization constant.

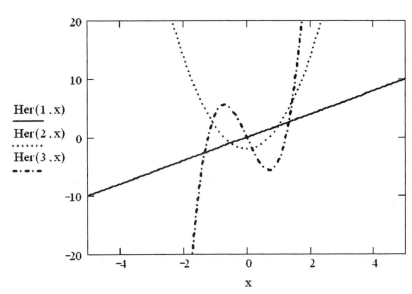

Figure 2d. The Hermite Polynomials. The Hermite polynomial Components are obtained with the Her(n,x) Mathcad function. Three Hermite polynomials are shown here. Students can generate other Hermite polynomials easily and discuss the function's contribution to the overall wavefunction.

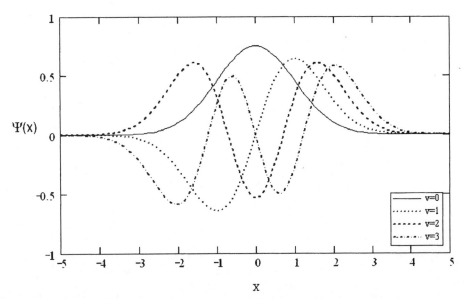

Figure 2e. Plots of four harmonic oscillator wavefunctions constructed from products of the three components. At this point students can plot any wavefunction easily and observe the function properties.

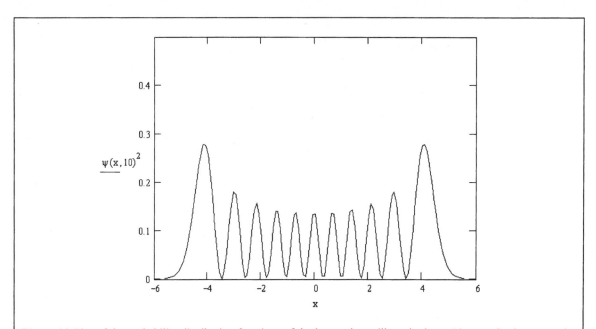

Figure 2f. Plot of the probability distribution functions of the harmonic oscillator in the v=10 state. Students can plot any distribution function by simply changing the value of v in the wavefunction parentheses.

Example 2. Visualizing the Statistical Thermodynamic C_V

The shape of the curves obtained from the equation for the constant volume heat capacity, Figure 3a and 3b, are neither easy to visualize nor easy to generate with a calculator. With Mathcad we can plot them for any diatomic molecule. The plots for four molecules are shown in Figure 3c. SymMath documents like this, when used for class lectures and/or homework, enrich the learning environment by empowering students to visualize more complex mathematical topics.

Figure 3a	$$C_v(T, \theta, gas) := 1.5 \cdot R + R + \frac{R \cdot \left(\dfrac{\theta}{T}\right)^2 \cdot \exp\left(\dfrac{\theta}{T}\right)}{\left(\exp\left(\dfrac{\theta}{T}\right) - 1\right)^2}$$
Figure 3b	$$\theta = \frac{h}{2 \cdot \pi k_b} \cdot \sqrt{\frac{k}{\mu}}$$

Figure 3c

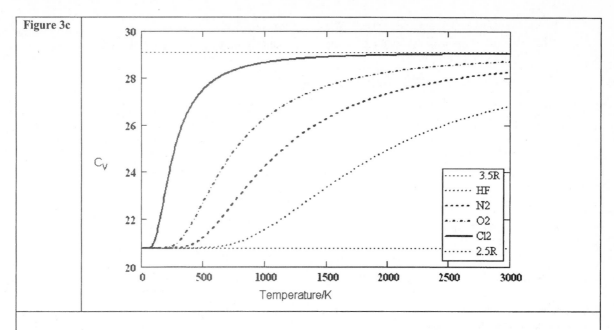

Figure 3a-c. C_v as a function of T from Statistical Thermodynamic calculations using Mathcad. 3a is the equation for C_v. 3b is θ which depends on the force constant and reduced mass of the molecule. The final curves appear in 3c.

The SymMath Collection

Since 1996 the SymMath collection has grown to over 100 documents/worksheets written by over 40 teaching chemists. The collection expands by eight or more new worksheets every year. The collection contains primarily Mathcad templates but there are a few Mathematica notebooks and Maple worksheets. The collection consists of both peer reviewed and 'open review' documents. The peer-reviewed documents are archived at http://www.jce.divched.org/JCEDLib/SymMath/index.html, The *Journal of Chemical Education JCE DLib* SymMath site, The abstracts, pdf view, and relevant information about all documents can be seen by anyone at the JCE site. A JCE subscription is required to download active SME documents from the JCE peer reviewed collection. The active SME worksheets of the 'open review' portion of the collection are available for download at the JCE site. Each open review document is copyrighted by the author and instructors can make these available to their students on a class intranet

The entire collection of SymMath documents has been included in the JCE Digital Library collection with appropriate search meta-data for. All of the SymMath documents found in the JCE Dlib are either learning objects or teaching assets. Assets are shorter documents that can be used as components in a larger presentation of a topic. Learning objects are fully developed interactive lessons on a topic. As of August 2007 over 90% of the documents in the collection were learning objects and were written using guidelines that foster student learning through guided inquiry. Learners can use these documents for independent study assignments or faculty can select documents for class assignments or to assist students to more efficiently handle data collected in the laboratory.

Adding to the SymMath Collection

Authors can find the guidelines for preparing publishable SymMath documents at http://www.jce.divched.org/JCEDLib/SymMath/authors/index.html. SymMath documents should contain some essential element that cannot be readily reproduced in the traditional print medium or easily completed by students using paper, pencil, and a calculator. The documents should contain clear goals and objectives for the student user. Excellent documents have interactive components that foster student learning; embedded interactivity is one of the most important components of a pedagogically effective

SymMath document. A document should also give clear instructions to enable students to use the document effectively; hints on SME syntax are especially important for inexperienced students and new faculty users.

Goals and Objectives in Well Crafted Documents

Designing goals and objectives is not something with which most teaching chemists are facile. Pedagogically, goals and objectives are different, a distinction not made in dictionaries. A goal is an overarching idea of the content or skills we want to provide to students. Objectives are the outcomes we expect after students use a resource, namely, what they should be able to do after completing an assigned activity or section of instruction. Each objective is driven by the goal we set for that activity.

Objectives do not state that they will:

- <u>Give</u> students knowledge about activity coefficients;

- <u>Teach</u> students about acid rain; and

- <u>Show</u> students non linear curve fitting.

Objectives are written with action words and include such statements as: After completing this exercise, students should be able to:

- <u>Determine</u> the limiting value for E' for any amalgam mixture given the potentials as a function of concentration;

- <u>Prepare</u> a multivariable diagram for concentrations of components of rainwater;

- <u>Explain</u> the method of determining the best fit of a polynomial to experimental data, etc.;

- <u>Determine</u> the rate constant for a reaction using non-linear curve fitting;

- <u>Determine</u> the standard deviations in the fitting parameters when non-linear curve fitting is done; and

- <u>Calculate</u> the temperature of a flame using the adiabatic flame temperature model.

- <u>Plot</u> $C_P(T)$ and <u>explain</u> the significance of the plot.

Active Learning with SymMath Documents

The emphasis on active participation as a mechanism to enhance learning is an important aspect of any SME document. Active participation results in students achieving greater depth of understanding, entertaining fewer misconceptions, and displaying longer retention of learned concepts. Furthermore, with digital materials faculty are not constrained by page limits. Faculty can create experiences that lead students to explore models and applications of chemistry that normal classroom and study time would preclude. When students analyze realistic data sets interactively within an SME template, they gain deeper understanding of concepts and physical models used in chemistry. Plots of data or model systems can be created, modified, and examined interactively using guided inquiry questions provided by the faculty author. That digital interaction leads to increased retention and greater understanding of concepts conforms to the success reported for active learning, hands-on–minds-on teaching strategies. With SME templates, inexperienced students avoid de novo data processing, programming, and algorithm development which detracts from the development of conceptual understanding of the chemistry. Digital documents also increase efficiency of learning by removing the tedium of hand calculations and allow students to achieve higher levels of mastery of concepts and techniques. This does not mean that students should not create their own documents. Through faculty documents and templates students learn the syntax of the software and become sensitive to the elements of style in document preparation; students can then later adapt the faculty created templates to their own projects and reports. As students progress by using many model documents they also gain confidence in their ability to use the software for original reports and homework.

Critical Thinking

Developing students' critical thinking skills is a central concern when creating SME worksheets. Perhaps the most effective ways to do this is by using the Socratic Method and active learning strategies. Fully developed digital documents can include both. Embedded questions can focus student thinking and reflection. Requests for students to practice the concepts by interacting with the document enhance comprehension and retention. Well-crafted exercises and mastery-level problems help students develop the ability to apply learned concepts to new situations and create independent SME documents including choosing the approach, mathematical model, and simplifying assumptions.

The SymMath Documents

A generic Table of Contents (Table 1) is the mechanism for organizing the topic areas in the SymMath collection.

Generic Physical Chemistry Table of Contents	
• Gases	• Fourier Methods
• Kinetic Theory	• Spectroscopy
• First Law	• Multi-electron Atoms
• Thermochemistry	• Diatomic Molecules
• Thermodynamics	• Polyatomic Molecules
• Second Law	• Computational Chemistry
• Third Law	o Classical Mechanics
• Free Energy	o MM/MD
• Phase Equilibria	• Symmetry/Group Theory
• Statistical Thermodynamics	• Molecular Spectroscopy
• Chemical Kinetics	• NMR
• Electrochemistry	• Solid State/Crystallography
• Quantum Chemistry	• Lasers
o Foundations	• Numerical Methods
o Particle in a Box	o Statistics
o Harmonic Oscillator	o Curve Fitting
o Rigid Rotor	o Mathcad Skills
o Hydrogen Atom	• Advanced Chemistry Topics
o MO Theory	

Table 1. Generic Physical Chemistry Table of Contents

There is at least one SME document in each category. For those documents that are JCE peer reviewed, the usage policy states that faculty may choose those documents that fit their instructional needs and then distribute one copy of each document to students in their classes if they have a JCE subscription or their campus has an IP based subscription to the Journal. Instructors only need to provide a list of the documents they are using to *JCE* for copyright tracking. Students have access to any published documents in the SymMath collection if the campus has the IP based subscription. Instructors also have access to the collection through their personal *JCE* subscriptions for students in their classes and for use in course intranet collections. There is no journal subscription requirement for open access documents. Since individual authors hold the copyrights to the open review documents, instructors may distribute copies to students via a class intranet but cannot publish them elsewhere without permission of the authors.

Because the SME collection contains over 100 documents, faculty must consider curricula goals and objectives and student SME skills when choosing documents to use in courses. If a campus does not support the published SME for a given worksheet, then a translation can be made using the accompanying pdf file as a guide. Translations are welcome additions to the SME collection and should be sent to *JCE* for inclusion in the collection. Translations are published in future appearances of the SymMath feature column with credit to the translators.

Making SymMath Documents Work in your Classes

The most effective mechanism to implement SME documents in courses is to require their use from the first day of a course and then build opportunities for students to learn the software as they complete homework and write laboratory reports throughout the semester. Thus one could start with a training exercise for the SME and follow with simple calculations and exercises as part of every homework assignment. As the semester proceeds one can introduce skills for doing derivations that support the course concepts. A first choice in a thermodynamics course might be the integration of $C_P(T)$ to obtain the amount of energy required to warm a sample of some material. In a quantum chemistry course one might start with Plank's radiation law and the relationship between λ_{max} and temperature. It is important to emphasize to students that although at first using the SME may seem harder than using paper and pencil, it is actually easier in the long term after they have had some practice and have collected a spectrum of their own files upon which to draw for future assignments or build solutions to more complex problems. After basic skills are learned by students they can be given more advanced worksheets which can be used in group projects, as templates for laboratory assignments, as homework, and as independent learning tools.

Freeing classroom time for discussion of difficult topics is a valuable outcome from using SME worksheets. When students learn and practice some of the simpler concepts for a topic through the worksheets free, class time for discussion of the more abstract features of that topic become available. One example is to provide the preliminary exercises for learning 1st and 2nd order kinetics, often a review of work done in general chemistry, followed by a more in depth study of reversible, series reactions, oscillating reactions, and more complex reactions for which no specific order can be easily written. Such an approach would permit instructors to use real data to teach students how to think about more complex kinetics and determine complex mechanisms (Hinsberg & Houle, 1996.).

When using SME throughout a course, i.e. in homework, laboratory, and focused topical studies, an instructor must be willing to provide constant support to students as they use the software. Although the learning curves are not steep, some students have the notion that they should not be required to move beyond using the calculator and pencil and paper for work in any chemistry course. Faculty need to demonstrate the use of the software in lecture and laboratory classes. Students must be given the opportunity to practice with the software during class or laboratory sessions when the instructor is present to smooth initial rough moments. It is also important to blend using the SME and homework in a way that helps students focus on learning the chemistry concepts rather than SME coding. Providing the students with templates that contain data facilitates their work toward mastery of concepts. Also providing students with sample templates for routine type calculations helps them move forward with the chemistry while they are learning the use of the SME. The key objective for the instructor is to provide a more efficient and richer learning environment than that represented by standard lecture and traditional homework assignments of the plug and chug or derive till I die styles.

Over the course of my career I have seen various technologies develop for use in the physical chemistry classroom. These technologies span the range from slide rules, through mechanical calculators, hand-held calculators, graphical calculators, higher level programming languages, and now SME software. It is in the SME software that I see the greatest quantum leap toward fostering student learning. The SMEs provide instructors the opportunity to make learning more flexible and efficient. Students can be more focused on the chemistry and not on the details of the number crunching or programming. Instructors can turn their creative energies to developing worksheets that combine study of the chemical concept, the mathematical model, and the scientific conclusions that can be drawn from data interpreted with models. The need for logical critical thinking is still required from students using SME templates. Students must be able to use the template and meet performance objectives set by their instructors. Students and instructors alike can no longer hide behind layers of mathematical manipulations. They must respond as thinking scientists to the use and application of SME software and templates as tools for learning and doing science.

In My Classroom

In addition to requiring that numerical homework problems be completed using Mathcad, I use a variety of SME documents in my physical chemistry courses. These include both peer reviewed and open review materials as well as some documents that I have created that are not yet available in the SME collection.

The quantum chemistry lecture and laboratory semester includes:

- An Introduction to Mathcad
  http://bluehawk.monmouth.edu/~tzielins/mathcad/tjz/doc001.htm

- Playing with Waves
  http://bluehawk.monmouth.edu/~tzielins/mathcad/tjz/doc007.htm

- Blackbody Radiation
  http://bluehawk.monmouth.edu/~tzielins/mathcad/GShalhoub/doc003.htm

- Exploring Orthonormal Functions (T. J. Zielinski, 2007)

- Harmonic Oscillator Wavefunction Explorations (T. J. Zielinski, 2007)

- Introductory Explorations of the Fourier Series
  http://bluehawk.monmouth.edu/~tzielins/mathcad/tjz/doc003.htm

- Properties of the Radial Functions
  http://bluehawk.monmouth.edu/~tzielins/mathcad/GShalhoub/doc004.htm

- Introduction to Franck-Condon Factors (T. J. Zielinski & Shalhoub, 1998)

- The Iodine Spectrum (Long & Zielinski, 1998)

- Exploring the Morse Potential (T. J. Zielinski, 1998)

- Vibronic Spectra of Diatomic Molecules and the Birge-Sponer Extrapolation (Shalhoub & Zielinski, 1998)

Documents used in the thermodynamics/dynamics course include:

- Computing a Flame Temperature
  http://bluehawk.monmouth.edu/~tzielins/mathcad/JNoggle/doc001.htm

- Computing a Liquid-Vapor Phase Diagram (Chen, 2005a)

- The Entropy of Lead
  http://bluehawk.monmouth.edu/~tzielins/mathcad/GHardgrove/doc001.htm

- Work Done During Reversible and Irreversible Isothermal Expansion of an Ideal Gas (Ferguson, 2004)

- Calculating Enthalpies of Reactions
  http://bluehawk.monmouth.edu/~tzielins/mathcad/tjz/doc010.htm

- van der Waals and Redlich Kwong: Fitting Two Parameter Equations to Gas Data
  http://bluehawk.monmouth.edu/~tzielins/mathcad/tjz/doc008.htm

- Modeling Stratospheric Ozone Kinetics, Part I (Harvey & Sweeney, 1999a).

- Modeling Stratospheric Ozone Kinetics, Part II (Harvey & Sweeney, 1999b).

- Maxwell Distribution of Gas Molecule Velocities
  http://bluehawk.monmouth.edu/~tzielins/mathcad/GHardgrove/doc003.htm

- Fitting a Polynomial to C_P vs. T for Ag
  http://bluehawk.monmouth.edu/~tzielins/mathcad/tjz/doc002.htm

Caveats for SME in the Curriculum

There are some factors that instructors should keep in mind when starting to use SME applications in their courses. The major caveat is that software changes frequently; some SME companies issue new versions every two years, e.g. Mathcad. This can be frustrating to instructors who must then check/update documents for each class. It is also frustrating for archivists who are faced with the job of updating older versions of published templates. Older Mathematica, Maple, and Mathcad documents may need to be rewritten in order to be used with newer versions of the SME. The only solution to this problem is a vigilant monitoring of the templates by users who then send updated versions to the archival site.

Another aspect of SME version enhancements is that it is not possible to archive documents in all versions of an SME that may be in use at any given time. At the SME archive site some documents were created with Mathcad 6 and others created with version 8, 2000, 2001, 2001i, 11, 12, and 13. Templates created with the current version of Mathcad (Mathcad 14) will not open in an older version of the software. Documents created with an older version of Mathcad will open with Mathcad14 but there may be some incompatibilities such as units or the way some functions work. When this happens the instructor is left with a debugging task that could be time consuming. Instructors are encouraged to share their updates of various templates with the wider audience of users via the SymMath archive. Another aspect of this is that many departments, especially at smaller campuses, cannot upgrade software as often as developers make new versions. Thus they are restricted to documents created or archived using formats that are older or concurrent with their version of the software. Here a pdf file of the worksheet would help the instructor create their own new template for the version of the software at hand. Document users can also request a colleague with the newest version to save, SaveAs, the worksheet in the older format. This would at least minimize some of the keying required for a recreation of an entire document.

Because of the potential software version incompatibilities, all SME documents at the SymMath archive are published in both native SME format and pdf format. The pdf file contains all the worked out components that an instructor can use to recreate the worksheet or debug a badly behaved worksheet. The pdf files also facilitate translation of a worksheet from one SME format to another, e.g. from Mathcad to Maple or Mathematica. This broadens the potential user base as colleagues adapt, rewrite, or translate documents and share their work through the SymMath collection.

Final Questions

Some might ask which SME is the best to use. There are advocates for each available SME. The key, however, is not which SME to use but to decide to use one and move forward with that decision. But you might ask, shouldn't all students have experience with the same SME? I don't think so. The fundamental logic of developing solutions to new and interesting problems and an understanding of the underlying chemical concepts is transferable from one SME to the others. Once one SME is learned it is easier to move to another SME later. Users may develop a preference for one of the SME products but that choice may change during a career.

The main barrier to the use of SME in teaching may be the crowded curriculum and concerns about adding one more components to an already crowded advanced chemistry course. This barrier seems insurmountable. However, physical chemistry instructors are often overly concerned about 'covering' the curriculum, the cannon, of the subject. Once one recognizes that it is impossible to cover all of physical chemistry in two or even three semesters of instruction, it becomes easier to choose the topics for any course. Remember that the same course does not fit all types of students or programs. The engineers would want a course different from the chemists who in turn want a course that is different from the biochemists etc. The important results are the skills students develop while learning any topic deeply and logically through use of an SME document. With this skill students later can learn any other topic independently and well

Conclusions for Best Practice in Teaching Physical Chemistry

The best practices for teaching physical chemistry require a vigilant instructor who is willing to make curriculum choices based on the type of course and the students in that course. It is impossible to cover all topics in two semesters of physical chemistry instruction. Choices are necessary and should be consistent with the growth of thinking skills in students and the creation of flexibility in their ability to learn new things. There is not enough time during a standard semester for students to do the practice required to develop understanding of concepts with standard paper and calculator computation. Consequently in my opinion using SymMath documents in a physical chemistry course is essential. This in turn requires faculty to provide students with templates that at least cut some of the tedious data entry and permit them to focus on the concepts, comprehension of scientific and mathematical models, and interpretation of data. Faculty should also use the software during lecture and have students present their SymMath solutions in class. Physical chemistry is not a programming course; thus faculty should provide students with a way to use the software that it does not detract from the science and scientific models. It is almost as if students need to learn the software by osmosis so that they can thrive with the chemistry. This is where the SymMath collection can serve as a starting point for infusing more abstract thinking and model manipulation into the physical chemistry curriculum. Students can succeed beyond traditional expectations if given the tools and support during a course. SymMath materials have done this for my students. It is a best practice in my classroom.

Acknowledgements

Partial support for various physical chemistry projects was provided to TJZ and colleagues through: NSF DUE #9354473 Guided Inquiry Materials/SymMath; NSF DUE #9455928 - New Traditions - UW – Madison – SymMath; NSF DUE #9950809 PCOL; NSF DUE #9653440 Numerical Methods Workshop - Jeff Madura, Andrzei Wierzbicki, and Sidney Young; NSF DUE #0127291 for "Quantum States E-Book"; NSF DUE #0226244 The JCE Dlib – UW Madison; DUE-0632303 for "Collaborative Project: ChemEd Digital Library: An NSDL Pathway for Chemical Sciences Education"; and numerous colleagues who contributed documents to the SymMath collection

References

Atkins, P., & de Paula, J. (2002). Explorations in Physical Chemistry: A resource for Users of Mathcad. New York: W. H. Freeman and Company.

Cady, M. P., & Trap, C. A. (2000). *A Mathcad Primer for Physical Chemistry*. New York: W. H. Freeman and Company.

Chen, F. M. C. (2005a). Computing Liquid–Vapor Phase Diagrams for Non-Ideal Binary Mixtures. *J. Chem. Educ., 82*, 1100.

Coleman, W. F. (1990). The use of equation solvers in teaching chemistry. *J. Chem. Educ., 67*, A203-A205.

Cooper, R., & Casanova, J. (1991). Two-Dimensional atomic and molecular orbital displays using Mathematica. *J. Chem. Educ., 68*, 486-488.

Cropper, W. H. (1998). *Mathematica Computer Programs for Physical Chemistry*. New York: Springer.

Ferguson, A. (2004). Work Done During Reversible and Irreversible Isothermal Expansion of an Ideal Gas. *J. Chem. Educ., 81*, 606. http://www.jce.divched.org/JCEDlib/SymMath/collection/031/index.html (accessed March 2008).

Harvey, E., & Sweeney, R. (1999a). Modeling Stratospheric Ozone Kinetics, Part I: The Chapman Cycle. *J. Chem. Educ., 76*, 1309.

Harvey, E., & Sweeney, R. (1999b). Modeling Stratospheric Ozone Kinetics, Part II: Addition of Hydrogen, Nitrogen and Chlorine: Ozone. *J. Chem. Educ., 76*, 1310.

Hinsberg, W. D., & Houle, F. A. (1996.). *Chemical Kinetics Simulator, v1.01*. Retrieved August, 2005, CKS may be downloaded at no charge at URL http://www.almaden.ibm.com/st/computational_science/ck/?cks (accessed March 2008)

Long, G., & Zielinski, T. J. (1998). The iodine spectrum: IodineSpectrum.mcd. *Journal of Chemical Education, 75*(9), 1192-1192.

Madura, J. D., & Metiu, H. (2005). *The merging of physical chemistry and computer algebra systems. Abstract of Papers,* 230th National Meeting of the American Chemical American Chemical Society, Washington DC; American Chemical Society: Washington, DC; COMP 48.

Metiu, H. (2006) *Physical Chemistry* Volumes 1-4. New York: Taylor and Francis.

Noggle, J. H. (1996). *Physical Chemistry Using Mathematica*. New York: HarperCollins.

Noggle, J. H. (1997). *Physical Chemistry Using Mathcad*. Newark: Pike Creek Publishing.

Noggle, J. H., & Wood, R. H. (1992). Calculation of vapor pressure using Mathematica. *J. Chem. Educ., 69*, 810-811.

Rioux, F. (1992). Quantum Mechanics using Mathcad 3.0. *J. Chem. Educ., 69*, A240-A242.

Rioux, F. (1994). Enriching quantum chemistry with Mathcad. *J. Chem. Educ. Software*, 1D2.

Rioux, F. (1995). Enriching quantum chemistry with Mathcad. *J. Chem. Educ. Software*, 3D1.

Rioux, F. (1997). Enriching quantum chemistry with Mathcad (Program for Mac OS-compatible computers). *J. Chem. Educ., 74*, 1016.

Rioux, F. (1998). Group Theory with Mathcad: Issue 9801MW for Mac OS and Windows. *J. Chem. Educ., 75*, 644.

Scarlete, M. (1999). *WWW Living-Book of Physical Chemistry*. Quebec CA: BU Press. The individual volumes included in the collection can be found at http://www.ubishops.ca/ccc/div/sci/chem/publications/pub-scarlete.html (accessed March 2008).

Shalhoub, G. M., & Zielinski, T. J. (1998). Vibronic spectra of diatomic molecules and the Birge-Sponer extrapolation. *J. Chem. Educ., 75*(9), 1192.

Smith, W. R., & Missen, R. W. (1997). Using Mathematica and Maple to obtain chemical equations. *J. Chem. Educ., 74*, 1369-1371.

Zdravkovski, Z. (1991). Using MathCAD in chemistry calculations. *J. Chem. Educ., 68*, A95-A97.

Zdravkovski, Z. (1992). Mathcad in Chemistry Calculations II: Arrays. *J. Chem. Educ., 69*, A242-A244.

Zielinski, T. J., & Shalhoub, G. M. (1998). The Franck-Condon factors: *J. Chem. Educ., 75*(9), 1192. http://www.jce.divched.org/ JCEDLib/SymMath/collection/003/index.html (accessed March 2008)

Zielinski, T. J. (1998). Exploring the Morse potential: MorsePotential.mcd. *J. Chem. Educ., 75*(9), 1191. http://www.jce.divched.org/ JCEDLib/SymMath/collection/article.php?id=1 (accessed March 2008).

Zielinski, T. J. (1998). Mathcad in the Chemistry Curriculum. *J. Chem. Educ., 75*, 1189-1192.

Zielinski, T. J. (2004). Helping Students Learn Mathematically Intensive Aspects of Chemistry. *J. Chem. Educ., 81*, 155-158.

Zielinski, T.J. (2007a). Exploring the Harmonic Oscillator Wave Function Components. *J. Chem. Educ., 84*, 1232. http://www.jce.divched.org/JCEDLib/ SymMath/collection/article.php?id=54 (accessed March 2008).

Zielinski, T. J. (2007b). Exploring Orthonormal Functions. *J. Chem. Educ.*, *84,* 1888. http://www.jce.divched.org/JCEDLib/SymMath/collection/article.php?id=59 (accessed March 2008)

Part III

Teaching and Learning Chemistry Outside the Classroom

16

Chemistry Is in the News: The Why and Wherefore of Integrating Popular News Media into the Chemistry Classroom

Kathleen M. Carson
Department of Educational Leadership and
Policy Analysis
University of Missouri-Columbia

Deborah L. Hume
Department of Psychological Sciences
University of Missouri-Columbia

Yongqiang "John" Sui
Department of Chemistry
University of Missouri-Columbia

Susan Schelble
Department of Chemistry
Metropolitan State College of Denver

Rainer E. Glaser
Department of Chemistry
University of Missouri-Columbia

Abstract

Chemistry Is in the News is a curriculum incorporating popular news media into the chemistry classroom. Its design and adoption have been driven by the desire to improve student learning by emphasizing the connection of the classroom content to real world events, to improve classroom atmosphere through the use and support of student collaborative groups, and to better prepare students to operate in the information age by meaningfully integrating the use of general and discipline specific Information and Communication Technologies (ICT) into the curriculum. Here the philosophical and pedagogical basis of this approach is presented to provide future *CIITN* faculty with the justification for its implementation (webportal: http://ciitn.missouri.edu). *CIITN* has achieved many of the goals it was to accomplish; however, many challenges remain and opportunities for further evolution of the curriculum exist.

Biographies

Kathleen M. Carson, a research assistant in the Department of Chemistry at the University of Missouri-Columbia, received a B.A. in International Studies at MU in 2003 and a M.A. in Educational Leadership and Policy Analysis at MU in 2005, and she is currently working toward a Ph.D. in Political Science at St. Louis University. She has focused on interdisciplinarity in the pursuit of her education, having a background in both hard science and social science and combining her graduate classroom experience in the College of Education with research experience in the Department of Chemistry. She is the recipient of the 2006 MU Distinguished Master's Thesis Award.

Dr. Deborah L. Hume is a social psychologist with interests in the application of social psychological principles to issues in health, education, and social justice. She has taught statistics and women's studies at Stephens College, and a variety of graduate and undergraduate courses in psychology at both Stephens College and the University of Missouri-Columbia. As an Instructional Development Specialist at the Program for Excellence in Teaching at MU, she was able to employ her interests in the development and assessment of effective teaching methods. Dr. Hume is currently Resident Instruction Assistant Professor in the MU Department of Psychological Sciences.

Yongqiang "John" Sui studied at Beijing University of Chemical Technology and received a B.S. in chemistry with a minor in computer science in 1995 and an M.S. in management engineering in 1998. He joined the MU Department of Chemistry in 2003, earned an M.S. degree in 2004, and is now working toward a Ph.D. on butadiene-based materials chemistry combining experimentation and solid state electronic structure theory. He is the co-developer of the *Chemistry Is in the News* web tool.

Dr. Susan Schelble is an Assistant Professor in the Chemistry Department of Metropolitan State College of Denver. She has a background in physical organic chemistry and chemical education. Her research interests are centered around undergraduates student majoring in chemistry or biology with an interest in health careers or education. Dr. Schelble's research lies in two distinct areas. The first is in chemical education where she works with future high school teachers in the Denver Public Schools, and in developing peer-reviewed group projects for college and high school students. The laboratory research focuses on mechanistic studies of novel organo-phosphorus compounds and the preparation of new synthons for pseudo-peptides. Dr. Schelble currently is a councilor for the American Chemical Society, representing the 2400 member Colorado Section.

Dr. Rainer E. Glaser, Professor of Chemistry, studied chemistry and physics in Tübingen, at Berkeley, and at Yale. His major lines of research are in bioorganic chemistry and toxicology (carcinogenesis, DNA base deamination), materials chemistry (polar, anisotropic, optical), and astrochemistry (interstellar nucleobase synthesis). He published 145 articles, including 22 papers in the *Journal of the American Chemical Society* and 9 papers in *Angewandte Chemie* and *Chemistry-A European Journal*. He has collaborated extensively with chemists, biochemists, physicists, mathematicians, astronomers, educators, and journalists. His research involved 32 undergraduate, 25 graduate, and 5 postdoctoral students. His undergraduates went on to graduate studies at Stanford, MIT, Tübingen, Manchester, SUNY's CSH Lab, his graduate students to postdocs at Harvard, Berkeley, OSU, UAB, and ETH Zürich, and six former students won professorships. In 1995, Glaser began his Education Research with the novel curriculum, *Chemistry Is in the News* (*CIITN*), that he designed for chemistry education of science majors. He was a JSPS Fellow in 1997 and was elected AAAS Fellow in 2004 and Fellow of the Royal Society of Chemistry in 2006.

Introduction

The pace of the expansion of the frontiers of science is increasingly making science education, as it is generally practiced, obsolete. The gap between the way students are taught and how students might employ scientific knowledge has become nearly unbreachable. This is particularly true in introductory chemistry courses where the overwhelming majority of students do not pursue chemistry beyond theses courses. Yet these students are taught chemistry concepts in isolation from the process of discovery or the concepts' actual applications. Judith Ramaley, assistant director of the NSF Directorate for Education & Human Resources, highlighted this problem, stating at the 2003 ACS Society Committee on Education Conference that 'the major challenge facing contemporary higher education is to enhance its relevance and connectedness to the issues and problems faced by the broader society, as these problems are defined by community members and not by academics acting independently of the views of others' (Jacobs, 2003, p. 34) (Figure 1).

Figure 1. The gap between traditional content and students' needs in the scientific society.

In order to meet that challenge, we have reviewed various approaches that facilitate the construction of these connections, and have developed a taxonomy of 'Authentic News Media Based Learning Activities' in the *Chemistry Is in the News* (*CIITN*) project (Glaser & Carson, 2005) (Table 1). This taxonomy describes the levels of implementation of the *CIITN* project and provides the theoretical foundation needed for teaching innovation (Gabel, 1999). This project is designed for science majors to draw explicit connections between real-world issues and classroom content. It has been implemented in sophomore-level organic chemistry courses at the University of Missouri-Columbia (MU) in various forms since 1997 (Glaser & Poole, 1999; Hume, Carson, Hodgen, & Glaser, 2005). Faculty development workshops and several multi- and one-day con-ferences have been offered since 2001 and have reached over 50 faculty members in 20 states and 3 countries (Figure 2). These have led to the implementation of formal *CIITN* activities at the University of Colorado-Denver since 2002, at Florida State University and the University of Ontario Institute of Technology since 2004, and at St. Louis University and Miami University since 2005. Many of the workshop participants also have implemented local versions of *CIITN*. International *CIITN* collaboration is being carried out with students at the University of Paderborn, Germany; the first international residence took place in the fall of 2005 with the German students visiting Columbia to present their portfolio to their American peers at MU. International collaboration is also being pursued with the University of Haifa, Israel. These implementations, both formal and local are breaking new ground by adapting *CIITN* for other levels of instruction, other areas of chemistry, and even other science disciplines.

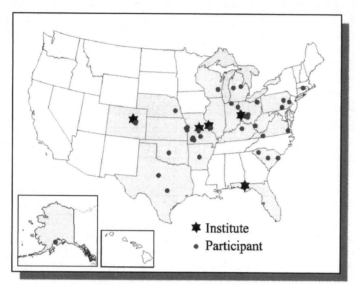

Figure 2. *CIITN* Dissemination.

To fully appreciate *CIITN* activities, one must discuss the philosophical and pedagogical aspects of the learning activity as well as the logistics of implementation. Why is it important to make the connection between course content and real world issues, particularly via the news media employing news portfolios? How best can these activities facilitate increased communication and interaction among students and between students and the instructor so as to make the course less impersonal through collaborative group work? How does one accomplish this in a course of 300 students? How do you integrate the news and still "cover the material"? One must show how these activities provide opportunities for the development of process-oriented learning skills central to scientific inquiry and valuable for students' educational and career goals (e.g. collaboration, communication, research skills) and why portfolio creation is essential in promoting these competencies.

Overall, the goal of the *CIITN* project is to create a more effective learning environment within a large lecture science course to promote students' learning of organic chemistry. In order for the wider implementa-tion of *CIITN* to occur in a sustainable fashion, faculty

> Showing us how what were learning applied to our every day lives really made the Cs and Hs a lot more interesting. By turning a board full of zig zag [sic] lines into how the ozone is being depleted or how hydrogen cars work really brought my interest in chemistry up dramatically. I also found myself becoming a way more involved reader in that I would actually try to apply what I learned.
> Evan C., Aug. '05, Organic I WS04

members must understand, accept, and advocate the philosophical and pedagogical basis of *CIITN* in addition to understanding how to successfully implement it in their own classroom. With this understanding in place, one can begin to convince colleagues and students. However, without well-reasoned commitment, faculty will likely become discouraged even from "normal" levels of resistance to any curricular change encountered from students and colleagues. In order to equip faculty members with the tools to affect this lasting curriculum change, we have sketched the logistics of implementing *CIITN* and described in depth the pedagogy and philosophy of *CIITN* and how the principles of this pedagogy are accomplished with the *CIITN* curriculum.

Implementation

The taxonomy of 'Authentic News Media Based Learning Activities' has six levels of implementation requiring varying degrees of time commitment and involvement (Table 1). Beginners and those not able to commit to full implementation can integrate Level 1 or 2 into their curriculum, possibly gradually working up to the higher levels. While others can pursue full implementation at Level 4 through 6 but still adjust the level of implementation from term to term to best fit their schedules, available resources, and student bodies.

Chemistry Is in the News **Taxonomy of Activities.**

Level	Activity	Quality Review	Resource	Focus
1	Read News Article	None	Online News Media	Issue Awareness & Interest
2	Read News Portfolios	None	*CIITN* Online Database	Knowledge & Comprehension
3	Read & Create News Portfolios	Instructor Review		Application, Analysis & Synthesis
4	Read, Create & Judge News Portfolios	Intra-Class Peer Review	*CIITN* Software Tools	Evaluation Constructive Review
5	Read, Create & Judge News Portfolios	Inter-Class Peer Review		Awareness of Diversity
6	Read, Create & Judge News Portfolios	International Peer Review		Awareness of the International Context

Table 1. *Chemistry Is in the News* Taxonomy of Activities.

Level-1 to Level-5 activities have been implemented within large lecture organic chemistry courses and are pursued outside of class in groups of three to six individuals. In Level-1, students are asked to read the newspaper and identify science-related news. Students engage in Level-2 activities by studying online instructional 'news portfolios' created to accompany each major course topic. These news portfolios provide access to selected newspaper articles and include interpretive comments, questions tying the article to course content, and links to other pertinent sites on the World Wide Web. At Level-3, the students select online news articles relevant to course topics and create news portfolios for display on the World Wide Web. Intra-class peer review of the created news portfolios elevates the activities to Level-4. At Level-5, inter-class peer review is carried out; these activities are more recent developments and they are currently being evaluated. Finally, international inter-class peer review is the goal of Level-6 and has been accomplished, albeit in a modified form, for the first time in 2005.

All *CIITN* activities are supported by the *CIITN* webtool (ciitn.missouri.edu) and *CIITN* support staff (Wu & Glaser, 2004; Wu, Sui, & Glaser, 2005). The webtool is hosted by MU (Figure 3),

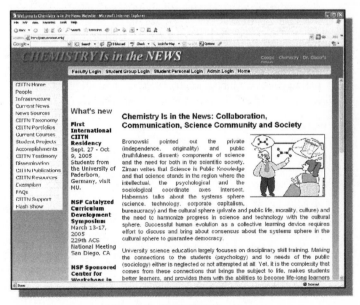

Figure 3. *CIITN* Web Portal

and is free of charge to all participants. It has both publically accessible content and content that requires registration, namely the portfolio creation software and a database of student-created portfolios. Because of this support, only supervisory and directive roles are left for the teaching staffs at participating institutions and thus the only requirement of participants is Internet access.

CIITN *webtool and curriculum content*. The publically accessible content is comprised primarily of content for those who are interested in adopting *CIITN* and those who are implementing Levels 1 and 2. Here one can find the instructional portfolios, some student-created portfolios, assignments, possible Level-5 collaborators, and *Exempli*, in which various levels of implementation are illustrated.

CIITN *webtool and curriculum tools*. The *CIITN* webtool also hosts the tools which are used to facilitate the curriculum. This content requires a login name and password, which can be obtained by contacting the *CIITN* support staff. These tools include a portfolio creation tool, the inter-group peer review tool (students peer review other students' portfolios) used for Levels 4-6, and the intra-group peer review tool (students peer review their group members' contribution to the process). The use of these tools is fully supported by the *CIITN* staff and all records produced are permanently stored and are continually accessible in the *CIITN* database, including the student portfolios and all review scores and comments. With these tools, the logistics of implementation are well provided for. With these tools, the adoption of *CIITN* hinges primarily upon faculties' adoption of *CIITN*'s pedagogical basis.

Connections to Societal Issues

The pedagogical basis for *CIITN* begins with the necessity of connecting course content to the real world. The importance of students constructing the connection between the content of chemistry courses and real world issues has been emphasized by numerous educators and researchers (National Science Foundation, 1996). As stated by Zoller, Fastow, Lubezky, and Tsaparlis (1999), 'The development of students' higher-order cognitive skills in the context not only of the specific content and processes of the science disciplines but also of the interrelationships of science, technology, environment, and society has become one of the most important goals of chemistry and science education' (p. 112). However, the difficulty of doing so has also long been recognized; as Poincaré pointed out (Root-Bernstein & Root-Bernstein, 1999), for students 'the world of science and that of reality are shut off in water-tight compartments' (p. 17).

Figure 4. Cipro® in the news

Despite the difficulty, merging the 'compartments' of science and reality is necessary for several reasons. First, the ability to see *the connection is valued in and of itself*: it is important to understand the impact that science has on our lives and our society. Particularly in a democratic society, it is essential that the citizenry is able to understand and make informed decisions about the consequences of various consumer, political, and economic choices, which increasingly require scientific competency (AAAS, 1990). This means that one needs not only knowledge of chemical concepts and principles, or science literacy, but one must also understand the implications of these concepts and principles for real issues in modern life, scientific literacy.

> In conversation I can recall facts and statistics about current scientific issues... What I came away from your class with was a confidence in my ability to talk, think, and reason as a scientist. For the first time I related science to life and came away with a deeper love for it. Thank you for the opportunity to expand my knowledge and to refine my thinking...
> Allison H. May '03, Organic II W.S03

Second, to recognize connections is *important for pedagogical reasons*. Understanding the connections with familiar issues provides a cognitive framework or context that can facilitate students' learning, understanding, and remembering the chemistry content (Taylor, Gilmer, &

Tobin, 2002). The result is a more complex conceptual understanding, rather than mere memorization of disjointed facts (Bransford, 1979; Cracolice, 2005). If students can tie new material to something familiar, they will have greater success in incorporating that new information into their knowledge structures, and a greater probability of retrieving that information from memory.

A third reason for encouraging students to see connections with real world problems is that these links *enhance students' interest*, motivating them to spend more time and effort learning the subject matter. If students are taught the connects as opposed to dry facts that are entirely divorced from anything that interests or concerns them, they are more likely to remain in science courses, major in science disciplines, and appreciate the value of scientific research and the importance of government funding for such research (Felt, 2000; Pringle, 2004).

Consequently, emphasizing the connections between chemistry and the real world serves both as an end of chemical education and as a means to facilitate learning. However, unless students view these connections as personally relevant, their engagement is limited (Wink, 2005). In addition, to really meet pedagogical needs and promote higher order cognitive skills, which will provide true scientific literacy (Zoller; 2000), students must <u>do</u> something with the connections— something more complex than just recognizing that they exist (Domin, 1999). Without this engagement, such efforts may fall short of leading to a sound conceptual understanding and the exercise of critical examination of the connec-tions between science and the real world issues. If students are to become truly scientifically literate, they need a conceptual under-standing of the science content and practice in evaluation of evidence.

(a) **Computer Room Activity—Information Retrieval.** Use the ChemFinder online database to find the structure of ciprofloxacin and draw the structure below. Pay attention to the following instructions:

> Draw all lone pairs (as dashes).
>
> The cyclopropane ring should be on top.
>
> The piperazine ring (6 ring with 2 N) should be in the upper left.
>
> The carboxylic acid group should be drawn in such a conformation that the hydroxyl group of the COOH group is in a position to form an H-bond to the proximate carbonyl group. Draw a dashed H-bond.

Lewis-Kekule structures of Cipro (4 points)

Provide the requested information (16 points total; 2 points each item)

Molecular formula:	$C_{17}H_{18}FN_3O_3$
Molecular mass:	331.3459
Number of chiral centers:	0
Give the typical bond length of a C–C single bond (value & units):	1.54 Å
Give the typical bond length of an aromatic CC bond (value & units):	1.40 Å
Give the typical bond length of a C=O single bond (value & units):	1.20 Å
Give the typical bond angle at an sp^3-hybridized atom (degrees):	109°
Give the typical bond angle at an sp^2-hybridized atom (degrees):	120°

Figure 5. Part of Cipro® exam question (FS01)

Using current news, as in *CIITN*, provides an excellent means to accomplish these objectives. The articles reflect timely issues that are of concern in our society, thus providing students with an authentic and meaningful task directly tied to the content of the course. In addition, current issues are multifaceted, which fulfills another educational demand (Eisen, Cimino, Aparicio, Marsteller, & Kushner, 2003; Jones & Merritt, 1999).

At every level of *CIITN*, the connection to societal issues is integrated with the material. At Level 1, students are required to read the newspaper. This requirement is reinforced in three ways. First, in the general lecture, the lecturer introduces new topics or exemplifies a concept by bring in current news articles that illustrate it and students are encouraged to also be watching for articles that tie into the course somehow. For example, during the anthrax scare of 2001, the drug Cipro® was frequently in the news (Figure 3). As opposed to using a generic example of chirality for example, one instructor used a chiral center of the Cipro® molecule to have students practice determining chirality. Second, the web portal (ciitn.missouri.edu) is continually being updated with links to news items illustrating chemistry that would be of interest to students. Third, every exam has one or more multi-part questions that are based on a recent news article; students are given the article and all of the additional information they might need to form the correct answer, but those who are in the habit of reading the newspaper for science content are better prepared (Figure 5).

> Organic chemistry really made me see the relevance of the other science classes I had taken; finally the information had practical applications in part due to CIITN projects.
> Laura B., Jan. '05, Survey Organic, FS04

At Level 2, the connection is made more explicit through the instructional news portfolios that are accessed throught the *CIITN* web portal. The portfolios are created to address each main content area of the course and are being continually updated and expanded to cover additional topics. In the instructor-created news portfolios, which students read and work on together with their collaborative groups, the activity engages students in active learning, evaluation, and critical thinking. Students are encouraged to wrestle with the issues, thinking about them at more than a superficial level. Instructors may, and do, base exam questions on these portfolios, requiring students to read and be familiar with them. *This is the key to utilizing soctietal issues to teach chemistry: consistently use the real-world examples to illustrate concepts.* Thus, one is still able to "cover the material," but is also able to do it in a meaningful way which will help students understand and remember the concepts better than a purely abstract presentation of the material.

Levels 3 through 6 offer the additional benefit of the students creating the connections between the news and the course content. In creating their own group news portfolios via the *CIITN* webtool, students engage in a fuller range of cognitive skills, from comprehension and application to synthesis and evaluation, and explore multiple knowledge dimensions, including factual, conceptual, and procedural (Bloom, Engelhart, Frost, Hill & Krathwolh, 1956; Krathwohl, 2002; Worsnop, 2003). The particular concept they choose to illustrate in their portfolio becomes their own in a sense that cannot be accomplished through the lecture/exam format of a traditional class.

The *CIITN* exercise is made complete by the process of peer review in Levels 4 through 6, in which the skill of evaluation is explicitly exercised when students quantify and justify their assessment of their fellow students' work. Peer review provides the additional benefit of exposing students to a number of different concepts using alternative explanations and unique connections provided by their fellow students, often helping them understand it better than if they had only had it explained by the instructor and textbook.

Communication, Community and Classroom Climate

In addition to the call for connecting science to real-world issues, one of the persistent challenges in teaching chemistry at the university level concerns the quality of educational experiences within a large lecture classroom. Meeting the requirements of good teaching and achieving the desired outcomes for undergraduate science education is no small task in classes with one hundred or more students. Although the limitations of the large lecture have been widely recognized and documented, it nevertheless remains the most frequently used mode of teaching in higher education (Davis, 1993; Theilens, 1987). The primary drawbacks of lecture are that it encourages

> ...in life and in our careers especially science careers it is imperative that one can learn how to successful comprehend text. For these reasons I believe the curriculum you are trying to intro-duce serves the students educational needs,... although we might not always want to realize it!
>
> Anne-Marie A., April '04, Organic II WS03

students to assume a passive rather than an active role, limiting their engagement with the course material and offering few opportunities for critical thinking, problem solving, and other higher-level cognitive activities, and that it precludes student-teacher and student-student interactions leading to student isolation and alienation (Cooper & Robinson, 2000; McKeachie, Pintrich, Lin, & Smith, 1986; Yair, 2000). As a result, the large lecture format has limited impact in the development of multiple intelligences (Gardner, 1993). Consequently, the lecture is neither the preferred nor the most beneficial teaching format (Kovac, 1999; Nurrenbern, Mickiewicz, and Francisco, 1999; Spencer, 1999). However, there is no denying that large lecture courses have some advantages and that they will remain a central fixture in higher education (Bartlett, 2003, Parini, 2002). Therefore, it is necessary to restructure large lecture classes in order to provide more effective learning environments, making them complex and interactive (Carbone, 1998; Clouston & Kleinman, 1999; Winn, 2002).

Collaborative group tasks is valuable for promoting interaction and communication among students and for encouraging active engagement with the material, of which the educational benefits have been extensively documented (Hertz-Lazarowitz & Miller, 1992; Kovac, 1999; Nurrenbern, Mickiewicz, & Francisco, 1999; Spencer, 1999; Cooper, 2005; Varma-Nelson & Coppola, 2005). One is that they have a *positive impact on retention* of students, which is sought by educators at the undergraduate level owing to the decline in the number of students choosing physical sciences as a major and the relative lack of interest in scientific topics by non-science majors. This impact is being attributed to a link between classroom climate and student retention (Spencer, 1999). The communication and interaction promoted by the activites make a large lecture course less impersonal, decreasing the psychological isolation students frequently experience in this setting (Carbone, 1998).

Figure 6. Collaborative group working in computer laboratory (from left: Christopher Scrivner, Beverly Mills, Laura Comotto, Kristin Rahner).

CIITN courses employ collaborative group projects as part of the course requirements and further encouraged students to use their collaborative groups for other course-related tasks (viewing visualization centers, working problem sets, working with the instructor-created news portfolios, and studying for exams) and increasing interaction among students (Figure 6). This cooperative classroom climate is also enhanced by an absolute grading or criterion-referenced scale (Royse, 2001). The absolute grading scale is used as opposed to the commonly used relative grading scale, which has been cited for producing a competitive atmosphere and decreasing the amount of cooperation between students (Seymour, 1995). Communication and interaction were further supported by provision of an electronic discussion list, as well as email access with prompt responses from the professor, regularly scheduled review sessions, and office hours.

> I wanted to let you know how much I enjoyed today's discussion/lecture. I earned my first degree from University of A., where once upon a time I was an environmental science major. I changed my major due to the fact that I hated organic chemistry and my teacher there, and ended up just getting my minor in this subject...
> Melissa N., Nov. '04,
> Survey Organic FS04

Utilizing collaborative groups in a course of 300 or more can make it more managable. At MU, students are given an outline of what will be accomplished in collaborative groups and criteria to consider when selecting group members. They are then given two weeks to form a group of four to five students and email the group name a group members to the teaching staff. This process is facilitated by the instructor announcing a meeting of those without group immediately follow class one or more times during the two weeks as well as the electronic discussion broad. Once the groups have been formed and the teaching staff has been notified, they enter the group name into the *CIITN* webtool and gives the group members a temporary password to access their group account. The group is then responsible for entering each group member's name into the roster, which creates individual accounts for each member.

Requiring students to enter their own names into the *CIITN* webtool serves two pusposes. First, it requires the group to firmly establish who is in the group. Second, it forces students to join a group. They are informed that without a group, they are not able to create an individual account and without an individual account, no final *CIITN* score recorded for them. Using the webtool in conjunction with collaborative groups means that the instuctor and teaching staff's only administrative tasks are introducing the students to the webtool, entering approximately 60 group names into the webtool, and reviewing the group rosters to make sure the group have the correct number of students. In addition, the instructor is now interacting with 60 groups of 4 to 5 students instead of 300 individual students.

Development of Process-Oriented Skills

In addition to promoting an effective learning environment and assisting students in making the connection between chemistry and social issues, an additional benefit of the collaborative group project described here is the opportunity it provides for students to develop a range of learning skills. These skills are an important component of both the undergraduate educational experience and scientific research (Gosser & Roth, 1998). Henderleiter and Pringle (1999) pointed this out, stating 'A chemist must also be able to communicate with other chemists and nonchemists, work as a member of a team, evaluate data, and make decisions and recommendations based on the data collected', suggesting that teaching of these skills should be integrated into scientists' education.

CIITN engages students in a variety of communication exercises through the collaborative group work in which students create a portfolio and through the peer evaluation process (Carson, Hodgen, & Glaser, submitted). The skills exercised, working effectively in collaborative settings to solve problems, accomplishing tasks, and evaluating based on evidence, are important for many aspects of students' lives— achieving educational goals and preparing for their future careers (Demers, 2003; McLoughlin & Luca, 2002). Focusing on these skills also plays an important role in building the science and engineering pipeline. Students are exposed to the core processes of science and engineering and attain the competencies necessary to participate in them, particularly those involved in the peer review process (National Science Board, 2005). Increasing the number of students interested in and prepared for careers in science and engineering, strengthens the quality of the research performed (National Academies, 2005).

Addressing Berka and Berka's (1996) suggestion that 'It is impor-tant for science and engineering students to be able to read, under-stand, and convey the

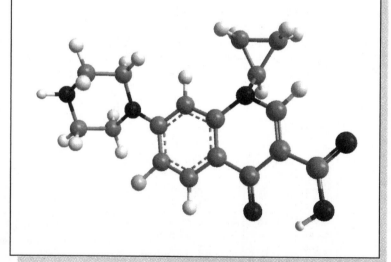

(b) Computer Room Activity—Molecular Modeling. (15 points)

PHASE 1: Build the molecule Cipro in Chem3D. Under the MM2 menu, select "minimize energy." make sure the piperazine ring is a chair. Make sure there is a hydrogen-bond between the -COOH group and the proximate carbonyl.

PHASE 2: Adjust the display to "cylindrial bonds." "pattern by element," depth ratio 50%, 25% size, show element symbols. Arrange the orientation of the molecule as much as possible to match your drawing of the Lewis structure. Then print the molecule in color and glue it or tape it nicely on this page ("nicely" is worth points).

Figure 7. Part of Cipro® exam question (FS01)

essence of published information in their field of study, communicate results of their own work to specialists and nonspecialists alike, and relate the results to societal needs and concerns', students research their topic through online resources and synthesize this information into a portfolio. For their project to succeed, individuals need to communicate well with their team members, and the groups need to effectively communicate the results of their efforts to the class as a whole.

Successful projects also require the ability to work with elec-tronic sources of information to locate the articles on topics relevant to course content and to locate relevant links of good quality to supplement the news portfolios. Other skills developed are those related to presenting informa-tion in an electronic format as well as the development of skills related to designing web pages (Figures 7 & 8), though web-design is not a re-quirement of the project.

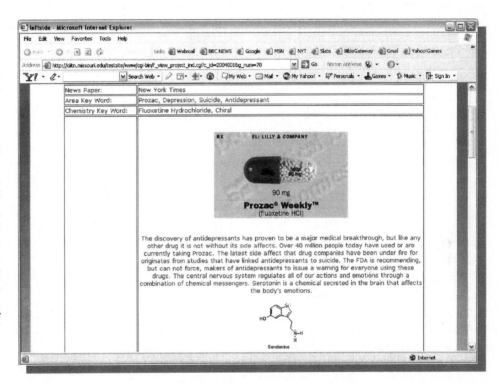

Figure 8. Student-created *CIITN* portfolio

Promises and Challenges

It is well known that Thomas Kuhn (1970) wrote "In science novelty emerges only with difficulty, manifested by resistance, against a background provided by expectations," (p. 64); and it is also well known to science educators that science teaching novelties face obstacles to their implementation before their full acceptance. Paradigm shifts progress through three stages. First, the innovators must demonstrate competency; second, persuaded by the innovators arguments and expertise, new converts are drawn to the new methods; and third, the innovation becomes supported by evidence and accepted by the mainstream community. Hence, assessment has always been an essential pillar of *CIITN*. We have published a study on ICT facilitated collaborative group work (Glaser & Poole, 1999), an assessment of student attitudes (Hume et al., in press), and a study of intra-group peer review (Carson, 2005), and other studies are ongoing.

These assessments do show that *CIITN* fulfills many of its promises through the integration of popular news media, ICT, and collaborative group activities into the chemistry classroom. The student commentary, some of which are highlighted throughout this chapter, illustrates this and it is also born out by student evaluations and retention data.

Retention and student success rate. The number of students staying in *CIITN* courses has not declined and, if anything, the data suggests improvement over the non-*CIITN* courses. More significantly and more strongly reflected in the data, the percentage of students advancing from courses utilizing *CIITN* has increased. Non-*CIITN* courses featured a ceiling of 80% successful completion, while *CIITN* courses have consistently been above 80% and averaging 89.3% advancing, and the trend has been very positive.

Restoring natural distribution of success rates. The collaborative groups provide social support and additional resources for students, which also contribute to lower attrition rates. There is clear evidence that the alternative learning and assessment strategies used with *CIITN* encourage students who do not fare well in the traditional classroom to persist and succeed. This is not to say that their grades are artificially inflated. In fact, the class average has been maintained or even decreased in large part due to the number of students completing the course (Schelble, Lupo, Angles, Carson, Wu, & Glaser, submitted).

Teaching evaluation scores. The teaching evaluation from large lecture courses have been fairly consistent, most falling in the range of 2.9 - 3.3 out of 4. The one expection was the score of 2.6 in Winter Semester 2004, and it coincides with one change in teaching strategy, namely Dr. Glaser's decision to no longer provide lecture notes. This association is supported by the near whole point decline in the specific categories of "Organization and preparedness of lecture" and "Ability to lecture in a manner which is easily followed." The decision to not provide students with lecture notes was made to encourage students to read the assigned textbook—instead of just lecture notes or even just PowerPoint® slides—and other textbooks, and to explore the wide variety of resources available on the World Wide Web. This is in keeping with the philosophy of *CIITN*, which aims to teach students in an active manner not only the prescribed course content but also how to continually access and use relevant information. One immediate consequence of this more active learning environment was that there was a higher rate of class attendance. This is particularly evident in the interesting 'anomaly' of the high percentage (94%) of teaching evaluations returned that semester. Though the large increase in the evaluations returned is not totally explained but, regardless of the students' motivation, the increase illustrates that students are more engaged in the class.

> The best part of the course, I can say, is when we had the opportunity to actually make our own "Chemistry is in The News" Project with our groups. It was fun in the sense that we not only learned about team work, but the main idea was to use the Internet to find articles relevant to Chemistry. Maria Holleb, Dec. '01, Honors Organic I FS01

The stability of the scores, combined with the increase in retention, indicate that students respond well to this curriculum. The evaluations, however, fail to truly illustrate this because the standard evaluations required by the MU Department of Chemistry do not include categories for large courses that utilize teaching methods other than lecture. The questions in the evaluation are teacher-centered, for example, asking about the quality of lecture. While in a more student-centered classroom, lecture often takes a backseat or is frequently interrupted and thus may seem disjointed or ill-prepared. Despite the fact that the lecture is not the focus of the class period, a quality learning experience can still have been provided. The focus on lecture as the primary, if not sole, method of teaching is problematic because evaluations are often pointed to when resistence to the curriculum crops up, regardless of how well the standard evaluations reflect the actual student experience. In fact, in independent assessment of the course, students reported that their group work experience, a core organizational principle of the course, was positive and had a positive effect on their overall course experience (Carson, 2005). This indicates that novel teaching methods require novel assessment tools.

Challenges. Despite the improvement in classroom climate that authentic learning activities such as *CIITN* can achieve, resistance exists on several levels. The changes in classroom structure and assessment that are necessary can be unsettling for both students and faculty members, including faculty members not involved in the implementation of the curriculum.

Faculty members not involved in the implementation of learning activities like *CIITN* can be the source of some of the most difficult resistance to such a curriculum. The complaints and concerns are manyfold. Their primary concern is that students will not learn 'the content'. They are particularly concerned about this when the students are taking a sequence of courses and often fight the implementation of any 'new' curriculum the hardest on this point, despite the lack of evidence. It will be interesting to see the results of longitudinal studies that follow cohorts of *CIITN* students; these data exist and they need to analyzed.

Colleagues are also concerned that such curricula are too time-consuming for all concerned. In addition, they complain that students engaged in the learning activities require too many additional resources, namely education materials and the use of computers (*CIITN* students at MU and elsewhere use departmental computer labs to include ChemDraw® and Chem3D® images in their portfolios). Faculty resistance is a significant obstacle to implementation, but it is most difficult when it is teamed with student resistance.

The most concrete form of resistance is that from students. Accustomed to the traditional large-lecture learning environment, many students experience anxiety in an active learning environment. The students who are the most vocal about their discomfort are the 'mediocre A-students'. These students have been successful at achieving the desired grade in the past by 'following the rules'; however, they are not practiced at nor are they comfortable doing activities for which there is not a defined course of action nor a 'right' answer. They often struggle with both the *CIITN*-based, multi-part exam questions and *CIITN* portfolio creation and, as a result, frequently spend a great deal of time asking the professor and TAs how they can 'get a better grade'. These students frequently express intense dislike for the peer review process, viewing their fellow students as incapable of grading fairly or accurately and the peer review process as inappropriate for an undergraduate class. There are two striking consequences of these students who generally perform well in traditionally structured classes not achieving the grade they have come to expect.

> I was the student Thursday who said he wanted to learn "basic" textbook organic chemistry... I realize, even when you were explaining yourself to me in class, that you were right... I don't want to be a person who only knows textbook facts, I want to know how things work around us, how chemistry is involved in our lives... When Friday's lecture came I think it was the best lecture I have heard so far and it's because I finally decided to... not just sit in my chair and gripe about how I thought you were wasting time going over the NY Times. Don't get discouraged..., if you can change my view I know you can change others.
> Charles P., March '03, Organic II WS03

The first is that the gains made by the students at the lower end of grade distribution—who benefit greatly from alternative forms of assessment and who have long suffered under traditional forms—are offset by a loss at the higher end of the grade distribution. The curve at the end of the semester is thereby compressed but the average does not change much, if at all, from semesters taught without *CIITN*.

The second is that these students tend to be the most vocal about their dislike for a course, the professor, his/her methods, and the curriculum. This is a likely explanation for the stability of the scores of the student evaluations of the course. While more students mark the course positively, these 'mediocre A-students' are marking the course more negatively.

Conclusion

Overall, *CIITN* has been a positive experience for all involved. The design and development process has involved many talented faculty and teaching support staff, who have brought in a wide variety of perspectives and new ideas. This has contributed to making the teaching experience of this new curriculum invigorating and satisfying for the professors. The teaching assistants have by necessity explored new areas of both chemistry and education and have also had the opportunity to contribute in areas of expertise previously untapped. Finally, students have responded in an overwhelmingly positive manner and have shown great growth in their academic lives. It is clear to everyone involved that science teaching is much more than the acquisition of disjointed facts and everyone draws excitement from the attempt to teaching science in its complexity.

Acknowledgement

Funding by the University of Missouri System, the Camille & Henry Dreyfus Foundation, and the National Science Foundation enabled the creation of the *CIITN* web portal, dissemination to engage *CIITN* collaborators at other institutions in Missouri, in the US, as well as in Canada, Germany, and Israel, and to conduct research on collaborative learning, peer review, and media literacy.

Suggested Further Reading

Habermas, J. (1991). *The Structural Transformation of the Public Sphere: An Inquiry into a Category of Bourgois Society*. Cambridge, Mass.: MIT Press.

Reeves, R. (1998). *What the People Know, Freedom and the Press*. Cambridge, Mass.: Harvard University Press.

Gregory, J., & Miller, S. (2000). *Science in Public: Communication, Culture, and Credibility*. Cambridge, Mass.: Perseus Publishing.

Kleinman, D. L. (2005). *Science And Technology In Society: From Biotechnology To The Internet*. Malden, Mass.: Blackwell Publishers.

Gilmer, P. J. (2002). *Opalescence at the triple point*. In P. C. Taylor, P. J. Gilmer, & K. Tobin (Eds.). *Transforming undergraduate science teaching*. New York, NY: Peter Lang Publishing, Inc., pp. 423-462.

References

American Association for the Advancement of Science. (1990). *Science for All Americans: Project 2061*. New York: Oxford University Press.

Bartlett, T. (2003, May 9). Big, but not bad. The best teaching doesn't always happen around a seminar table. p. A12. *The Chronicle of Higher Education*.

Berka, K. M., Berka, L. H. (1996). Developing student speaking skills: a project/independent study in forensic science. *J. Chem. Educ.* 73, 931-933.

Bloom, B. S., Engelhart, M. D., Frost, E. J. Hill, W. H., & Krathwohl, D. R. (1956). *Taxonomy of educational objectives. Handbook I: Cognitive domain*. New York: D. McKay.

Bonwell, C. C., & Eison, J. A. (1991). *Active learning: Creating excitement in the classroom*. Washington, D.C.: The George Washington University, School of Education and Human Development.

Bransford, J. (1979). *Human cognition: Learning, understanding, and remembering*. Belmont, CA: Wadsworth Publishing Co.

Bransford, J. D., Brown, A. L., & Cocking, R. R. (2000). *How people learn: Brain, mind, experience, and school*. Washington D.C.: National Academy Press.

Carbone, E. (1998). *Survival skills for scholars: Vol. 19. teaching large classes: Tools and strategies*. Labella, P. (Series Ed.). Thousand Oaks, CA: SAGE Publications, Inc.

Carson, K. M. (2005). *Chemistry Is in the News*: Assessing intra-group peer review (M.A. thesis, University of Missouri-Columbia, 2005).

Carson, K. M., Hodgen, B., & Glaser, R. E. (2006). Teaching dissent and persuasion. *Educ. Res. Rev.* 1, 115-120.

Clouston, L. L., & Kleinman, M. H. (1999). The design and synthesis of a large interactive classroom. *J. Chem. Educ.* 76, 20-21.

Cooper, J. L. & Robinson, P. (2000). The Argument for Making Large Classes Seem Small. In Svinicki, M. D, (Series Ed.), MacGregor, J., Cooper, J. L., Smith, K. A., & Robinson, P., (Vol. Eds.). *New Directions for Teaching and Learning: Vol. 81. Strategies for Energizing Large Classes: From Small Groups to Learning Communities*. San Francisco: Jossey-Bass.

Cooper, M. M. (2005). An introduction to small-group learning. In N. J. Pienta, M. M. Cooper, & T. J. Greenbowe (Eds.), *Chemists' guide to effective teaching*. Upper Saddle River, NJ: Pearson/Prentice Hall, pp. 117-128.

Cracolice, M. S. (2005). How students learn: Knowledge construction in college chemistry courses. In N. J. Pienta, M. M. Cooper, & T. J. Greenbowe (Eds.), *Chemists' guide to effective teaching*. Upper Saddle River, NJ: Pearson/Prentice Hall, pp. 12-27.

Davis, B. G. (1993). *Tools for teaching*. San Francisco: Jossey-Bass Publishers.

Demers, N. E. (2003). Issues in science and technology. *J. Coll. Sci. Teach.* 32, 332-337.

Domin, D. S. (1999). A content analysis of general chemistry laboratory manuals for evidence of higher-order cognitive tasks. *J. Chem. Educ.* 76, 109-112.

Eisen, A., Cimino, A., Aparicio, H., Marsteller, P., & Kushner, H. (2003). Race and Science. *College Teaching.* 51, 46-51.

Felt, U. (2000). Why should the public 'understand' science? Historical perspective on aspects of the public understanding of science. In Dierkes, M., von Grote, C. (Eds.) *Between understanding and trust.* 7-38. London: Routledge.

Fujishige, S., Takizawa, S., & Tsuzuki, K. (2001). A simple preparative method to evaluate total UV protection by commercial sunscreens. *J. Chem. Educ.* 78, 1678-1679.

Gabel, D. (1999). Improving teaching and learning through chemistry education research: A look to the future. *J. Chem. Educ.* 76, 548-554.

Gardner, H. (1993). *Multiple intelligences.* New York: Basic Books.

Glaser, R. E., & Carson, K. M. (2005). 'Chemistry Is in the News': Taxonomy of authentic news media based learning activities. *Int. J. Sci. Educ.* 27, 1083-1098.

Glaser, R. E., & Poole, M. J. (1999). Organic chemistry online: Building collaborative learning communities through electronic communication tools. *J. Chem. Educ.* 76, 699-703.

Gosser, D. K., Jr., & Roth, V. (1998). The workshop chemistry project: peer-led team-learning. *J. Chem. Educ.* 75, 185-187.

Hertz-Lazarowitz, R., & Miller, N. (1992). *Interaction in Cooperative Groups.* New York: Cambridge University Press.

Henderleiter, J., & Pringle, D. L. (1999). Effects of context-based laboratory experiments on attitudes of analytical chemistry students. *J. Chem. Educ.* 76, 100-106.

Hume, D. L., Carson, K. M., Hodgen, B., & Glaser, R. E. (2006). *Chemistry Is in the News.* Assessment of Student Attitudes toward Authentic News Media Based Learning Activities. *J. Chem. Educ.* 83, 662-667.

Jacobs, M. (2003). Education chemists for the future: Conference explores different ideas on how to reform chemistry curricula and inspire students. *Chem. Engin. News.* 81, 34-35.

Johnson, D., & Johnson, R. (1975). *Learning together and alone.* Englewood Cliffs, NJ: Prentice Hall.

Jones, P. C., & Merritt, J. Q. (1999). JGHE symposium: The TALESSI project. *J. Geogr. Higher Educ.* 23, 335-348.

Kovac, J. (1999). Student active learning methods in General Chemistry. *J. Chem. Educ.* 76, 120-124.

Krathwohl, D. R. (2002). A revision of bloom's taxonomy: An overview. *Theor. Pract.* 41, 212-225.

Kuhn, T. (1970). *The Structure of Scientific Revolutions* (2nd ed.). Chicago: University of Chicago Press.

McKeachie, W. J., Pintrich, P. R., Lin, Y. G., & Smith, D. A. F. (1986). *Teaching and learning in the college classroom: A review of the research literature.* Ann Arbor, MI: National Center for Research to Improve Postsecondary Teaching and Learning.

McLoughlin, C., & Luca, J. (2002). A learner–centred approach to developing team skills through web–based learning and assessment. *Br. J. of Educ. Technol.* 33, 571-582.

National Academies. (2005). *Rising above the gathering storm. Energizing and employing American for a brighter economic future* [prepublication copy]. Washington, DC: National Academies Press.

National Science Foundation-Division of Undergraduate Education. (1996). *Shaping the future: New expectations for undergraduate education in science, mathematics, engineering, and technology.* Arlington, VA: National Science Foundation.

National Science Board. (2005). *National Science Board 2020 vision for the National Science Foundation* [draft for public comment]. Arlington, VA: National Science Foundation.

Nurrenbern, S. C., Mickiewicz, J. A., & Francisco, J. S. (1999). The impact of continuous instructional development on graduate and undergraduate students. *J. Chem. Educ.* 76, 114-119.

Parini, J. (2004, January 16). The well-tempered lecturer. p. B5. *The Chronicle of Higher Education.*

Pringle, P. (2004, May 13). Dense matter indeed; With taxpayers footing the bill for much of their research, scientists try to illuminate for the layperson what seems incomprehensible. *Los Angeles Times*, A1.

Root-Bernstein, R., & Root-Bernstein, M. (1999). *Sparks of Genius.* New York: Houghton Mifflin Company.

Royse, D. (2001). *Teaching tips for college and university instructors.* Boston: Allyn & Bacon.

Schelble, S., Lupo, E., Angles, E., Carson, K. M., Wu, Z., & Glaser, R. E. (submitted). Intra- versus inter-class peer review: A study of calibration.

Seymour, E. (1995). Revisiting the "problem iceberg": Science, mathematics, and engineering students still chilled out. *J. Coll. Sci. Teach.* 24, 392-400.

Spencer, J. N. (1999). New directions in teaching chemistry: a philosophical and pedagogical basis. *J. Chem. Educ.* 76, 566-569. 0

Slavin, R. E. (1988). *Educational psychology: Theory into practice* (2nd ed.). Englewood Cliffs, NJ: Prentice Hall.

Taylor, P. C., Gilmer, P. J., & Tobin, K. (2002). *Transforming undergraduate science teaching*: Social constructivist perspectives. New York: Peter Lang.

Thielens, W. (1987). Paper presented at the annual meeting of the American Education Research Association.

Vygotsky, L. S. (1993). *The Collected Works of L. S. Vygotsky,* (Vol. 2.) Knox, J., Stevens, C., (Trans.). New York: Plenum Press.

Varma-Nelson, P., & Coppola, B. P. (2005). Team learning. In N. J. Pienta, M. M. Cooper, & T. J. Greenbowe (Eds.), *Chemists' guide to effective teaching.* Upper Saddle River, NJ: Pearson/Prentice Hall, p. 155-169.

Wink, D. J. (2005). Relevance and learning theories. In N. J. Pienta, M. M. Cooper, & T. J. Greenbowe (Eds.), *Chemists' guide to effective teaching.* Upper Saddle River, NJ: Pearson/Prentice Hall, p. 53-66.

Winn, W. (2002). Current trends in educational technology research: The study of learning environments. *Educ. Psychol. Rev.* 14, 331-351.

Woolfolk, A. E. (2001). *Educational Psychology,* 8th ed. Boston: Allyn & Bacon.

Worsnop, C. M. (2003). A taxonomy is not a sequence. *Education Week.* 23, 36.

Wu, Z., & Glaser, R. E. (2004). Software for the synergistic intergration of science with ICT education. *J. Inform. Tech. Educ.* 3, 325-339.

Wu, Z., Sui, Y., & Glaser, R. E. (2005). *Chemistry Is in the News* [webtool]. Accessed at ciitn.missouri.edu

Yair, G. (2000). Educational battlefields in America: the tug-of-war over students' engagement with instruction. *Sociol. Educ.* 73, 247-269.

Zoller, U. (2000). Teaching tomorrow's college science courses--are we getting it right? *J. Coll. Sci. Teach.* 29, 409-415.

Zoller, U., Fastow, M., Lubezky, A., & Tsaparlis, G. (1999). Students' self-assessment in chemistry examinations requiring higher- and lower-order cognitive skills. *J. Chem. Educ.* 76, 112-113.

17

Chemistry at a Science Museum

Robert G. Silberman
Department of Chemistry
SUNY – Cortland

Abstract

In recent years there has been a strong interest in outreach program for chemistry. After I retired I became involved in outreach efforts at a small local science museum. Although I began as a volunteer trying to build simple science exhibits my efforts evolved into a series of activities involving visitors and high school students in interactive chemistry activities, the development of interactive floor programs, and chemistry activities run by trained high school students. This article recounts my experiences as I was developing these programs.

Biography

Dr. Silberman is Professor Emeritus of Chemistry at the State University of New York at Cortland. He has authored more than 50 papers in chemical education. He is a co-author of the first and second editions of Chemistry in Context the American Chemical Society's curriculum for non-science major college students and was also co-author and edited of the laboratory program for Chemistry in Context. He developed 16 original lab exercises for the program.

Dr. Silberman has designed and given teacher workshops through out the United States and in 4 foreign countries on such topics as ChemCom, Chemistry in Context, Microscale Chemistry, Teaching Chemistry Labs on Shoestring, Laboratory Assessment Strategies and New Developments in Laboratory teaching. In past years he has been a member of the Chemistry Olympiad Examination committee specializing in designing the laboratory section of the National Chemistry Olympiad Exam. He was visiting Senior Research Fellow at the ACS Examinations institute and at the University of Glasgow. While at the ACS exam institute he wrote the ACS Small-Scale Assessment Activities text.

Dr. Silberman was an active member of the Chemical Education Division of the American Chemical Society he held the post of national program chair for the Division. He has also organized seven symposiums at national meetings of the American Chemical Society. At Cortland he taught Organic Chemistry, a general studies chemistry course and a graduate course for high school teachers titled Modern Chemistry in the High School Curriculum. Since his retirement from SUNY Cortland he has become the volunteer resident chemist at the Sciencenter in Ithaca and developed a series of hands on chemistry activities for visitors, a high school student run chemistry program, and built or helped build twelve free-standing exhibits at the Sciencenter.

Chapter: Chemistry Outreach

I wish I could say there was some special approach or formula for a starting an outreach program. There doesn't seem to be one. In my case I was looking for a volunteer activity I would enjoy after I retired. Like many of my colleagues as I neared retirement I began to think about what I would do if I retired. A few years before I retired we moved from Cortland to Ithaca, because Ithaca offered more in the way of social and cultural activities than Cortland. It also seemed to offer several possible retirement activities, because of the very large academic community. The Ithaca community strongly supports cultural and education endeavors. One of these is a small science museum that had started in a storefront and by time I moved to Ithaca it had progressed to the old sewage treatment plant office building. I decided to see if they needed volunteers. After all, their mission statement seemed to nicely sum up much of what I was trying to do in my teaching career:

> Sciencenter mission statement: To inspire people of all ages and backgrounds to discover the excitement of science through exhibits and programs that promote learning through interaction.

The museum welcomes volunteers and after spending some time as a member of the museums exhibits committee I decided to spend my final sabbatical, before I retired, as the resident chemist at the museum. The museum was just starting an expansion program that would triple the museum's size. At the time there was no chemistry at the museum. As in most science museums chemistry was the least represented science at the museum. Perhaps, it is because chemistry exhibits use up materials quickly, require frequent monitoring, and present potential safety issues. Most chemistry exhibits at museums focus on either physical analogies for physical chemical processes or, look-but-don't-touch" exhibits in glass cases[1]. The Sciencenter has a tradition and goal of making every exhibit interactive. The only non-interactive exhibits are a bee colony and a couple a of coral reef tanks. Introducing chemistry to the museum visitors became my goal.

I began by trying to build an exhibit using chemicals that did not require monitoring and did not need the chemicals to be replenished often. My first attempt involved the light activated reaction of thionin[2]. When a blue solution of thionin is exposed to strong visible light the solution become colorless. When the light source is removed the blue color reappears. The process can be repeated many times and the solution lasts for weeks. The exhibit consisted of three thionin solutions in flat-sided bottles spaced around a turntable. As the table was rotated the bottles were positioned in front of a strong light source at a different distance from the source. The intent was to show the reaction and that the rate of the reaction was related to the distance from the light source. Finally, I made some colored filters so visitors could determine the approximate wavelength of light that was needed to initiate the reaction. To many of my colleagues it seemed like I was on to something. Unfortunately, the exhibit was not very successful. As in many chemistry exhibits chemicals did not last as long as I had hoped and extraneous light interfered with reaction.

The typical Sciencenter visitor is a 4-12 year old and a parent. Explaining what was happening and why proved difficult. Both the child and a parent who is not chemically literate tended to view the exhibit as "magic". A second exhibit about polarized light was fascinating to the few science minded adults who read the lengthy explanation provided, but most visitors just played with the polarizers and looked at "magical " color changes. Perhaps the lesson to be learned is that color changes attract, but for a visitor to learn from the exhibit the explanation must be easy to understand and relatively short.

Although the polarized light exhibit has been on the museum floor for over two years it only interested a few visitors and does not really provide any of the flavor of chemistry that I enjoyed as a adolescent with a chemistry set. The more successful out reach activities started with the museum activity called show time. Twice a month the museum presents an interactive experience in the classroom or theater. The activities are designed for the child visitor with the adult as a helper. The program usually lasts between 30 minutes and one hour. I asked to do one these programs to give the visitor the kind of experience that interested me as a child and interested non-science majors in a college chemistry, mixing things to see what would happens. I think outreach to children works best if it is started with things they know about used in unexpected ways. I designed a simple acid base activity called "Acids, Bases and Beans, Oh My" that used indicators.

I think that a successful out reach activity for most individuals should start with familiar things. For this activity I began with common household acids and bases, seltzer, vinegar, lemon juice, strong soap, powdered dishwashing detergent and ammonia-based window cleaner. For an indicator I used a water extract of dried black beans. Each set up for a visitor had a 24 well wellplate, a pair of safety goggles, a few transfer pipettes and three Popsicle sticks. Each table had labeled plastic cup with black bean extract, vinegar, lemon juice, seltzer, dishwashing detergent, household ammonia diluted with water, and strong soap in water. The session started with an explanation for the goggles. I tried to relate to child's experience by asking "Did you ever get soap in your eye? How did it feel?" Then I explained that the goggles were to prevent that from happening today. Then I gave a brief talk about acids and bases.

> The talk: Acids come in several varieties. Most people think of acids as very dangerous and a few are very dangerous. However, many acids are not very dangerous and some are in the foods we eat. They give a sour taste to lemons and vinegar. Bases also can also be strong and very dangerous and they never appear in foods because they have a bad taste. Think about the taste of soap. They are often in cleaners. Acids and bases are opposites. If they are mixed together they use each other up. We can tell if a substance is and acid or base by using a dye that is one color in acid and another color in base. Chemists do not want to taste things because some acids and some bases can be dangerous. The dye is called an indicator. Today's indicator is made from black beans soaked in water. Lets begin our experiments.

The idea behind the talk was to introduce the activity briefly using as few chemical terms as possible. This is not a school class. Children in a museum do not sit through a long lesson. They want to do something that will be fun.

The instructions: 1. Using the droppers put a few drops of the "bean juice' in a well in the plastic plate in front of you. Add a few drop of vinegar. What happens? Now try all the other materials at the table with "bean juice". What happens? What color did you get with which materials? What color does bean juice turn in an acid, in a base? What happens if you start with bean juice and vinegar and slowly add ammonia solution to it? Try any other combinations you wish. Note; I allowed time for experimenting. I have another indicator that is in food, Blueberry juice. Can you find out what color it turns with acids and bases? A small bottle of blue berry juice is placed on each tale. After the visitors experiment I briefly ask what the colors they found in acid and base and how they did the experiment. Finally I say I have a trickier problem. I have indicator that is called a universal indicator, as an acid is used up by a base it changes many colors, How many colors can you find? A dropping bottle of Bogan's universal indicator is placed on each table. I warn that this indicator can stain clothing so be careful. Time for experimenting is given. A careful child or parent can find five colors, red, orange, yellow, green, and blue. During the experimenting time I walk around and briefly talk to and give help, if need, to the visitors. I encourage the children to experiment by mixing combinations, changing order i.e., start with base and indicator then add acid. When most of the children seem "finished" I conclude with a simple demonstration of "chemical magic trick" that they can do. I have a coke bottle filled with " bean Juice" and pour different "drinks" from the same battle. One glass has a few milliliters of vinegar; one has a few milliliters of household ammonia. So pouring bean juice in one glass produces a red liquid and in the other glass, a green liquid. Finally each child gets small packet containing black beans, two plastic test tubes, a piece of golden rod paper and a small transfer pipette, and instructions for simple experiments for the child to do together with their parent. Because many children will want to try "black bean" chemistry at home I usually give each parent a recipe for black bean soup. I wonder what happens at the dinner table if the parent actually makes black bean soup.

The acid base activity proved very successful judging by the interest by the participants. When the Sciencenter was asked to present a program at a Rotary club breakfast we used the acid base activity successfully. The event was held at a local restaurant and again it generated a great deal of interest.

A second Showtime that proved very successful was Bandana Chemistry. The activity was a version one published by Bob Becker[3]. The activity involves stretching a cotton cloth (a T shirt or square of cloth) over the opened end of a cylinder (coffee can) spotting the cloth with markers, followed by dripping 90% isopropyl alcohol drop wise on the spotted fabric. The cloth responds like the paper in paper chromatography and the marker colors spread out and separates forming patterns. Children really enjoyed this activity as evidence by the fact that I literally couldn't get them to leave. The activity was schedules for 30 minutes. After an hour and a half many were still experimenting with the colors and alcohol. Fortunately, I had plenty of cloth squares to hand out.

After the success of these show time activities I thought that the way to reach our museum visitors was by using simple hands on chemistry activities as interactive floor programs (IFP's). These activities involved a volunteer docent doing something with visitors at a table or cart set up on the museum floor. I began to think about doing IFP's involving chemistry. At the time the museum had no facilities for storing chemicals, preparing solutions, no chemical other than those found in a supermarket or facilities for actually doing these activities. Clearly several things would be needed before I started developing activities and doing these IFP's. Funding in small science museums is often in short supply. So I wrote a grant proposal that I submitted to the Dreyfuss Foundation under their special grants program. In the proposal I asked for all the facilities to develop an interactive chemistry program with 10 activities. In addition, funds were requested for evaluating the program and disseminating the activities. The materials requested included a rolling demonstration cart, storage cabinets, balances, glassware, plastic ware, goggles, and goggles sterilization cabinet and of course chemicals. Fortunately the proposal was funded.
Developing the activities

Because the activities were going to be designed for young children to do on a museum floor, I needed to set some strict guidelines for safety as well as tailoring the activities for children. My guidelines were, no flames, smoke, flammables, strong acids, bases or oxidizers. In addition, no highly toxic materials and no combinations in any one activity that could result in any of the above. These guidelines severely limit the kinds and types of activities that can be used. Many of the usual lab activities or demonstrations simply do not fit these guidelines. To further complicate the search for activities each activity would have some element of discovery or challenge. Finally, I considered the attention span of an elementary school child; no activity could take longer than a few minutes.

As I began to develop the activities I ran into a number of problems of the sort that result from not knowing my audience very well. For example I started by using transfer pipettes. Unfortunately many first and second graders had trouble controlling the drop rate from the pipettes, while older children found that transfer pipettes could act like squirt guns. Dispensing all liquids from dropping bottles solved this problem. No matter how hard these were squeezed liquid still came out a drop at a time.

A big help in designing activities came from testers. In my case they were the children of a colleague who were just the right ages 7 and 10. The first activity called finding colors in which children using vinegar and sodium carbonate solutions and were challenged to find all the colors that appeared when universal indicator was used as a indicator for titrating an acid with a base. The first run of this activity was simply done on a table set up on the museum floor. There were a few minor logistic problems such as no nearby sink. Young visitors seemed to enjoy the activity. We encouraged children to experiment and many did. Some decided to use five wells in a row to line up all the possible colors in a "rainbow formation", others tried titrating in both directions. This activity proved very successful.

Our next activity proved much les successful. We tried to get children to separate different plastics using density. Adding them to liquids of different densities could separate a mixture of plastic pieces. Children just weren't interested. "Some things float some don't, ho hum! Next," was the attitude. After this failure we realized that to hold children's interest something unexpected had to occur. From this point on we concentrated of simple reaction chemistry in which something visible or unexpected happened. The activities developed involved color changes, temperature changes, bubbles or fizzing, or noise making[4].

We also discovered young children's limitations in terms of patience, small motor control and cognitive ability. Children 6 and older and could usually do the activities with little difficulty and seemed to enjoy doing them. They stayed for a relatively longtime, called friend over to do the activity, and came back to try it again. One general observation was that girls spent more time with many activities than boys and showed particular interest activities involving color changes. As part of the grant proposal we had a professional evaluation team evaluate the program ref *Doug Spencer*. They found that most elementary school children who did the activities got the main concept we were trying to get across. Of course the concepts were relatively broad ideas:

1.   Acids and bases use each other up when mixed.

2.   Some chemicals get hot when mixed and some get cold.

3.   Some liquids and solids conduct electricity some don't.

4.   Bleach can change colors of some the colors of some stains.

5.   Some raw foods have chemicals called enzymes that can cause hydrogen peroxide to bubble.

6.   Cooking foods inactivates enzymes.

7.   The composition of unknown materials can be found by using chemical reactions.

8.   Some liquids are denser than others.

Another outreach possibility using teenagers presented itself at the museum. The museum had opportunities for high school students to volunteer as docents and it also had a program sponsored by Workforce New York for employing disadvantaged high school students.   As I began doing some of these IFP's with young visitors I noticed that some of the high school student seemed interested is doing some of the activities. Why not train some of the high school students to do these chemical activities with the younger museum visitors. This idea became the basis for a second grant proposal submitted to the Dreyfus foundation. Fortunately the Sciencenter has good record for securing grants and a staff member who is grants manager and proposal writer. So a proposal was submitted asking for funds to train High school students to present chemistry to the museum visitors. Some of the funds went for a teen docent trainer and manager and the bulk of the funds went for funding to pay teen docents for their time during the program.

The Teen Training Sessions

The teen training involved several steps, first the program manager recommended those teens in the workforce NY program that he thought would work well with students. This step was necessary because the workforce NY program selected participants primarily on the basis of financial need not necessarily on science interest or academic performance. The teen manager was an experienced social worker, who had considerable experience working with teens. The actual training involved a small group of students, at one time. First the trainer, me, explained the chemistry behind the activity and then modeled the student role by have the student role play visitors as he showed the visitors the activity and guided them through doing it. The students were encouraged to ask questions as they did the activity. Then one of the high school students led the activity. The others, including the trainer, role-played child visitors. The trainer made suggestion for improving the presentation as it proceeded. The purpose was not only to have the presenter become familiar with the chemistry but to also have presenter gain some confidence working with a small group. After each student had a turn we had a general discussion of the activity that lasted until all felt confident that they could conduct the activity. Finally each participant did the activity with museum visitors while the trainer observed from the sidelines. After this trial run the trainer had a short discussion with the participant to answer questions and make suggestions for improvements if needed. Typically most needed little extra practice or training. A very few of the students did not do well usually because they did not relate well to visitors.

The activity took place on the museum floor either on a rolling cart or at a demonstration counter that was built in one corner of the museum. All the materials for an activity were put together in kits stored in individual plastic bins in one central location for easy access. The bins were checked and restocked periodically. The program ran successfully and between 6-8 hours of chemical activity sessions were present each week reaching between 20 and 50 elementary school children a week depending on museum attendance A chemistry day at the museum was used as publicize the chemistry activities. Chemistry students and a faculty member or two from Cornell and Ithaca College were recruited to set up and man tables so that all of the activities could be run at one time. Each visitor could try any or all of the activities. Each child was also given a small kit containing golden rod paper, black beans and two plastic test tubes a transfer pipette and directions for a few acid base experiments, with parental help, at home. The event proved very successful with well over a hundred attendees.

The other outreach program with high school students involved training a select group to do chemistry demonstration shows in the museums amphitheater. I began by contacting the science department chair at Ithaca high school explained my idea and asked if she could recommend students who met the following criteria:

1. A grade of B or better in general chemistry or 90 or better on the Chemistry regents.

2. A strong interest in science.

3. The ability to speak comfortably in front of a group.

4. Good social skills, especially with young children.

5. Access to email.

6. Transportation to and from the Sciencenter.

I contacted these students explained the program and asked for volunteers. Five students enthusiastically responded. Now that I had the students I began to put together a group of demonstrations. The demonstrations proved to be a challenging problem because of the facilities and the intended audience. The amphitheater does not have good ventilation, a sink, gas line, or permanent demonstration table. It does have an extensive sprinkler system and smoke detector system. Our audience would be children and their parents. Because safety was one of our primary concerns I decide that we would have no flames, no smoke or noxious gases, no explosions, no strong acids bases or oxidizers and only small amounts of toxic materials. Also I wanted demonstrations that were easy to set up, explain and maintain. These limitations eliminate perhaps 90% of most chemical demonstrators favorite demonstrations. After searching through several standards chemistry demonstrations books and my own demonstration repertoire I came up with 13 interesting, easy to do, short demonstrations. A list is at the end of the chapter.

I had the students, the demonstrations, funding all I still needed was an able assistant named Igor. I got a Marcia instead. Marcia is a good friend and a retired high school chemistry teacher with a good sense of humor. An unanticipated problem was finding a meeting time. A group of very good high school students means a group teenagers that are involved in all kind of extra curricular activities sports, clubs, yearbooks, newspaper, community activities etc. Finding a meeting time for this group can really be a problem.

At our first meeting we had the usual introductions all around, I explained the program, then Marcia and I ran through all the demonstrations with minimal explanations. I asked students to think of a name for the group. We also had a question and answer session about he demos. I handed out directions for each demo and asked the group members to decide which demos they might like to do and to think about how they might present the demos. The session lasted almost two hours and I was happy to see that I had a very congenial group of very bright students. For team building activity we asked the students to suggest a name for the group and design a t-shirt for the group. They chose the Chemsations as the name for the group. At the next meeting new colorful safety goggles were handed out, the group decided on the t-shirt design and we began to discuss the demos in detail. Marcia or I would show the demo then we asked a volunteer to do the demo. It became obvious that the students needed some coaching related to presentation. We modeled the presentation again and speaking loudly with animation and with enthusiasm. We also talked about making eye contact, connecting with the audience, and being attentive to the audience. While each student practiced doing a demonstration the others model the audience by asking questions and making comments. Marcia and I coached each student's performance. After two sessions in the museum classroom during which we decided on who would do each demo and talked about a script we moved to the amphitheater.

In retrospect, I realized I should have started in the amphitheater because it provided a more realistic setting than the classroom and students got the sense that is was performance rather than a classroom lesson. For the run through I prepared a sketchy script and a set of large Q cards with title of each demonstration on a single card. I we began by showing the group how to set up the stage efficiently for the performance. Our plan was to make sure the students could set up and take down the demonstration with out help. Before the first run through I packed all the chemicals and materials for each demonstration in a separate labeled containers. Each container also included a simple set of directions for the demo as kind of "cheat sheet". Before I started the project I had decided that students would not have do the prep work for the demonstrations. I had a corner of the museum's educational outreach preparation room for my chemical preparation area.

The first run through of the program took about three times as long as the actual performance. Our stage is small and the logistics of tables, apparatus and people took some to work out. As much as possible we tried to have the students work out the details of the performance. Initially there was some confusion about the order of the demonstrations and who was responsible for lights, set up etc. After the initial run through the Chemsations began to form a cohesive group. During the next run through they really began to take ownership of the program. They began to develop dialog, ad-lib, modify the script add personal touches to the demonstration and interact with each other as team. One of the clever script additions related to the introduction, they used goldenrod paper to introduce the show and themselves. Each one came out with a sheet of apparently blank goldenrod paper followed by the narrator who sprayed each a paper with dilute sodium carbonate solution so the person's name appeared as they were introduced. Another change made by the group involved relating the simple demonstration a disappearing Styrofoam cup in acetone to the witch melting in the Wizard of Oz and changed the cup to a Styrofoam rectangle with a witch drawn on it.

After 2 run throughs we had a dress rehearsal to which museum staff members were invited. One demonstration involving a sequence of five different solutions apparent being poured from one pitcher seemed to be too complicated for a smooth presentation and explanation so it was dropped from the program. The Chemsations also made a few minor mix ups in their explanations of the demos, a problem easily corrected. The theme for the performance was 'Chemical Magic" explained. Each demonstration was first shown as "chemical magic trick" and then the chemistry was explained in simple terms.

The first performance before a real audience went well. The Chemsations were a hit. The Chemsations gave 8 performances from December to June during the school year. Some of the performance did not involve all of the members of the Chemsations because of exams, hockey games, crew team practice, and other extracurricular activities. Fortunately, the group was very flexible every member of the group was able to fill in for a missing person when it was needed. At the end of the school year I arranged for each Chemsation member to get a small monetary honorarium from the Dreyfuss grant.

Below are a few suggestions for this sort of program. Make contact with the local High school Science chair or Chemistry teacher. Seek out students who work well with people and if possible who have done some public speaking or acted in a school play. Everyone has to have an email address. Students who are high achievers tend to be involved in so many activities that it is difficult to reach them by other means. A group that has been helpful has been the Local ACS section that agreed to fund the program when the Dreyfus grant funds run out.

The second year of the Chemsations program was much easier to get started then first year. Three of the original Chemsations asked to continue in the program. They served as mentors and coaches for the new members. Four new students joined the group. As in the past the biggest problem, because of the students busy schedules, involved scheduling rehearsals and performances. The group has seven members and they will do the performances in groups of 3 or 4 students. I expect this to solve some of the scheduling problems. The Chemsations program was expanded to include students from other area high schools. The second year students have rewritten some of the script and one or two new demonstrations will be added. Recent articles in JCE footnote this suggested that students gain much from doing these sorts of demonstrations shows.

There are almost four hundred science museums in the country ranging size from massive institutions with hundreds of employees and multimillion-dollar budgets to one-man one-room museums with thousand dollar budgets. Almost all welcome volunteers, but your most significant impact can usually be made at the small museums, unless of course you are able to contribute large amounts of money along with you time and effort.

Other Outreach Programs

Chemist's long tradition of involvement in outreach programs is briefly summarize by John Moore in a recent JCE editorial.[5] A casual search through the Journal of Chemical education shows that outreach programs in Chemistry fall into several major categories, chemistry camps[6], science competitions[7], science fair mentoring[8], van programs, and demonstration programs involving may combinations of faculty members, college students, high school students and elementary school students. A few chemists and faculty members have reached the public by writing general interest books about chemistry and giving public lectures. Notable examples are Drs. David Harpp and Joseph Schwarcz. Their accomplishments can easily be found using a Goggle search (there are hundreds of citations for each of them) or checking amazon.com for their writings. Three variations on the faculty members, college students, high school students and elementary school students theme are described below.

At Williams College Brigit G. Koehler, Lee Y. Park and Lawrence J. Kaplan have developed an outreach program that targets 4th graders[9]. College students plan, develop and present hands on workshops to 4th graders. Children are invited to campus so that the campus labs and facilities can be easily used. They also see the college students as role models in this setting. The sessions are 2-hour workshops on a wide variety of topics, that involve the physical and biological sciences. Sample topics include forensic science, waves, pressure, chemistry and cooking, color and light, astronomy, and the senses.

A somewhat different approach is the Student-to-Student Science Initiative (SSCI) at Midwestern University in Wichita Falls TX.[10] High school students and their teachers from around the state come to the university for training. Both the both the teachers and their students are trained to perform demonstrations and present lesson related to the demonstrations. After training the students are encouraged to present the demonstration in local elementary school classrooms. 8. The demonstrations are simple ones aimed at the elementary school level. Examples include endothermic and exothermic reactions in plastic bags, simple acid base chemistry with indicators and house hold chemicals, reaction of Luminol with peroxide, and solubility demonstrations.

At Calvin College in Grand Rapids MI Larry l. Louters and Richard D. Huisman dispensed with the middle man[11]. They set up a program in which entire elementary school classes are invited to the College for demonstration programs. Two demonstration sessions are run each day for 40 to 50 fifth and sixth graders at a time. The sessions take place during the last week of college exams and are run by faculty and staff members. They site the following advantages, transportation of equipment and materials is eliminated, there is a one time set up, and more challenging demonstration can be done in the college facility, and a visit to the college can also benefit future recruiting efforts.

References

Ucko, D.A., Schreiner, R and Shakhashiri, B.Z., J. Chem. Ed. **1986**, 1081.

Chen, Phillip, Entertaining And Educational Demonstrations, Chemical Elements publishing 1974, p. 57-58.

Becker Bob, Twenty Demonstrations Guaranteed To Knock Your Socks Off volume 1, Flinn scientific. 1997.

Silberman Robert G., Trautmann Charles, Merkel Susan M., Chemistry at a Science Museum, J.Chem. Ed. Vol. 81, 51.

Moore John, J. Chem. Ed vol. 76, 1469.

Exstrom, Christopher L., Mosher, Michael D., A Novel High School Chemistry Camp As An Outreach Model For Regional Colleges And Universities, J. Chem. Ed. Vol.77, 1295.

Mathews, Fred J., J. An Outreach Program Of Competitive And Non Competitive Events For High School Students, Chem. Ed., vol.74, 452.

DeClue, Mary Ellen, Johnson, Kevin, Hendrickson, Howard, Keck, Pamela J., Stimulate High School Science Fair Participation By Connecting With A Nearby College, J. Chem. Ed. Vol.77, 608.

Koehler Brigit G., Park Lee Y. and Kaplan Lawrence J., Science for Kids Outreach Programs: College Students Teaching Science to Elementary School Students and Their Parents J. Chem. Ed., Vol. 78, 1505.

Voegel Phillip D., Quashnock Kathryn A., and Hall Katrina M., The Student-to-Student Chemistry Initiative: Training High School Students To Perform Chemistry Demonstration Programs for Elementary School Students, J. Chem. Ed vol. 81, 681.

Larry L. Louters and Richard D. Huisman, Promoting Chemistry at the Elementary Level A Low-Maintenance Program of Chemical Demonstrations, J. Chem. Ed., 76, 196.

Chemsations Program Demonstrations

Disappearing Ink
Spilled blue ink turns colorless when you blow on it .

Disappearing styrofoam cube in acetone
Styrofoam cup magically disappears when put in a bowl.

Ripping a Coke Can
A small child can tear a coke can in half an adult cannot.

Disappearing Water
Water is poured into a cup. The cup is turned upside down and the water seems to be gone.

Fake Snow
Water is added to a small amount of white powder and the container fills with snow. Available from Teachersource.com.

Acid Base Color Wand
A long tube is filled with universal indicator solution. Acid is added to one end base added to the other

Floating Bubbles
Soap bubbles float on a layer of carbon dioxide

Golden Rod Paper
Secret messages can be made to appear by spraying goldenrod paper with dilute ammonia

Bubble Drop
Large drop shaped bubbles drop out of the end of a tube shaped like a faucet.

Dry Ice added to large graduated cylinders containing indicator solution
The liquid in graduated cylinder changes color as dry ice bubbles in the containers

Red Green Solution
A sealed glass container is change colors when it is shaken.

Luminol Cold Light.
Two solutions are poured down a spiral tube and light is emitted.

18

The *Journal of Chemical Education* Digital Library: Enhancing Learning with Online Resources

John W. Moore, Elizabeth A. Moore, Jon L. Holmes, Rachel Bain & Ieva Reich
Journal of Chemical Education
University of Wisconsin-Madison

William F. Coleman
Wellesley College

Hans J. Reich
University of Wisconsin-Madison

Ed Vitz
Kutztown University

Theresa Julia Zielinski
Monmouth University

Abstract

The *Journal of Chemical Education* Digital Library (*JCE* DLib) is an integral part of the National Science Digital Library, an NSF-sponsored project that aims to bring high quality educational resources to teachers, students, and the public. *JCE* DLib currrently includes eight collections: *JCE* ChemInfo; *JCE* DigiDemos; *JCE* Featured Molecules; *JCE* LivText; *JCE* LrnComOnline*; JCE* QBank; *JCE* SymMath; and *JCE* WebWare. Each collection provides access through the Web to peer reviewed learning resources such as chemical demonstrations, molecular structures, homework and exam questions, and lessons based on symbolic mathematics software such as Mathcad®. In each *JCE* DLib collection you will find many items that will be useful to you and your students. Readers are invited to use and contribute to this unique, comprehensive collection. (This paper was written in early 2006 and its content was last updated in March 2006; publication has been delayed through no fault of the authors.)

Brief Biographies

John W. Moore is Editor of the *Journal of Chemical Education* and principal investigator on the *JCE* DLib NSF grant.

Elizabeth A. Moore is an Associate Editor of the *Journal of Chemical Education*.

Jon L. Holmes is an Associate Editor of the *Journal of Chemical Education* and Editor of *JCE* Online.

Rachel Bain is an Assistant Editor of the *Journal of Chemical Education*, working on *JCE* QBank.

Ieva Reich is an Assistant Editor of the *Journal of Chemical Education*, working on *JCE* QBank.

William F. (Flick) Coleman is Editor of *JCE* WebWare and Editor of *JCE* Featured Molecules.

Hans J. Reich is Editor of *JCE* ChemInfo.

Ed Vitz is Editor of *JCE* DigiDemos and the *JCE* Tested Demonstrations column.

Theresa Julia Zielinski is Editor of *JCE* SymMath, Co-Editor of *JCE* LrnComOnline, and Editor of *JCE* LivText.

Introduction

The *Journal of Chemical Education* Digital Library (*JCE* DLib) is part of the NSF-sponsored National Science Digital Library (NSDL). The NSDL consists of a central unit that provides a Web site and overall organization together with a loose aggregation of NSF-sponsored projects from nearly every science, technology, engineering, and mathematics (STEM) discipline. These projects have identified useful online resources and are collaborating through the NSDL to provide a single Web site where teachers, students, and the public can find and use high quality learning resources and tools that support innovations in teaching and learning. The NSDL Web site (http://nsdl.org/) is expected to become *the* portal for science, engineering, and mathematics education—*the* place to go on the Web if you have a question about STEM education. *JCE* DLib is not the only chemistry project in the NSDL, but it is a portal with a broad range of resources and also provides direct access to the NSDL site. Our discussion here will be limited to *JCE* DLib, but it should give much insight into the kinds of collections that populate the entire NSDL.

JCE DLib consists of eight collections, each containing a different category of online learning aids. All of these online learning materials are available to *JCE* subscribers and many are also available to everyone. *JCE* DLib learning aids are useful at educational levels from high school through graduate school and all have been carefully selected and edited to insure high quality. We encourage readers to explore the collections by going to http://www.JCE.DivCHED.org/JCEDLib/.

JCE DLib officially opened its virtual doors in January 2004. At that time there were four collections:

- *JCE* DigiDemos—digitized text, graphics, sound, video, and safety information for chemical demonstrations

- *JCE* QBank—Web-deliverable chemistry questions that provide a broad range of question types and modes of delivery (including course-management systems)

- *JCE* SymMath—documents for MathCad®, Mathematica®, Maple®, or MATLAB® that help students learn mathematically intensive aspects of chemistry

- *JCE* WebWare—Web-deliverable interactive animations, simulations, calculations, spreadsheets, and other items that provide new insights for students

The *JCE* DLib is continually being expanded, both by adding new collections with new kinds of materials and by increasing the number of items cataloged in each collection. Since the January 2004 grand opening, these four collections have been initiated:

- *JCE* ChemInfo—a wealth of data, nomenclature, and other useful chemistry information collected in one convenient location on the Web

- *JCE* Featured Molecules—molecular structures that have been described in *JCE* articles and that can be rotated and manipulated using Chime or JMol to show their 3-D structures

- *JCE* LivText—living textbooks of chemistry that support learning in a major portion of the curriculum

- *JCE* LrnComOnline—online instructional modules that encourage collaboration among students via the Web, creating virtual learning communities at any level of the curriculum

JCE encourages readers to submit their own work for inclusion in the *JCE* DLib, to submit entire new collections, or to suggest new kinds of collections that would benefit teachers and students of chemistry. In what follows we describe each of the existing collections and how it can be used to enhance learning at all levels.

JCE DigiDemos

JCE DigiDemos is a collection of chemical demonstrations online, based on the Tested Demonstrations column from *JCE* and enhanced by forums and other mechanisms to allow contributions from all chemical demonstrators. It is available at http://www.jce.divched.org/JCEDLib/DigiDemos/index.html. *JCE* DigiDemos is the culmination of a long tradition of lecture demonstrations, so it is useful to examine how the pedagogy of demonstrations has developed, and what the future may hold. Readers who are interested in chemical demonstrations should also consult Chapter 6, by Vickie Williamson, which describes visualizations in chemical education.

Figure 1. Magnesium reacting with air.

WHY DO DEMONSTRATIONS?

Successful teachers view lecture demonstrations as an effective, if not essential, element of their teaching. Without demonstrations, students may learn relationships between words very well, but never learn the relationship of the words to the objects they describe (their "referents"). If we expect students to apply what they learn, the connections to experience must be *demonstrated.*

> *To teach without demonstrations is to teach pure language or mathematics, not science. In a good demonstration, the science speaks.*

Good demonstrators not only show what they think about, but how they think about it; that is, how they do science. To quote Henry Bent (Bent, 1985):

> *Doing experiments in lecture frequently yields unexpected, interesting, and memorable observations; and something about Whitehead's First Law of Higher Education: "The chief aim of a university professor [should be] to exhibit himself in his own true character—that is, as an ignorant man thinking"...Nature's an ideal lecture assistant. She never fails....What may fail, however, is the lecturer's imagination. There are no failed experiments, only unimaginative responses to unexpected occurrences.*

It is important to learn science rationally. Jonathan Swift is said to have observed "You cannot reason a person out of a position he did not reason himself into in the first place." Misconceptions, once learned dogmatically, are difficult to unlearn. A corollary might be that a person does not really understand a position he did not reason himself into, and demonstrations are the foundation of scientific reason.

> *To teach without demonstrations is to teach dogma, not science.*

Because they are so pedagogically powerful, demonstrations have been used from antiquity to make a point memorable, even if the point was eventually falsified, such as the alchemists' transmutation of metals. In contrast to early alchemists, whose aim was to obscure their practice, early iatrochemists following Paracelsus developed the didactics of chemistry, formulating the subject in ways that would ease its dissemination, especially by demonstration. The power of demonstrations had already been proven in surgical training, so demonstrations were naturally adapted to the teaching of chemistry in early medical schools (Jensen, 1991). Nineteenth century chemistry texts were largely based on demonstrations, so the earliest separate demonstration book was not published until the 1876 text by Karl Heumann in Germany, which was followed in quick succession by others in Germany, England, and the United States (Kauffman, 1996). Heumann's text includes blank pages after each demonstration so that a lecturer could enter notes describing improvements or alterations. This feature proved valuable, and DigiDemos has

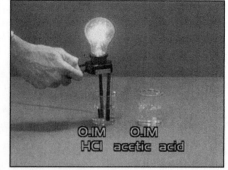

Figure 2. Measuring conductivity of 0.1-M HCl.

adopted and expanded it: Users' notes are online in a forum dedicated to each demo and accessible to all, not just readers of a particular book.

DEMONSTRATIONS IN JCE

The earliest published demonstration in the *Journal of Chemical Education* appeared in volume 1, "A New Lecture Table Outfit for Demonstrating Conductivity to Elementary Classes" (Davison, 1924). It described the well-known conductivity test using a 120-V light bulb. We have learned from this early work: *JCE* has since published many articles that describe apparatus with lower risk of electrical shock. Readers of earlier print versions would not become aware of these improvements unless they searched for and read all subsequent articles. Users of *JCE* DigiDemos on the Web, however, will find that safety warnings and other information are continually added and linked to the demonstrations, making it much easier to be up-to-date and safe.

Between 1924 and the early 1950s several authors published multiple papers describing demonstrations in *JCE*, notably Morris and Headley (1933, 1935, 1941) and Arenson (1940, 1941); even the *Journal of the American Chemical Society* carried at least one (Browne and von Hazmburg, 1926). *JCE* reported extensively on Symposia on Novel Lecture Demonstrations at the national ACS meetings in 1947 (Alyea, et al., 1947) and 1948 (Daugherty, et al., 1948), and *JCE* periodically printed abstracts of articles in other journals dealing with "Apparatus, Demonstrations, and Laboratory Practice" (Baker, 1935, 1936). Two bibliographies by Derrick had appeared by 1950 (Derrick, 1940, 1950). Many articles also appeared on the pedagogy of demonstrations, and a "Symposium on the Lecture Demonstration Method vs. Individual Laboratory Work" was held at the ACS National Meeting in 1935 and reported in *JCE* (Hunt, 1936).

A turning point occurred in 1955 when Hubert Alyea introduced "Tested Demonstrations" as a regular feature column in *JCE*. From then on all demonstration procedures were checked independently and the checker was identified to give credit for his or her work. This greatly increased the probability that even inexperienced demonstrators could execute a new demonstration with ease. To date more than 1000 articles and notes have been published describing demonstrations that have been thoroughly tested and assured to work. This valuable *JCE* service has been continued and enhanced in *JCE* DigiDemos, where each new Tested Demonstration that appears in print becomes available online immediately after publication, frequently with supplemental materials, such as videos or color photos that are not available in print. In addition we are currently adding to the collection most of the demonstrations from the *JCE* archives that were reprinted in the Alyea/Dutton/Dreisbach/Gilbert collection (Alyea and Dutton, 1965; Gilbert, et al., 1994).

WHAT WILL YOU FIND IN JCE *DIGIDEMOS?*

To summarize, *JCE* DigiDemos contains a large collection of demonstrations that have been tested and will enhance learning for students at all levels. The demonstrations are indexed in several ways to make them easier to find. Safety information and tips for performing demonstrations are linked to the demonstrations so that users of *JCE* DigiDemos will have the latest information at their fingertips. A discussion forum is available for each demonstration so that readers can comment on their use of the demonstration, and a demonstration newsletter is also accessible if you register for the forums, log in, and go to Demo Corner. If you use chemical demonstrations to enhance your students' learning, you will find *JCE* DigiDemos invaluable. It has been more than 80 years since the first demonstration appeared in *JCE*, and we have learned a lot since that time. *JCE* DigiDemos embodies all that we have learned.

Figure 3. Thermite reaction.

JCE **QBank**

JCE QBank is an online collection of thousands of test, quiz, and homework questions available on the Web to chemistry teachers everywhere. In many cases answers are also provided, but only to bona fide chemistry teachers. At present most of the questions are for general chemistry and organic chemistry courses, but submissions of questions are encouraged and the collection continues to grow. *JCE* QBank is available at http://www.jce.divched.org/JCEDLib/QBank/index.html.

One of the biggest challenges for any chemistry instructor is developing assessment materials. Writing homework, quiz and exam questions that are clear, concise and at a level that distinguishes those who understand the material from those who don't can be a time-consuming and difficult task, especially for relatively new instructors who do not have tried-and-true resources at their disposal.

In this digital age more instructors are searching online for relevant course material, but this too can be a time sink. For example, a Google search for the term "rate laws" returns nearly 30,000 hits. Few of these resources contain useful material for writing exam or homework questions, and the time it takes to find these few resources can be prohibitive. As one might imagine, using a digital library that specializes in scientific content can increase one's odds of finding useful questions. Searching for "rate laws" at the National Science Digital Library returns fewer than 70 resources; however, even here the majority of resources are either research papers or simulations dealing with rate laws. What chemistry instructors need is a repository of homework and exam questions that have been provided by other chemistry instructors.

WHAT WILL YOU FIND IN JCE QBANK?

The *Journal of Chemical Education* has created and continues to develop such a repository. The *JCE* QBank contains questions that have been used and submitted by chemistry instructors across the country. At present *JCE* QBank contains exam, quiz, and problem-set questions appropriate for undergraduate courses in General Chemistry and Organic Chemistry. There is also a large collection of ConcepTests and a collection of Conceptual Questions and Challenge Problems. We are extending coverage to courses in all areas and levels of chemistry.

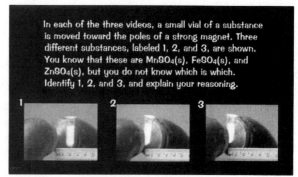

Figure 4. General chemistry question.

The questions in the General Chemistry section of *JCE* QBank cover the same material found in a standard general chemistry text book and are organized around topics in the typical chapter headings of general chemistry books. Question types include matching, multiple-choice, multiple-choice with more than a single choice allowed, and calculational with numeric answers entered. Many questions include color graphics and some are based on digitized videos showing chemical phenomena. These questions have been used with general chemistry students for more than half a decade and have been thoroughly tested and upgraded.

The Organic Chemistry collection contains questions of various types. There are multiple choice questions, questions requiring short answers, many of which are organic structures (products of reactions), synthesis questions, where a series of reactions constitute the answer and mechanism questions, where the answer is a detailed electron-pushing mechanism showing all intermediates. Access to the questions is freely open to students and instructors alike. Answers can be obtained by qualified instructors upon request.

6. Give the major product(s) of the following reaction.

Figure 5. Organic chemistry question.

The *JCE* QBank also contains a large collection of ConcepTests and a collection of Conceptual Questions and Challenge Problems. ConcepTests are available covering General, Organic, Analytical, and Inorganic Chemistry. These are multiple-choice questions to be used in the classroom setting to encourage student interaction and discussion. These can be accessed similarly by browsing according to topic. The

Conceptual Questions and Challenge Problems are more extensive questions designed to assess students' mastery of concepts and to provide more challenging, multi-part problems that students can work on in groups.

USING JCE *QBANK*

Questions are provided in a variety of formats; some can be copied and pasted from Microsoft Word or text documents, while others can be imported into course management systems such as WebCT or Desire2Learn for online homework and quizzes. Many of the questions even have answers provided to qualified teachers who request them. The questions have been reviewed by *JCE* staff and in many cases are peer-reviewed, so the quality of the questions is assured. Knowing that the collection consists of good-quality questions and that the questions have been used successfully by other instructors can reduce the time one might have to take to adjust or even rewrite the questions to fit one's own needs.

In the Organic Chemistry section, questions are arranged according to major topics that roughly correspond to chapters in most organic chemistry texts, such as Stereochemistry, Aldehydes and Ketones, and Aromatic Compounds. Under most major topics, questions are further subdivided. For example, under Aromatic Compounds, one finds Nomenclature, Hückel's Rule, Electrophilic Substitution, and Synthesis as subtopics. When writing an exam or problem set an instructor can browse the questions by topic and subtopic and copy and paste those that are relevant to the exam or problem set at hand. Alternatively, students can use these questions as a studying tool in preparing for exams.

Relevant questions can be identified in a variety of ways. One can browse *JCE* QBank by collection, which is particularly useful if the goal is to find questions by a certain author or in a specific format. Another option is to browse by topic, where a quick look through a list of general chemistry topics such as "Acids and Bases" or "Thermodynamics" is all that is needed to find all of the resources related to that topic. Browsing in this manner is advantageous because there is no need to be able to come up with just the right search terms to find the relevant questions.

An even easier way to find questions is being developed at *JCE* QBank. It is called "Textbook Table of Contents" (TToC), and it will work much like an online textbook supplement. An instructor will choose the textbook s/he is using from a list. The link will go to a page showing the table of contents for that textbook, and a click on the relevant chapter or section will return all of the QBank questions that are related to that section. This will eliminate all ambiguity in search terms and allow maximum return for an instructor's time. Thus not only the content but also the accessibility of the *JCE* QBank collection is constantly being upgraded.

SymMath Collection

JCE SymMath is a collection of Mathcad®, Mathematica®, Maple®, or MATLAB® documents designed to help students learn mathematically intensive aspects of chemistry. A more detailed description of the uses of symbolic mathematics software in the chemistry curriculum has been provided by Theresa Zielinski in Chapter 15. Built upon the foundation already established by the Only@*JCE* Online feature "Mathcad® in the Chemistry Curriculum", *JCE* SymMath provides peer-reviewed, high-quality examples of how chemistry teachers and students can use computer algebra systems (systems that do *sym*bolic *math*ematical manipulations). *JCE* SymMath provides 99 instructional peer-reviewed or open-review symbolic mathematics documents for use by the chemistry teaching community. The *JCE* SymMath content has been created by more than 40 different teaching colleagues and consists of 44 peer reviewed documents and 55 open-review documents available at http://www.jce.divched.org/JCEDLib/SymMath/index.html.

Each of the peer-reviewed *JCE* SymMath documents in the collection is a complete learning object, that is, a self-contained and comprehensive exposition of a chemistry topic. These conform to author guidelines that require explicit goals and objectives, pedagogical significance, and interactivity to promote student active learning. Most of the documents are suitable for use by undergraduate and first-year graduate students in physical chemistry. Some, especially those dealing with statistics and symmetry, are more suitable for advanced students and graduate students. Others address topics in analytical chemistry. The collection is open to any field of chemistry in which the mathematical aspects of chemistry and mathematical modeling can be made more accessible to chemistry students.

The topics areas in the SymMath collection are organized using a generic table of contents format that includes:

- Gases
- Kinetic Theory
- First Law
- Thermochemistry
- Thermodynamics
- Second Law
- Third Law
- Gibbs Free Energy
- Phase Equilibria
- Statistical Thermodynamics
- Chemical Kinetics
- Electrochemistry
- Quantum Chemistry

- Fourier Methods
- Spectroscopy
- Multi-electron Atoms
- Diatomic Molecules
- Polyatomic Molecules
- Computational Chemistry
- Symmetry/Group Theory
- Molecular Spectroscopy
- NMR
- Solid State/Crystallography
- Lasers
- Numerical Methods / Statistics
- Advanced Topics

Since the collection contains nearly 100 documents, faculty must choose which to use in a course. Five to six SymMath assignments per semester would provide students with a good foundation in the topics chosen and at the same time develop their skills with the software and thinking processes that they can carry forward throughout their careers.

We have learned that the most effective mechanism for embedding symbolic mathematics in a course is for an instructor to require use of the symbolic mathematics engine (SME) from the very start of a semester, building in opportunities for students to learn the software as they complete homework and write laboratory reports. Thus one might start with a training exercise for the SME and follow it with simple calculations and exercises in every homework assignment. As the semester proceeds, exercises that build skills for doing derivations that support the course concepts can be introduced. Simple introductory exercises could include gas expansion and work calculations in a thermodynamics semester or exercises on foundations of quantum chemistry in a quantum course. It is important to emphasize to students that although it may seem harder at first to use a SME than using paper and pencil, it is actually

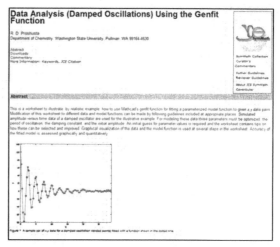

Figure 6. *JCE* SymMath Example: Damped Oscillations.

easier in the long term. After they have collected several of their own files, students can use these as examples upon which to draw for future assignments or to build solutions to more complex problems.

Faculty may need to provide templates to jump-start student work. Such templates are a valuable asset that should be shared with the teaching community. Good examples are welcomed as submissions for inclusion in the SymMath open-review *JCE* DLib collection. Completed learning objects are required for publication in the peer-reviewed section (which includes publication credit in the *Journal*). Some interesting examples of learning objects include *Exploring Harmonic Oscillator Wavefunctions* (Zielinski, 1996); *Orbital Graphing* (Ellison, 2004), *Linear Least Squares Regression* (Young and Wierzbicki, 2000) and *An Introduction to Statistical Mechanics* (Francl, 2005).

JCE WebWare: Web-Based Learning Aids

What is *JCE* WebWare? This is a not uncommon question and one that doesn't have a simple answer. By analogy to traditional libraries, much of what is in the *JCE* WebWare section might be classified as miscellaneous or eclectic. As the editor of *JCE* WebWare says "I may not be able to define it, but I know it when I see it." You can see it at http://www.jce.divched.org/JCEDLib/WebWare/index.html.

The idea behind *JCE* WebWare is to collect Web-based applications that

- assist teachers and students of chemistry,
- can be used in the classroom, the laboratory, and the dorm room, and
- involve an element of interactivity.

The *JCE* WebWare collection includes a peer-reviewed section and an open-review section. Applications in both sections have been thoroughly tested prior to publication, but peer-reviewed applications are usually more extensive and include more documentation than those in open review.

INTERACTIVE SPREADSHEETS

Many *JCE* WebWare applications are Excel-based and are referred to as interactive spreadsheets. They allow the teacher or student to easily and conveniently explore a plot of some property of a chemical system under a wide range of conditions. Such a spreadsheet is a much more effective means of presentation than a graph in a text, which can, at most, show only a few different conditions. For example, one of the early open-review submissions is an interactive spreadsheet that allows the user to construct species distribution diagrams and titration curves for acids with up to four protons (http://www.JCE.DivCHED.org/JCEDLib/WebWare/collection/open/JCEWWOR025/Sheets/alphanew.xls) Students quickly develop a sense for many aspects of polyprotic-acid chemistry and can more easily see the relationship between a buffer system and a titration curve. Topics such as how many equivalence points occur in a polyprotic acid titration are much easier to understand when the student can vary the pK_a values and immediately observe the change in the titration curve.

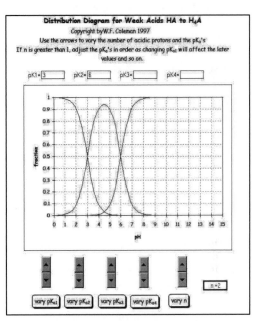

Figure 7. Example of an interactive spreadsheet.

JAVA APPLETS

An excellent example of peer-reviewed *JCE* WebWare is a Java-based application that allows students to explore the steady-state approximation in chemical kinetics (Haustedt and Goodman, 2003: see http://www.JCE.DivCHED.org/JCEDLib/WebWare/collection/reviewed/WW015/index.html). The applet allows students to compare the predictions from the steady-state and pre-equilibrium approximations to an exact solution for the concentration of species in the reaction $A \rightleftharpoons B \rightarrow C$. A useful exercise is to have students use a *JCE* WebWare application, either during class time or as outside work, and then have them write a short paper describing what they have seen—for example, have they uncovered general rules or particular dependencies on a certain variable? It is often productive to assign such an exercise *before* students have encountered the topic in lecture or in their readings.

Other *JCE* WebWare, such as Web-Based Interactive Animation of Organic Reactions (Stueker, 2003: see http://www.JCE.DivCHED.org/JCEDLib/WebWare/collection/reviewed/WW013/index.html), offer a rich source of assignments and study aids. Students who are having difficulty "seeing" organic reaction mechanisms will find this animation particularly useful, irrespective of how talented a two-dimensional artist their instructor is.

Several *JCE* WebWare publications, both in open review and in the peer-reviewed collection, deal with data analysis and statistics. These applications can be assigned as pre-lab exercises or made available to students for use in analyzing their own data. The interactive, visual nature of the programs helps students to gain both an intuitive and mathematical understanding of the issues involved in data analysis and of statistical methods for determining the reliability of data.

FLASH AND SHOCKWAVE ANIMATIONS

Flash and Shockwave animations make up a quite useful part of the *JCE* WebWare collection. Recently,

Charistos, Tsipis, and Sigalas (Charistos, 2004) translated a program illustrating vibrational modes (originally published in *JCE* Software as a Windows application) into a Shockwave animation. The result is available on *JCE* Online: http://www.JCE.DivCHED.org/JCEDLib/WebWare/collecti on/reviewed/WW022/index.html. It enables students at various levels in the curriculum to explore the vibrational modes of a number of different molecules. Introductory students might be asked which vibrations of a particular molecule would contribute to the molecule's being a greenhouse gas; upper-level students could be asked to explore the relationships between IR and Raman spectra and symmetry. (Symmetry is the topic of several other *JCE* WebWare applications, one of which, 3-D Molecular Symmetry, is by the same team of authors. A screen from 3-D Molecular Symmetry is shown here.)

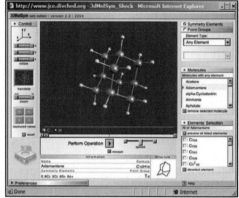

Figure 8. Screen from 3-D Molecular Symmetry

USING JCE *WEBWARE*

It is hard to think of any aspect of chemical education where students could not benefit from using a *JCE* WebWare application. In addition to encouraging you to make use of this resource, we also hope that you, your colleagues, or your students will be inspired to contribute additional applications. For example, students can be asked to produce their own interactive spreadsheets based on concepts they encounter in class or in the text. A video illustrating how to make such a spreadsheet is available at http://www.wellesley.edu/Chemistry/Flick/chem231/excelforms1.htm.

All of the examples mentioned, as well as all other items in the *JCE* WebWare collection, are designed to engage students with concepts that may seem rather turgid without an interactive component. There is a great variety of items in the collection, but all are designed to help students discover answers to questions and to encourage students to take a greater degree of responsibility for their learning. Many items lend themselves quite naturally to raising questions that are quantitative but at the same time require descriptive, essay-like, answers. Asking students to write about their understanding—in addition to asking them to demonstrate that understanding through calculation—is an invaluable part of teaching chemistry to all students at all levels. The *JCE* WebWare collection, both now and with future acquisitions, can be of great value to teachers and students in this endeavor.

JCE ChemInfo

JCE ChemInfo is a collection of Web pages containing data and information useful to teachers, researchers, and students. At present the collection involves organic chemistry, biochemistry, and medicinal chemistry. The pages have been selected for ease of use, broad applicability, and quality of coverage. Topics include structural information, organic reactions, nomenclature, physical properties, and spectroscopic data. *JCE* ChemInfo: Organic is located at http://www.jce.divched.org/JCEDLib/ChemInfo/organic/. In the bulleted lists that follow, each of the italicized titles is a Web site that can be accessed from this URL.

These existing pages will be updated as needed, and additional Web pages dealing with other subdisciplinary areas of chemistry will be added as they become available. We encourage others who have collected data useful to chemists or who regularly use Web sites that provide such data to contribute their information to this column.

NOMENCLATURE

Organic chemists delight in using acronyms and in naming important reactions, reagents, postulates, rules and effects after the chemists who first introduced or broadly applied them in the chemical literature. The resources below will help the mystified chemist or student who encounters such names in the literature.

- *Acronyms*: lists about 150 common acronyms along with their full names and structures

- *Named Reactions*: lists 95 of the most important named reactions in organic chemistry. Each is linked to a Web page that gives the primary reference and equations for one or more recent literature examples that illustrate the use of the reaction.

- *Named Reagents*: provides structures of more than 160 common reagents used in organic chemistry that are often referred to by the originator's name, by an acronym, or by a trade name.

- *Named Rules and Effects*: provides descriptions and structures of a number of named effects, rules, stereochemical models and hypotheses—from Baldwin's rules to the Zimmerman–Traxler transition state.

The International Union of Pure and Applied Chemistry has developed an extensive series of documents describing the nomenclature of organic compounds. IUPAC recommendations have been summarized at the sites listed below. The last site gives GIF structures of common reactive intermediates.

Class Names	*Carbohydrates*	*Bioinorganic Terms*
Organic Compounds	*Steroids*	*Reactive Intermediates*
Physical Organic Terms	*Stereochemistry*	*Heterocycles*

NMR SPECTROSCOPY

Chemists engaged in any form of organic synthesis spend a good fraction of their time analyzing proton and carbon-13 NMR spectra to assign and confirm structure, establish conformational preferences, and determine the composition of mixtures. The two sites listed below provide the chemical shifts and some coupling constants for thousands of organic compounds to serve as models for interpreting proton and carbon NMR spectra. Each collection is indexed by functional group and compound type, allowing individual compounds to be easily found and facilitating comparison of related structures. References to the source of the data for each compound are provided. A readily accessible collection of proton and carbon chemical shifts of this size is not available anywhere else—on the Web or in hard copy.

It is valuable to be able to see actual reproductions of spectra for comparison purposes, or for creating exercises and exam questions. The third Web site listed below provides a convenient source of NMR, IR, and Mass spectra, including more than 12,000 proton and carbon NMR spectra, more than 20,000 mass spectra, and almost 50,000 IR spectra. The Web site provides numeric summaries of the data, but does not provide vector images of the spectra, which would be the most useful. However, a GIF image of the actual spectrum, which is adequate for the simpler spectra, can be downloaded easily.

In summary, in the NMR section you will find

- *Proton Chemical Shifts*

- *^{13}Carbon Chemical Shifts*

- *NMR, IR, and Mass Spectra*

PK$_A$ VALUES

The pK_a values of CH, OH, NH, and SH bonds in organic molecules have tremendous value for understanding and predicting many aspects of their reactivity. The rates of deprotonation, leaving group abilities, anion nucleophilicity, rates of anionic fragmentation, activation of double bonds towards nucleophilic addition, ease of single electron reduction, and reactivity of organometallic compounds all correlate strongly with pK_as of the conjugate acids of the appropriate anionic species. The Web sites below provide many pK_a values of organic molecules in three different media: in solution in DMSO, in aqueous solution, and in the gas phase.

- *Bordwell pK_a Values in DMSO*: The late F. Bordwell of Northwestern University measured the pK_a values of thousands of organic compounds. This Web site makes some of the data he measured conveniently available to the chemical community, and provides literature references to the published data (the Web site also includes much unpublished data).

- *Aqueous pK_a Values*: This list was originally collected by W. P. Jencks and F. H. Westheimer and compiled by R. Williams.

- *Gas Phase Acidity*: This site provides a very comprehensive collection of thermodynamic data selected by the scientists at the National Institute of Standards and Technology (NIST).

JCE Featured Molecules

Each month an article in the current issue of *JCE* is chosen because it discusses molecules that are appropriate for *JCE* Featured Molecules. Chime (available at http://www.mdli.com/—free registration is required for download) and JMol (available at http://jmol.sourceforge.net/) models of selected molecules from the paper are then generated, placed in *JCE* Online, and linked to the table of contents. The structures of the molecules are taken either from crystallographic data or optimized using a variety of quantum-mechanical and non-quantum-mechanical methods. Originally these molecules could be viewed using the Chime plug-in, but more recently Jmol structures have been added. *JCE* Featured Molecules can be found at http://www.jce.divched.org/JCEWWW/Features/MonthlyMolecules/.

Although Web-based molecular structure collections have been readily available for the past decade, linking of the *JCE* Featured Molecules to articles that describe their functions and applications, and the care taken to produce structures that are as accurate as possible, makes *JCE* Featured Molecules a very useful collection for classroom use at all levels of chemical instruction. As an example of the importance of using optimized structures, there are many water structures available on the Web that have a bond angle of 109.5°, which is very confusing to students who have been taught VSEPR theory and know that the angle should be smaller.

USING JCE *FEATURED MOLECULES*

At the middle or high school level it is important for students to begin to appreciate the architecture of chemistry, and these students should be exposed to as many structural models as possible. It makes a great deal of sense to initiate that early exposure by using both hands-on and Web-based three-dimensional models prior to introducing students to the two-dimensional shorthand models that the printed page, and convenience, have forced chemists to adopt. Most students in introductory college-level courses, and perhaps higher-level courses as well, find the two-dimensional structures to be confusing and difficult to read. The more complex the molecule

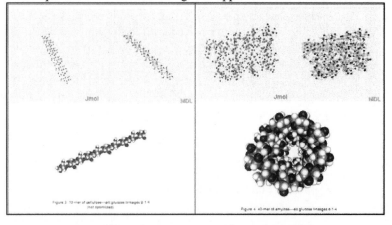

Figure 9. Cellulose and Amylose: *JCE* Featured Molecules for March 2006. See http://www.jce.divched.org/Journal/Issues/2006/Mar/abs413.html

becomes, the more problems students have when interpreting two-dimensional structures. Many students will always have difficulty with the mental conversion from two to three dimensions. The figure shows an example of amylose and cellulose, molecules selected to correlate with an article and a classroom activity based on popcorn.

Many of the *JCE* articles from which *JCE* Featured Molecules are chosen have been written at a level that is accessible to high school students and would make excellent one- or two-day assignments in high school or first-year college courses. If the molecules are complex, then students should be asked to look for familiar structural themes such as a tetrahedral or trigonal planar carbon, or an oxygen with two bonds. They can then use the Jmol version of the molecule to measure angles and bond lengths and to look for, and explain, deviations from idealized values.

Many of the published molecules exhibit both geometric and optical isomerism. In the July 2005 issue all eight stereoisomers of menthol are shown; students in organic or introductory chemistry could be asked to look at pairs of these isomers to decide whether they are diastereomers or enantiomers. Students in introductory chemistry readily understand why the staggered form of ethane is more stable than other rotamers, but by viewing *JCE* Featured Molecules they could be asked to look for similar structural features in more complex molecules. Students in a physical chemistry class might use computational software to explore the energy differences in the menthol isomers to see whether or not enantiomers have the same energy. Additionally, students in chemistry courses for non-majors will always benefit from being exposed to thinking at the molecular level. What better way to help them do that than through the use of interactive three-dimensional models.

It is never too early to have all students begin thinking about the complex relationships between molecular form and molecular function, the role of small and large molecules in biochemical systems, the structures and properties of solids, or the myriad ways in which molecular structure drives emerging fields such as nanotechnology. Molecular structure is what we are all about as chemists, and students should be taught that lesson as early and as often as possible. Remember that "a molecule a day keeps the physicists away".

JCE LrnComOnline

The goal of the *JCE* LrnComOnline feature column is to promote creation, dissemination, and utilization of well-crafted online instructional modules that span the chemistry curriculum. Each online module is a multiweek project that engages students in learning experiences that cut across traditional institutional or disciplinary boundaries and that can be used for both intercollegiate and intracollegiate collaboration among students. Modules are available in a peer-reviewed section and an open-review section. To find the modules, go to http://www.jce.divched.org/JCEDLib/LrnCom/index.html.

EXAMPLE MODULE

The first peer-reviewed module, Cl_2O_4 in the Stratosphere (Whisnant, *et al.*, 2005), provides students with a framework within which they can explore the properties of chlorine oxides and the mechanism for the destruction of the ozone layer. In this module computational chemistry is employed to illuminate the role of chlorine oxides in stratospheric ozone depletion. Students begin by drawing Lewis structures and conclude by conducting *ab initio* calculations to determine the molecular enthalpies of formation of all the species in the reaction of dichlorine tetraoxide with ozone. Using the calculated enthalpies, they predict the reaction's importance in the stratospheric oxygen cycle. Along the way students learn some history, apply group theory to predict normal-mode behavior, learn to distinguish semi-empirical from *ab initio* methods, employ simplifying assumptions

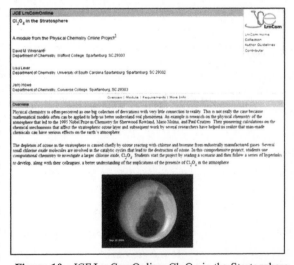

Figure 10. *JCE* LrnComOnline: Cl_2O_4 in the Stratosphere.

about entropy changes in gas-phase reactions, and conduct advanced molecular modeling calculations.

They directly apply the concepts they have learned in physical chemistry to answer a question relevant to their world. The project can be used in a class localized on a single campus or for intercollegiate collaboration across several campuses via the Internet.

GOALS AND OPEN-REVIEW MODULES

The goals of the Chem-Online feature include improving collaboration among faculty, encouraging research into teaching methods, and providing module resources in an easily accessible format. The open-review modules are at http://bluehawk.monmouth.edu/~tzielins/PCOLWEB/ChemOnLine/. They include:

- Be My Guest: Thermodynamics of Inclusion Compounds, Theresa Julia Zielinski, Alex Grushow, Erica Harvey, George Shalhoub (Spectroscopy, Thermodynamics)

- Ozone Kinetics, Erica Harvey, Robert Sweeney (Kinetics, Numerical Modeling)

- Real Gases, Theresa Julia Zielinski (Thermodynamics)

- Spectroscopy of I_2, George R. Long, Deborah G. Sauder (Spectroscopy)

- Polymer Elasticity: Bungee Jumping, George Shalhoub, Theresa Julia Zielinski (Thermodynamics)

- Polymers are Us, Lisa Lever, David Whisnant (Materials Science, Thermodynamics)

- Laser Dyes and Molecular Modeling: The Shady Laser, George Shalhoub (Spectroscopy, Computational Chemistry)

- How Hot is That Flame, Theresa Julia Zielinski (Thermodynamics)

- Computational Chemistry and Hair Dyes, David Whisnant, Deborah Sauder, Melissa Reeves (Computational Chemistry)

- Carbon Clusters, David Whisnant, Lisa Lever, Jerry Howe (Computational Chemistry)

- Apple Enzyme Kinetics, Erica Harvey, Robert Sweeney (Kinetics, Biochemistry)

- Chirality, Michael Waxman, George Long (Spectroscopy)

- Contrails, Franklin Chen (Thermodynamics)

- The DNA Melt, Don Estes (Biophysical Chemistry)

Each of the modules has been field tested in several physical chemistry courses over the past five years. There is a handbook for faculty that supports each module and indicates where the module fits in the curriculum. The modules can be used in both lecture and laboratory courses. Because of their modular nature and the fact the they require a significant commitment of time, they are best used in parallel with other course activities.

CONTRIBUTE TO JCE *LrnComOnline*

Prospective *JCE* LrnComOnline projects and summaries should be sent to the feature editors Theresa Julia Zielinski at tzielins@monmouth.edu or George Long at grlong@iup.edu. Instructions for authors of a *JCE* LrnComOnline module can be found at http://www.jce.divched.org/JCEDLib/LrnCom/authors.html and at the Chem-Online site at http://bluehawk.monmouth.edu/tzielins/PCOLWEB/ChemOnLine/. The ChemOnLine collection of on-line modules for physical chemistry contains many good examples that demonstrate the level and scope of materials being solicited for *JCE* LrnComOnline.

JCE LivText

We often refer to the *Journal of Chemical Education* as a "living textbook of chemistry", a phrase coined by Neil Gordon, the first editor of *JCE*, and popularized by former editors Bill Kieffer and Tom Lippincott. The idea is that with each month and each issue of the *Journal* we add more to the textbook. In this age of online digital libraries, we are able to extend this concept to embrace a textbook that not only grows and changes over time, but also comes alive with animations and interactivity. In December 2005 we brought this idea to fruition by introducing *JCE* LivText: Living Textbooks for Chemistry, the newest collection of the *JCE* Digital Library.

The mission of the *JCE* LivText collection is to make available several living textbooks in digital form. Each textbook will consist of several chapters, and each chapter is intended to provide a coherent and organized body of materials that support instruction in a specific topic and that can be easily incorporated into the classroom and disseminated to students. Chapters may be written by different authors or teams of authors, but all chapters in a given living textbook will be overseen by an editorial board of experts in the field and reviewed by *JCE* peer reviewers. In addition to serving as the basis for traditional classroom instruction, *JCE* LivText also aims to support those who need to learn topics in chemistry independently as background for their work in other fields of science such as biology, geology, etc.

Items in the *JCE* LivText collection differ from other *JCE* DLib resources in that their coverage of a particular area of chemistry is of the same breadth and scope as a textbook. Unlike traditional textbooks, each *JCE* LivText includes interactivity, hyperlinks, and moving media to help students explore its topic. You can find *JCE* LivText at http://www.jce.divched.org/JCEDLib/LivTexts/.

JCE LivText PHYSICAL CHEMISTRY

The initial offering of *JCE* LivText is in the area of physical chemistry. The *JCE* Living Textbook of Physical Chemistry aims to develop a collection of instructional resources spanning the physical chemistry curriculum. The structure of the collection parallels the textbook chapter format. Each chapter is a full exposition of a physical chemistry topic written in a conversational style that facilitates independent study as well as classroom use. Each chapter includes links to supplementary learning objects. These learning objects may include background material for review, fuller development of derivations, supplemental advanced treatment of topics, complete interactive symbolic mathematics lessons, and supplemental exercises and longer projects supporting student learning.

The *JCE* LivText Physical Chemistry is monitored by an editorial committee of volunteer physical chemists who will keep the collection current, add new chapters, and add new links to existing chapters. Potential components submitted for inclusion in the collection will be fully peer-reviewed by the editorial committee and other *JCE* reviewers to assure accuracy and compatibility with the collection.

QUANTUM STATES OF ATOMS AND MOLECULES

In December 2005 *JCE* published Quantum States of Atoms and Molecules, the first set of chapters in *JCE* LivText Physical Chemistry (Hanson, et al., 2005). Quantum States of Atoms and Molecules is an introduction to quantum mechanics as it relates to spectroscopy, the electronic structure of atoms and molecules, and molecular properties. A digital, living textbook, it provides opportunities not found in conventional textbooks, encouraging students to develop skills in information processing, critical thinking or analytical reasoning, and problem solving that are so important for success.

Figure 11. *JCE* LivText Example: Quantum States.

In contrast to many quantum chemistry textbooks, the relevant properties of atoms and molecules become part of the discussion immediately. Concepts are introduced at a concrete level and then generalized, and put in mathematical form at a later stage in the presentation. The goal is to establish the fundamental principles of quantum chemistry and their consequences in a rigorous way while not delaying the discussion of molecular properties until the end. This approach is based on the experience that a concrete verbal description paves the way for a more fundamental, mathematical approach.

The design goals of Quantum States are:

- Make the concepts and methodologies of quantum chemistry accessible and meaningful to all students.

- Develop an understanding of atomic and molecular properties in terms of quantum chemistry.

- Establish the fundamental principles of quantum chemistry and their consequences in a rigorous way while not delaying a discussion of molecular properties until the end.

- Encourage the development of information processing, critical-thinking, and problem-solving skills.

- Set the challenge for each assignment at a level that encourages the growth of critical-thinking and problem-solving skills, yet that can be achieved reasonably, though not always easily, by a student learning team facilitated by a master learner, the instructor.

Quantum States is suitable for a one-semester undergraduate or graduate course and can be part of a two-semester sequence in physical chemistry.

JCE is actively soliciting contributions to *JCE* LivText in all areas of chemistry. All submissions will be peer-reviewed by an editorial committee and other *JCE* reviewers. Abstracts of accepted submissions will be published in the *Journal of Chemical Education* so that authors receive publication credit for their work. If you are interested in developing a new living textbook, have already developed one and would like to contribute it, or are interested in serving on the editorial committee in a particular area of chemistry, please contact *JCE* editor John Moore (jwmoore@chem.wisc.edu).

Conclusion

There is a wealth of excellent, peer-reviewed digital content in the *JCE* Digital Library. Resouces available to you range from single-concept interactive graphs or animations to entire living textbooks consisting of many chapters containing videos, animations, symbolic mathematics manipulations, and hyperlinks to resources that enhance student learning. In every one of the eight *JCE* DLib collections you will find many items that will be useful to you and your students. We invite you to use and contribute to this unique, comprehensive collection. Join with us and many of your colleagues across the country to make the *Journal of Chemical Education* and its Digital Library a true living textbook for the 21st century!

Acknowledgment

Work reported here has been supported by the National Science Foundation's Division of Undergraduate Education through grants DUE #9354473, USE #9455928, DUE #9950809, DUE #0127291, and DUE #0226244, by the Pew Grant Program in Course Redevelopment, and by the UW-Madison Chancellor's Enhancement Fund for course improvement. All figures have been obtained from *JCE* Online or from the Chemistry Comes Alive! collection of *JCE* Software and are used with permission.

References

Alyea, H. N. (1948). Demonstration Techniques. *Journal of Chemical Education, 25*, 249-261.

Alyea, Hubert N.; Dutton, Frederic B. (1965). *Tested Demonstrations in Chemistry*, 6th ed., *Journal of Chemical Education*: Easton, PA.

Arenson, S. B., (1940). Lecture demonstrations in general chemistry. *Journal of Chemical Education, 17*, 434-436.

Arenson, S. B., (1940). Lecture demonstrations in general chemistry. *Journal of Chemical Education, 17*, 469-472.

Arenson, S. B., (1940). Lecture demonstrations in general chemistry. *Journal of Chemical Education, 17*, 513-515.

Arenson, S. B., (1941). Lecture demonstrations in general chemistry. *Journal of Chemical Education, 18*, 168-169.

Baker, R. A. (1935). *Journal of Chemical Education 12*, 44-45.

Baker, R. A. (1936). *Journal of Chemical Education 13*, 395-6, and others starting in 1925 under abstracters' initials.

Bent, H. A. (1985). What Do I Remember? The Role of Lecture Demonstrations in Teaching Chemistry. In Shakhashiri, B.Z. *Chemical Demonstrations: A Handbook for Teachers of Chemistry*, Vol. 2, pp. xiv-xv. Madison, Wisconsin: The University of Wisconsin Press, 1985; adapted with additional and deletions from Bent, H.A.; Bent, H.E. (1980) *Journal of Chemical Education, 57*, 609.

Browne, A.W. and von Hazmburg, R. S. (1926). Lecture Experiments with the New Halogenoid, Azido-Carbondisulfide. *Journal of the American Chemical Society, 48*, 2383-5.

Charistos, Nickolas D. *et al.* (2004). 3-D Normal Modes Shockwave: Three-Dimensional Perception of Molecular Normal Modes on the Web. *Journal of Chemical Education, 81*, 1231.

Daugherty, T. H. *et al*, (1948). Sequestration, dispersion, and dilatancy-lecture demonstrations. *Journal of Chemical Education, 26*, 482-499.

Davison, H. F. (1924). A new lecture table outfit for demonstrating conductivity to elementary classes. *Journal of Chemical Education, 1*, 74. [Note that when this was published in April 1924 only 73 pages had preceded this article in 4 months of JCE!]

Derrick, J. O. (1940). One hundred high-school chemistry projects. *Journal of Chemical Education, 17*, 492-4.

Derrick, J. O. (1950). A bibliography of chemistry projects and demonstrations, 1940-49. *Journal of Chemical Education, 27*, 562-4.

Elder, A. L. (1936). Applicability of the lecture demonstration method to certain groups of students. *Journal of Chemical Education, 13*, 65-68.

Ellison, Mark. (2004). Orbital Graphing. *Journal of Chemical Education, 81* 158.

Francl, Michelle M. (2005). An Introduction to Statistical Mechanics. *Journal of Chemical Education, 82*, 175.)

Gilbert, George L.; Dreisbach, Dale; Dutton, Frederic G.; Alyea, Hubert N. (1994). *Tested Demonstrations in Chemistry*, Vol. I and Vol II, Department of Chemistry, Denison University: Granville, OH.

Hanson, David; Zielinski, Theresa J.; Harvey, Erica; Sweeney, Robert (2005). Quantum States of Atoms and Molecules. *Journal of Chemical Education, 82*, 1880.

Haustedt, L. O.; Goodman, J. M. (2003). How Accurate Is the Steady-State Approximation? *Journal of Chemical Education, 80*, 839.

Hunt, H. (1936). Demonstrations as a substitute for laboratory practice in general chemistry. *Journal of Chemical Education, 13*, 29. Describes the eighty-ninth meeting of the American Chemical Society, New York City, April 25, 1935. "Cost" was a big factor in economically depressed times.

Jensen, W. B. (1991). To Demonstrate the Truths of "Chymistry". *Bulletin of the History of Chemistry, 10*, 3-15.

Kauffman, G. B. (1996). Lecture Demonstrations, Past and Present. *The Chemical Educator,* 1(5) 1430-1471.

Morris, S., Headlee, A. J. W. (1933). Lecture experiments in general chemistry: I. The rusting of iron. II. Spontaneous combustion. III. The halogens *Journal of Chemical Education, 10*, 637.

Morris, S. Headlee, A. J. W. (1935). Lecture experiments in general chemistry: IV. The law of partial pressures, V. The law of diffusion of gases. *Journal of Chemical Education, 12*, 355.

Morris, S., Headlee, A. J. W. (1941). Lecture experiments in general chemistry: VI. The liquefaction and fractionation of air. VII. The liquefaction and fractionation of natural gas. *Journal of Chemical Education, 18*, 79.

Stueker, O. (2003). Web-Based Animation of Organic Reactions. *Journal of Chemical Education, 80*, 583.

Whisnant, David M.; Lever, Lisa; Howe, Jerry. (2005). Cl_2O_4 in the Stratosphere: A Module from the Physical Chemistry On-Line Project. *Journal of Chemical Education, 82,* 334.

Young, S. H.; Wierzbicki, A. (2000). Linear Least-Squares Regression. *Journal of Chemical Education, 77* 669.

Zielinski, T. J. (1996). Exploring Harmonic Oscillator Wave Functions. http://bluehawk.monmouth.edu/ ~tzielins/mathcad/tjz/doc006.htm.